A SURVEY OF
MATHEMATICS
Elementary Concepts and Their Historical Development

A SURVEY OF MATHEMATICS

Elementary Concepts and Their Historical Development

Vivian Shaw Groza

SACRAMENTO CITY COLLEGE

HOLT, RINEHART AND WINSTON
New York   Chicago   San Francisco   Atlanta
Dallas   Montreal   Toronto   London

To my husband Bill, for his continuous encouragement,

and

*To my daughter Laurinda Joan Koblick, for her assistance
in writing the Greek historical background*

Preface

This book is the result of amplifications and developments of lecture notes used by the author for several years in teaching a one-semester college course in mathematics. The course is designed as a terminal course in mathematics in the general education curriculum and does not assume any algebraic or geometric background on the part of the student. The objective of the course is to acquaint the student with the various branches of mathematics and to develop an appreciation and understanding of the relationship of mathematics to the modern world. The concepts that are introduced in today's elementary schools are covered in depth and are related to the historical background from which they developed.

The mathematical topics are presented in a historical setting. The contents of the book are divided into four chronological periods: the prehistorical, the ancient Oriental, the Greek, and the Hindu-Arabic-European. There are many advantages from such an arrangement. First, the history serves as a unifying thread weaving together the various topics of mathematics into a whole that is meaningful to the student. The arrangement also serves to help the student appreciate the cultural significance of developments in mathematics and perhaps to motivate him by relating mathematics to areas that are probably more comfortable and familiar to him.

Since a student unfamiliar with the subject of mathematics would have great difficulty understanding a chronological history of mathematics, certain changes are made in the historical order. Some topics from modern mathematics are discussed at earlier times for various reasons. The topic may help the student to understand better the material developed at an earlier period, or the topic may be fundamental to the discussion of the material following this topic, or the topic may complete the unit on a certain subject.

For example, elementary set theory is introduced during the prehistorical period because the set concept is basic to that of number and because set theory forms a foundation for other branches of mathematics. Symbolic logic is presented during the Greek period because it completes and simplifies the subject of logic.

With some exceptions, then, the over-all arrangement of the mathematical topics is in historical order. These topics are arranged in chapters and are separated from the general historical backgrounds presented at the beginning of each of the different periods. The reading of these sections may be left to the student when this is desirable.

More material is included in the book than can normally be presented during a one-semester course. This permits the instructor to select certain topics in accordance with the needs and interests of a particular class of students. It also provides the individual student with additional information in a subject area of special interest to this student. Certain sections, labeled "optional," could be used in this supplementary way.

The development and presentation of the basic mathematical disciplines of number, space, and logic in this historical manner, as man himself created them, has proved to be a very effective method of instruction. It is with great pleasure that one observes the transition from a negative "I've always hated mathematics" to the more positive "Why didn't someone tell us these things before? It makes everything so much more interesting and meaningful."

VSG

Sacramento, California
January 1968

Contents

Bibliography

Aaboe, Asger, *Episodes from the Early History of Mathematics*. New York: Random House, Inc., and the L. W. Singer Company, 1964.

Bell, E. T., *Men of Mathematics*. New York: Simon and Schuster, Inc., 1937.

Cajori, Florian, *A History of Mathematical Notations*, 2 vols. La Salle, Ill.: The Open Court Publishing Company, 1928–1929.

Cajori, Florian, *A History of Mathematics*, 2nd ed. New York: The Macmillan Company, 1919.

Conant, L. L., *The Number Concept, Its Origin and Development*. New York: The Macmillan Company, 1923.

Dantzig, Tobias, *Number, The Language of Science*. New York: The Macmillan Company, 1954.

Eves, Howard, *An Introduction to the History of Mathematics*, rev. ed. New York: Holt, Rinehart and Winston, Inc., 1964.

Heath, T. L. *History of Greek Mathematics,* 2 vols. New York: Oxford University Press, 1921.

Hilbert, David, *The Foundations of Geometry*, tr. by E. J. Townsend. Chicago: The Open Court Publishing Company, 1902.

Midonick, Henrietta, *The Treasury of Mathematics*. New York: Philosophical Library, Inc., 1965.

Newman, James, ed., *The World of Mathematics,* 4 vols. New York: Simon and Schuster, Inc., 1956.

Ore, Oystein, *Number Theory and Its History*. New York: McGraw-Hill Book Company, Inc., 1948.

Smith, D. E., *History of Mathematics,* 2 vols. Boston: Ginn & Company, 1923–1925. (Also New York: Dover Publications, Inc., 1958.)

Struik, D. J., *A Concise History of Mathematics*, 2nd ed. New York: Dover Publications, Inc., 1948.

Swain, R. L., *Understanding Arithmetic*. New York: Holt, Rinehart and Winston, Inc., 1957.

Turnbull, H. W., *The Great Mathematicians*. New York: New York University Press, 1961.

Van der Waerden, B. L., *Science Awakening*, tr. by Arnold Dresden. Groningen, Netherlands: P. Noordhoff, N.V., 1954.

A SURVEY OF MATHEMATICS

Elementary Concepts and Their Historical Development

PART I

THE PRE-HISTORICAL PERIOD

The concept of number and the principles of counting developed during the prehistorical period of man's existence. This period includes the Paleolithic, or Old Stone Age, during which man survived by gathering plants and by fishing and hunting with stone weapons. He lived in caves, built fires, and buried his dead. During the last 15,000 years of this period, man enriched his life with creative art forms, small statues, and paintings.

Around 8000 B.C., when the ice sheet covering Europe and Asia began to melt, man entered the Neolithic, or New Stone Age. During this time he learned to farm and to domesticate animals. During a period of 6000 years man invented weaving, pottery, the wheel, writing, copper, bronze, the mill, the cart, the plow, and the boat. When we enter the period of recorded history, we find that man has already developed the calendar, numeral systems, and systems of weights and measures. Man created numeral systems in order to keep permanent records. He was most concerned with records of taxes and other governmental matters and with records pertaining to trade and commerce. The records in turn reflected the increasing complexity of man's existence as he began to live in cities.

Although we have no written records, we can still advance a plausible theory of the development of counting, ending with the creation of a numeral system. This theory is based on three sources of information:

1. Archeological findings in paleolithic caves in France, Spain, and Italy and in neolithic ruins and excavations.
2. Anthropologists' reports of present-day primitive peoples still living in paleolithic or neolithic conditions.
3. Modern studies concerned with numbers and counting.

CHAPTER I

Counting

> "Can you do Addition?" the White Queen asked.
> "What's one and one and one and one and one and
> one and one and one and one and one?"
> "I don't know," said Alice. "I lost count."
> "She can't do addition," the Red Queen interrupted.
>
> *Through the Looking-Glass,* Lewis Carroll

The probable sequence of ideas in the development of counting is as follows:

1. Number sense, the concept of more or less or equal.
2. Tallying, the concept of one-to-one correspondence between sets.
3. Vocal sounds for numbers of concrete objects.
4. Abstract number words.
5. Extension of number words, by addition using small number bases.
6. Finger counting, the use of bases 5, 10, 20, or combinations of these.
7. Numerals, written symbols to designate numbers.
8. Systems of numerals, to record large numbers.

Each of these ideas will be discussed in order in this chapter.

1. NUMBER SENSE

The number concept, the ability to distinguish the difference between two sets of numbers whether presented simultaneously or successively, is undoubtedly innate with man. No primitive tribe has been discovered without this ability, even though their language may be lacking in numeral words. Certain studies have indicated that the direct visual number sense of the average civilized man rarely extends beyond four.

Scientific studies (see References) show that some birds and insects possess a number sense. An example is stated concerning a suspicious crow, and a man wanting to shoot the crow. Whenever the man entered the watch house, the crow would fly away and would not return until after the man had left. To deceive the crow two men were sent to the house, one remaining after the other had left; but the crow would not return. The next day three men went, one staying after two left. Still the crow was not deceived. It was necessary to send five or six men to the house before the crow would return. From this behavior it was inferred that the crow could "count" to four.

Another example concerns the habits of wasps. One species supplies its young with 1 large caterpillar; another, 5; and others, 10, 15, and even 24. The number is constant for each species. How does the wasp know when it has brought its required number? It does not do this by filling the cell because if some caterpillars are removed, the wasp does not fill the cell but only brings the required number. It might be argued that the wasp has some mysterious or innate tendency to provide exactly a certain number. Even if this were an explanation, it would not agree with the facts. In one genus, the males are smaller than the females, and if the egg is male, 5 victims are supplied; if female, 10 victims are supplied. Does the wasp count?

Scientific experiments by Koehler indicate that animals can be taught to "count" or think unnamed numbers in the real sense of the word — to recognize differences between unequal sets of dots, or rows of marks, and to take action, to reason, on the basis of quantitative differences. Koehler states that his studies are especially significant because they point to forms of prelinguistic thinking that higher animals and man have in common.

One of the experiments Koehler describes concerns a jackdaw. The bird was supposed to open certain boxes until it had eaten exactly five baits. In this particular experiment, the baits were distributed in the first five boxes in the order 1, 2, 1, 0, 1. The jackdaw returned to its cage after it had opened only the first three boxes. Just as the experimenter was about to record an incorrect solution, the bird went through a remarkable performance. It went back to the line of boxes, bowed its head once before the first box; twice before the second box; once before the third; opened the fourth, which was empty; opened the fifth, removed the bait, and then returned to its cage with an air of finality. Certainly this bird was "counting" or "thinking unnamed numbers" in the true sense of the word.

REFERENCES

Newman,[1] *The World of Mathematics*, Vol. 1:

Conant, L. L., "Counting," pp. 432–441.
Koehler, O., "The Ability of Birds to 'Count'," pp. 489–496.

2. TALLYING

2:1 One-to-One Correspondence

Tallying is an example of a more general mathematical concept, that of a one-to-one correspondence between the elements of a set. A **set** in mathematics means a collection of objects, called **elements,** or members, of the set. We are thinking of the same concept when we speak of a set of dishes or a set of golf clubs.

Two sets are said to be in **one-to-one correspondence** if the elements of one set can be paired with the elements of another set so that each element of the first set has exactly one matching element in the second set and each element of the second set has exactly one matching element in the first set.

For example, sets *A* and *B* below are in one-to-one correspondence:

$$\text{Set } A = \{\text{France, England, Germany}\}$$
$$\updownarrow \qquad \updownarrow \qquad \updownarrow$$
$$\text{Set } B = \{ \text{ red, \quad white, \quad blue } \}$$

This enables us to establish a foundation for the concept of equality. We say that set *A* has objects **equal** in number to that of set *B*.

On the other hand, sets *C* and *D* below are *not* in one-to-one correspondence:

$$\text{Set } C = \{\text{pencil, paper}\}$$
$$\updownarrow \qquad \updownarrow$$
$$\text{Set } D = \{\text{penny, nickel, dime}\}$$

No matter how we try to match or pair off the elements of sets *C* and *D*, there is always an element of set *D* left over. In this case, we say that set *D* has **more** elements than set *C*, or that set *C* has **fewer** elements than set *D*.

---

[1] Full bibliographic data for key books cited herein are given in the Bibliography.

Tallying is a special case of a one-to-one correspondence between sets. Exactly one tally mark is made for each object or event to be recorded and no tally mark is made which does not represent an object or event. A modern example of tallying is the use of check marks to record numbers of objects:

$$\text{НН}\quad\text{НН}\quad 111$$

2:2 Tallying: The Recording of Unnamed Numbers

A variety of methods for tallying, or recording numbers, has been found in different civilizations. Among these are

1. Scratches in dirt or on stone.
2. Knots in a string or rope, used by the Incas of Peru.[2]
3. Collections of pebbles or sticks, such as the Chinese computing rods.[3]
4. Notches in bone or wood, such as the English tally sticks used until 1826.[4]

The oldest example of a tallying device is a tally stick found in Moravia, dating back to paleolithic times. It is the bone of a young wolf, 7 inches long, engraved with 55 deeply incised notches, of which the first 25 are arranged in groups of 5. These are followed by a simple notch twice as long, which ends the series; then, starting from the next notch, also twice as long, a new series runs up to 30.[5]

Charles Dickens, in an address on administrative reform delivered a few years after 1834 when the tally sticks were burned, gives an entertaining account of these tallies, their abolishment, and their burning. They were burned in a stove in the House of Lords and the fire from this burning reduced both the House of Lords and House of Commons to ashes.[6]

Many conjectures have been offered regarding man's motivation for tallying. It seems reasonable to assume that his most urgent motivation was associated with a struggle for survival. Locations of fish and game are related to the time of year and to a knowledge of direction. By observations of the sun, moon, and stars and by the process of tallying man could determine time and direction and even a primitive calendar.

---

[2] Midonick, *The Treasury of Mathematics*, "The Peruvian Quipu," pp. 643–659.
[3] Midonick, *The Treasury of Mathematics*, "Sun-Tsu," pp. 751–758.
[4] Ore, *Number Theory and Its History*, p. 9.
[5] Struik, *A Concise History of Mathematics*, p. 4.
[6] Dantzig, *Number, The Language of Science*, pp. 23, 24.

3. VOCAL SOUNDS FOR "CONCRETE" NUMBERS

Vocal sounds soon developed as a word tally. At first there were different sounds for different types of sets, even though their number would be the same. Thus there were different sounds for two sheep, two men, and two spears. This multiplicity of words for the same number can be found in the English language with respect to the number two. Thus we speak of a brace of pheasants, a span of horses, a couple of days or a married couple, and a pair of gloves. Philosophers believe that it requires many years for a primitive tribe to evolve the general concept or the word "two" to describe all these special cases.

The Thimshian language of a tribe in British Columbia illustrates this point and also indicates a progress toward complete abstraction. There are seven sets of words for each number they know. That is, there are seven different words for "two," seven others for "three," and so on, as far as they count. One set is for animals and flat objects, one for time and round objects, one for human beings, one for trees and long objects, one for canoes, one for measures, and one for miscellaneous objects not in the other six categories.

4. ABSTRACT NUMBER WORDS

Primitive man next abstracted the number words for "one," "two," and "many." Perhaps the abstract word was the one used to describe the objects in the miscellaneous category.

Many primitive tribes have a very limited knowledge of number words. "One, two, many" is their complete counting system. This primitive system is found today among the forest tribes of Brazil, the Bushmen of South Africa, and some native races of Australia and Polynesia.

Our own ancestors were probably not better equipped than this because all European languages bear traces of such early limitations. The English "thrice," like the Latin "ter," has the double meaning of three times and many. Similarly, there is a strong relationship between the French "très," many, and "trois," three.

5. EXTENSION OF ABSTRACT NUMBER WORDS

By combining the words for "one" and "two" man was able to obtain more number words, such as "two one" and "two two." Since the numbers being named were to be added to obtain the new number being named, we say he extended his number words by addition. Also man established a **base** for his counting system. The base of a counting system using words means the number of different number words from which the other number names are compounded.

For example, if man said "One, two, two one, two two, two two one" for our sequence "One, two, three, four, five," his system would have a base of two. If he said, "One, two, three, three one, three two," his system would have base three.

The complete counting systems of some Australian tribes are given in Table 1.1. The first four of these systems are binary (base two) and the fifth is a ternary system (base three).

TABLE 1.1 COUNTING SYSTEMS OF AUSTRALIAN TRIBES

DARLING RIVER	BELGANDO RIVER	MURRAY RIVER
1. Neecha	1. Wogin	1. Enea
2. Boolla	2. Booleroo	2. Petcheval
3. Boolla Neecha	3. Booleroo Wogin	3. Petcheval Enea
4. Boolla Boolla	4. Booleroo Booleroo	4. Petcheval Petcheval

TORRES STRAITS	KAMILAROI
1. Urapun	1. Mal
2. Okosa	2. Bulan
3. Okosa Urapun	3. Guliba
4. Okosa Okosa	4. Bulan Bulan
5. Okasa Okasa Urapun	5. Bulan Guliba
6. Okasa Okasa Okasa	6. Guliba Guliba
Ras (many)	

6. FINGER COUNTING

Eventually man formed a one-to-one correspondence between his numbers and his fingers. His fingers enabled him to enlarge his knowledge of numbers by helping him with his counting and by helping him to perform simple arithmetical calculations. Since both fingers and toes can be used for counting, we would expect that 5, 10, or 20 would be the bases most often selected. Ethnological studies verify this. Of 307 number systems of primitive American peoples investigated by W. C. Eels,[7] 146 were

---

[7]W. C. Eels, "Number Systems of North American Indians," *American Mathematical Monthly,* **20,** 1913, p. 293.

decimal; and 106 were quinary (base 5), vigesimal (base 20), or combinations of 5, 10, and 20.

The counting system of the Luli of Paraguay illustrates the transition from a small number base to a finger base. We see an initial use of base 4 but once 10 is reached, base 10 dominates the counting pattern.

1. alapea
2. tamop
3. tamlip
4. lokep
5. lokep moile alapea (four and one) *or* is alapea (one hand)
6. lokep moile tamep (four and two)
7. lokep moile tamlip (four and three)
8. lokep moile lokep (four and four)
9. lokep moile lokep alapea (four and four one)
10. is yaoum (both hands)
11. is yaoum moile alapea (hands and one)

.

.

.

20. is eln yaoum (hands, feet)
30. is eln yaoum moile is yaoum (hands, feet, hands)

In most primitive languages the word for the number "five" is the same as the word for "hand" and the word for "ten" is the same as that for either "two hands" or "man." Also, in many primitive languages the number words from one to four are identical with the names given to the four fingers as they are used in counting.

An interesting example that illustrates counting by fingers and toes is the system of the Greenland Eskimos. This system is quinary-vigesimal, that is, base 20 dominating an earlier use of base 5.

1. atauseq
2. machdlug
3. pinasut
4. sisamat
5. tadlimat
6. achfineq-atauseq (other hand one)
7. achfineq-machdlug (other hand two)
8. achfineq-pinasut (other hand three)
9. achfineq-sisamat (other hand four)
10. qulit

11. achqaneq-atauseq (first foot one)
12. achqaneq-machdlug (first foot two)
13. achqaneq-pinasut (first foot three)
14. achqaneq-sisamat (first foot four)
15. achfechsaneq
16. achfechsaneq-atauseq (other foot one)
17. achfechsaneq-machdlug (other foot two)
18. achfechsaneq-pinasut (other foot three)
19. achfechsaneq-sisamat (other foot four)
20. inuk navdlucho (a man ended)

The counting now proceeds by 20s.

Since the number words of our modern European languages originated such a long time ago, it is almost impossible to trace their derivations. However, we can find some relationships to finger counting. For example, the Sanskrit "pantcha" meaning "five" is related to the Persian "pentcha" meaning "hand." The Russian "piat" (five) is related to "piast" (the outstretched hand). The English word "digits," derived from the Latin "digitus," refers both to the fingers and toes and to the numbers from one to nine and zero.

There are examples of base 20 words in certain European languages; for example, the English "score" and the French words "quatre-vingt" and "quatre-vingt-dix" meaning four score and four score ten, respectively. In Paris there is a hospital originally built for 300 blind veterans. Its name is "Quinze-Vingt," meaning 15 score, or 15 times 20, or 300.

It is possible that 20 was the limit of our counting at one time, since "score" also means "many" in some of our expressions, such as "a score of times." "Score" is also used to indicate a total or summing up as in the "score" of a game. The word "score" meaning 20 is derived from the Anglo-Saxon word "skar," which meant "scratch" or "tally." Both our modern words "scar" and "score" come from the same source.

7. NUMERALS

7:1 Differences between Numbers and Numerals

A **number** is an abstract concept. We associate with it the idea of how much or how many. A **numeral** is a *symbol* that is the name of a number.

For example, the numeral "7" is the symbolic name of the number we call "seven." The numeral "7" is not the number, just as the word "chair" is not the object we sit upon but the name of this object.

Study Table 1.2 and note that the statements on the left concern numerals whereas those on the right are about numbers.

TABLE 1.2 NUMERAL AND NUMBER STATEMENTS

NUMERAL STATEMENTS	NUMBER STATEMENTS
1. a. One half of 8 is 0.	b. One half of 8 is 4.
2. a. Twice VII is XII.	b. Twice VII is XIV.
3. a. 2 is larger than 7.	b. 7 is larger than 2.
4. a. His 6s look like 10s.	b. The sum of 6 and 10 is 16.

7:2 Creation of Numerals

The first numerals were probably created as the result of the efforts of primitive man to keep written records of numbers. The first numerals reflect the process of tallying, as illustrated in Figure 1.1.

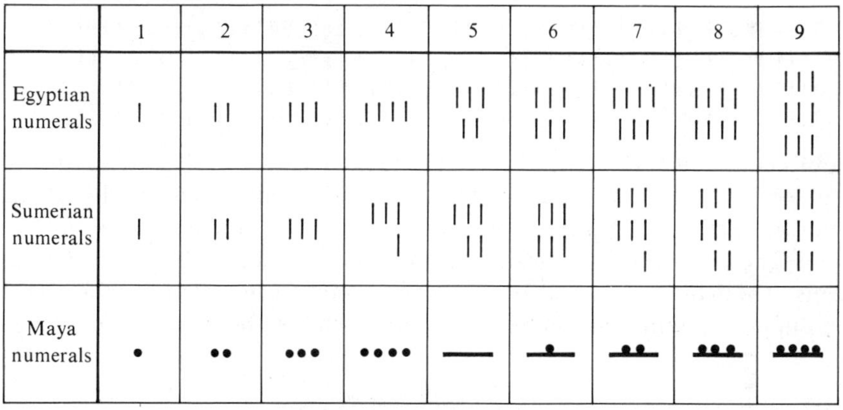

Figure 1.1

8. NUMERAL SYSTEMS

8:1 Development of a Simple Grouping Numeral System

Numeral systems most likely developed as the result of man's necessity for making permanent records of very large numbers. It would have been both awkward and difficult for man to remember 100,000 different number names or to write a tally symbol 100,000 times. Thus man devised the scheme of arranging his numbers in groups. Whatever scale he used to determine the size of his groups became the base of his numeral system.

For example, if his base were 10, he would group 10 objects together and create a symbol for this amount, such as "X." His next larger group

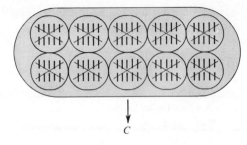

X C

Figure 1.2

would be 10 of these 10s, or 100 objects, and he would create a symbol for this number, such as "C" (Figure 1.2). Then, to record the number representing

11111 11111 11111 11111 11111 11111 11111 11111 11111 11111 11111 11111
11111 11111 11111 11111 11111 11111 11111 11111 11111 11111 11111 11111
11111 11111 11111 11111 11111 11111 11111 11111 11111 11111 11111 1111
11111 11111 11111 11111 11111 11111 11111 11111 11111 11111 11111

objects, he would write "CCXXXIIII," meaning 100 added to 100 added to 10 added to 10 added to 10 added to 1 and 1 and 1 and 1. Using our modern numeral system we would write this number as 234.

The early Egyptians had a simple grouping numeral system such as this. The Roman numeral system we use today is an example of a simple grouping system and was derived from that of the ancient Egyptians.

8:2 Development of a Positional Numeral System

The simple grouping system served the purpose for which it was probably invented, that is, to record large numbers. However, it proved to be inadequate for man's computational needs. Thus, as the problems and arithmetic of his civilization became more complex, man evolved the concept of a positional numeral system as an answer to his computational necessities.

In a positional numeral system, the position that a symbol occupies determines the value of the group size represented. The symbol itself determines how many of these groups are being represented. Our modern Hindu-Arabic numeral system is an example of a positional system with base 10.

For example, 234 means two 100s added to three 10s added to four 1s. Each position has a value 10 times that of the one on its right. Since 10 is being used as the multiplier to determine group sizes, the base is 10.

The concept of a positional numeral system was known to the ancient Babylonians, who used a base of 60 and a base of 10. One disadvantage

CHAPTER II

Sets

The number of a couple
is the set of all couples.

Set theory was created by the mathematician Georj Cantor during the period 1874–1895 when his works on this subject (called "Mengenlehre" in German) were published. Cantor (1845–1918) had Danish parents, was born in Russia, and was educated in Germany, where he lived and taught.

1. THE SET CONCEPT

1:1 "Well-defined" Concept

Definition: *A set is a well-defined collection of objects called "elements" or "members" of the set.* Mathematicians use the word "set" in the same spirit that is used in everyday language when one speaks of a set of dishes, or a coin collection, or the class of freshman students.

A collection is **well defined** if it is always possible to determine whether or not a particular object or element belongs to the set.

For example, all former presidents of the United States is a well-defined collection, and therefore a set, because it is always possible to decide whether a particular person was a former president or not.

---

of their system was the lack of an absence symbol, or zero, to hold the place if certain groups were not being represented. For example, the zero in our numeral 305 means that there are no groups of 10. Finally, man did invent the number zero and created a symbol to represent it. The first historical appearance of zero in our culture was on a document found in India dated 738 A.D. Exactly when zero was first introduced is a matter of conjecture. Some historians believe it to be 400 A.D. A period or symbol such as a punctuation mark acting as a placeholder appears on Babylonian tablets dating around 300 B.C. However, it was not used consistently and was used only in the middle of a numeral and never at the end. Probably there was a gradual development from before 300 B.C. to 800 A.D. In Chapter 3 we shall study the numeral systems of various civilizations.

In retrospect, we can now see that in the development of counting, man began with 1 and ended with 0.

EXERCISES

1. Explain how the mathematical concept of one-to-one correspondence is involved in each of the following.
    a. Two children, dividing candy, say "A piece for you, a piece for me. . . ."
    b. An instructor determines if any students are absent without counting.
    c. The name of a football player is determined from the number on his jersey.
    d. A hostess determines if she has enough napkins for each place setting without counting.
2. Establish a one-to-one correspondence of the letters of the word "lime" with themselves so that the order of the letters again forms a word. Repeat this with the words "earn," "tar," "onset," and "devil."
3. Determine which of the following matchings are examples of a one-to-one correspondence.

    a. Eyes of people matched with their owners.
    b. Players on a baseball team matched with the positions they play.
    c. Cups at each place setting on a dinner table matched with their saucers.
    d. Knives at each place setting on a dinner table matched with their forks.
    e. The votes for a political candidate, each vote matched with the voter.

4. For each of the following pairs, use the concept of one-to-one correspondence to determine whether set *A* is equal to, larger than, or smaller than set *B*.
   a. *A* = set of days in a week
      B = set of planets in our solar system
   b. *A* = set of days in the week
      B = set of letters in the word "numeral"
   c. *A* = set of days in the week
      B = set of fingers on one hand

5. In how many ways can the set {N, O, W} be placed in one-to-one correspondence with itself?

6. What is the difference between a number and a numeral?

7. Determine whether the italicized word in each of the following designates a number, a numeral, or neither.
   a. A *five* is difficult for a young child to write.
   b. *Seven* is longer than ten and also has more letters.
   c. *Six* was a difficult concept for some primitive men to understand.
   d. Some numeral systems have base *twenty*.
   e. The *five* in your address 753 Main Street means *five* times ten.

8. a. How many objects are in 3 gross, 5 dozen, and 7?
   b. Express 530 in the gross-dozen system.
   c. What is the base of the gross-dozen system?

9. a. How many cups are in 6 quarts, 1 pint, 1 cup?
   b. Change 31 cups to quarts, pints, and cups.
   c. What is the base of this measuring system?

10. What base is associated with each of the following systems of measurement?
    a. Cycle, kilocycle, megacycle, used by radio engineers.
    b. Measuring spoons of housewives.
    c. Seconds, minutes, hours, used to measure time.

11. Determine the base of each of the following counting systems and extend each system. The last system is that of the African Pygmies.

one	dit	do	eeny	a
two	dot	re	meeny	oa
three	dot dit	mi	miny	ua
four	dot dot	fa	mo	oa oa
five		sol	eeny mo	oa oa a
six		sol do	meeny mo	oa oa oa
seven		sol re	miny mo	
eight				
nine				
ten				
Base				

12. The coinage system of the planet "Terto" consists of the following coins.
    3 sens = 1 nik
    3 niks = 1 bit
    3 bits = 1 kwat
    3 kwats = 1 halb
    3 halbs = 1 bill
    What is the least number of coins needed to pay for an item costing
    a. 500 sens?
    b. 242 sens?
    c. 81 sens?

13. The exchange rate of the currency of a foreign country is given below.
    1 ot = 1¢
    1 bot = 5¢
    1 cot = 25¢
    1 dot = $1.25
    1 lot = $6.25
    Convert the following amounts of U.S. money to the currency of this new country so that you will have the least number of coins to carry.
    a. $3.78
    b. $12.63
    c. $25.00
    d. $33.40

On the other hand, all the large cities in the United States is *not* a well-defined collection and thus is *not* a set. It is impossible to decide whether some cities should be included or not until the meaning of "large" is clarified, for example, by requiring a large city to be one with a population of 200,000 or more.

1:2 Set Membership and Notation

Set membership is indicated by the notation $a \in S$, which means that the object whose name is a is an element or member of the set whose name is S.

For example, let T be the set of textbooks of a certain student; an algebra book a, a chemistry book c, an English book e, and a history book h. Then

$$a \in T \text{ means} \begin{cases} a \text{ is an element of } T \\ \qquad or \\ a, \text{ the algebra book, is a member of } T, \text{ the set of} \\ \text{textbooks} \end{cases}$$

2. METHODS FOR DEFINING PARTICULAR SETS

Particular sets may be defined by two general methods, the listing method and the description method.

2:1 Definition by Listing

In this method the set is defined by listing or stating the names of its members. For example,

$$A = \{\text{red, white, blue}\}$$

This has the meaning, "A is the name of the set whose members are the colors, red, white, and blue."

When using this method, it is important to use the symbols exactly as indicated. That is, separate the elements of the set by commas and enclose the members of the set with braces, { }, and *not* parentheses, ( ), or brackets, [ ].

2:2 Definition by Description

In this method the set is defined by describing the set or stating a property possessed by each member of the set. For example,

$$A = \text{the set of colors on the flag of the United States}$$

This method of definition is logically more fundamental. The listing method can always be replaced by the description method, but the opposite cannot always be done, even theoretically. For example, it would be difficult to list the set of persons in the world having blue eyes. It would be impossible to list the set of all decimal fractions.

3. SPECIAL SETS

There are two special sets that we shall want to consider: the empty set and the universal set.

3:1 Empty Set

Definition: *The* **empty set** *is the set that has no members.* In symbols, we write

$$\varnothing \qquad \text{or} \qquad \{\ \}$$

Mathematicians consider that there is just one empty set; it is of no concern whether the set has no persons in it or no books in it. Each of the following is a description of the empty set.

> The set of persons over 12 feet tall.
> The set of persons who have been to Mars.
> The set of women on your college football team.

3:2 Universal Set

Definition: *A* **universal set,** *U, is a set to which the elements of all other sets in a particular discussion must belong.* For example, let

$$U = \{1, 2, 3, 4, 5, 6, 7, 8, 9\}$$

Now, if A is the set of multiples of 3, then A must be $\{3, 6, 9\}$. A cannot have the number 12 as a member because 12 does not belong to the universal set that we selected.

As another example, suppose we consider various clubs on campus. Each club would be a set of students. A universal set for our discussion could be the set of all students on campus. Or we could pick as our universal set the set of all college students in the state. Thus it is possible for more than one set to serve as a universal set for a particular discussion. However, we always state what universal set we do select.

4. RELATIONS BETWEEN SETS

4:1 Subsets

Definition: *The set A is a* **subset** *of the set B if every element of A is an element of B.* In symbols, we write $A \subset B$.[1]

The above definition is the same as saying that there are no elements of A that are not elements of B.

For example, the subsets of the set $\{x, y, z\}$ are as follows:

$$\{x\}, \{y\}, \{z\}, \{x, y\}, \{x, z\}, \{y, z\}, \varnothing, \text{ and } \{x, y, z\}$$

The set $\{x, y, z\}$, being all the set, is called an **improper subset** of itself. All the other subsets are called **proper subsets.**

Mathematicians have agreed to regard the empty set as a subset of every set. This does not violate the definition of subset, since there is no element in the empty set that is not in every other set.

We can now state that a universal set is a set that contains all the sets of a particular discussion as its subsets.

4:2 Equal Sets

Definition: *Two sets are said to be* **equal** *if and only if $A \subset B$ and $B \subset A$.* In symbols, we write $A = B$.

Thus $\{x, y, z\} = \{z, x, y\}$. We notice that the order in which the elements are written is not important. It is only necessary that the two sets have exactly the same objects in them. Equal sets are also called **identical sets.**

4:3 Equivalent Sets

Definition: *Two sets, A and B, are said to be* **equivalent** *if and only if their elements can be placed in one-to-one correspondence.* In other words, it must be possible to pair the elements of A with the elements of B in such a way that for every element of A there corresponds exactly one element of B and for every element of B there corresponds exactly one element of A. In symbols, we write $A \leftrightarrow B$.

---

[1] Some authors prefer to use $A \subseteq B$ to mean "A is a subset of B" and $A \subset B$ to mean "A is a proper subset of B."

For example, {red, white, blue} ↔ {x, y, z} because we can exhibit the one-to-one correspondence:

$$\text{red, white, blue}$$
$$\updownarrow \quad \updownarrow \quad \updownarrow$$
$$x, \quad y, \quad z$$

There are other ways in which the matching could have been made, but it is only necessary to find one such correspondence.

We can *think* of equivalent sets as sets having the same number of elements but we cannot *say* this and be mathematically correct, because we have not defined the concept "number." This will be done at the end of this chapter by the use of the more fundamental or basic concept of equivalent sets.

5. VENN DIAGRAMS

By letting the points inside a rectangle represent the universal set U, and the points inside circles represent subsets of U, it is possible to illustrate our knowledge of sets with geometric figures. These figures are called **Venn diagrams.**[2] (See Figure 2.1.) The four possible ways that two

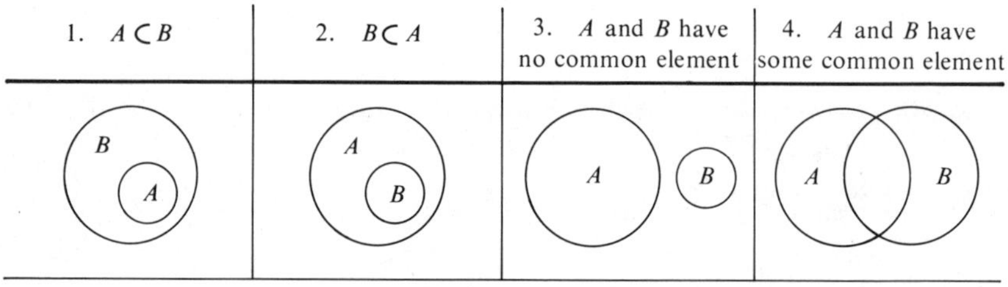

1. $A \subset B$	2. $B \subset A$	3. A and B have no common element	4. A and B have some common element

Figure 2.1

[2]John Venn (1834–1923) used these diagrams to illustrate logic in his work *Symbolic Logic*, published in 1881. (See Midonick, *The Treasury of Mathematics*, pp. 774–785, and read this work in its original form.)

John Venn was an English logician; he was ordained as a priest in 1859, but resigned his order in 1883 to devote all his time to the study and teaching of logic. He remained profoundly religious all his life.

The use of circles to illustrate principles of logic was also employed by the Swiss mathematician Leonard Euler (1707–1783). Thus these diagrams are sometimes called **Euler's circles.** However, Venn was the first to use them in the general way described above.

unequal sets may be related are shown. However, to save ourselves the trouble of having to draw four figures for each of our general discussions, we shall consider the fourth figure to be the general case and draw only this figure. Note in Figure 2.2 that the area inside the rectangle is divided into four compartments, each indicated by one of the numerals 1, 2, 3, or 4. Now, if we consider compartment 2 to be empty, our diagram represents the first figure in Figure 2.1. If we consider compartment 4 empty, we illustrate the second figure in Figure 2.1, and, if we consider compartment 3 empty, we illustrate the third figure. In this way we use only one diagram to represent all the cases possible.

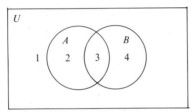

Figure 2.2

6. OPERATIONS ON SETS

There are three basic operations that are performed on sets: complementation, union, and intersection.

6:1 Complementation

Definition: *The* **complement** *of a set A that is a subset of the universal set U is the set of all elements of U that do not belong to A.*

In symbols, we write $\bar{A}$ for the complement of A. (Other notations that are used for $\bar{A}$ are A', $\tilde{A}$, $\sim A$, and $-A$.)

EXAMPLE 1. If the universal set is the set of all students at your college, and if A is the set of all male students at your college, then $\bar{A}$ is the set of all female students at your college.

EXAMPLE 2. Let $U = \{1, 2, 3, 4, 5\}$ and $A = \{2, 4, 5\}$; then $\bar{A} = \{1, 3\}$. The shaded area of Figure 2.3 illustrates $\bar{A}$.

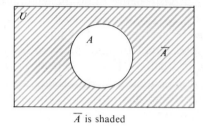

$\bar{A}$ is shaded

Figure 2.3

6:2 Union

Definition: *The **union** of two sets, A and B, is the set of all elements that are in A, or in B, or in both A and B. In symbols, we write $A \cup B$.*

EXAMPLE 1. If $A = \{1, 2, 3, 4\}$ and $B = \{3, 4, 5\}$, then $A \cup B = \{1, 2, 3, 4, 5\}$.

EXAMPLE 2. Let A be the set of all blonde persons, and let B be the set of all brown-eyed persons. Then $A \cup B$ is the set of persons having either blonde hair, or brown eyes, or both.

The shaded area of Figure 2.4 illustrates $A \cup B$.

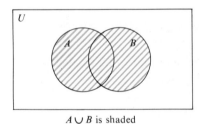

$A \cup B$ is shaded

Figure 2.4

6:3 Intersection

Definition: *The **intersection** of two sets, A and B, is the set of all elements that are in both A and B. In symbols, we write $A \cap B$.*

EXAMPLE 1. If $A = \{1, 2, 3, 4\}$ and $B = \{3, 4, 5\}$, then $A \cap B = \{3, 4\}$.

EXAMPLE 2. Let A be the set of all blonde persons and let B be the set of all brown-eyed persons. Then $A \cap B$ is the set of all brown-eyed blondes.

The shaded area of Figure 2.5 illustrates $A \cap B$.

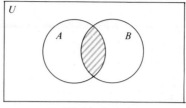

$A \cap B$ is shaded

Figure 2.5

Disjoint Sets. Two sets, A and B, are said to be disjoint if their intersection is empty, that is, if $A \cap B = \emptyset$.

Figure 2.6 illustrates two disjoint sets.

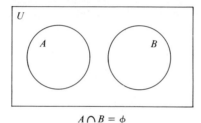

$A \cap B = \phi$

Figure 2.6

7. COMBINATIONS OF OPERATIONS

The three basic operations, complementation, union, and intersection, may be combined in a variety of ways to form other sets.

For example, let $U = \{a, b, c, d, e\}$, $A = \{a, c, e\}$, and $B = \{c, d, e\}$. Then $\bar{A} = \{b, d\}$, $\bar{B} = \{a, b\}$, $A \cup B = \{a, c, d, e\}$, and $A \cap B = \{c, e\}$. From the above sets we can now form new sets by repeating the basic operations. Thus

$$\bar{A} \cup B = \{b, c, d, e\}, \quad \bar{A} \cap B = \{d\}, \quad \bar{A} \cup \bar{B} = \{a, b, d\},$$

$$\bar{A} \cap \bar{B} = \{b\}, \quad \overline{\bar{A} \cup B} = \{a\}, \quad \overline{\bar{A} \cap B} = \{a, b, c, e\},$$

$$\overline{A \cup B} = \{b\}, \quad \overline{A \cap B} = \{a, b, d\}$$

In this example, note that there are two pairs of equal sets above:

$$\bar{A} \cup \bar{B} = \overline{A \cap B} \quad \text{and} \quad \bar{A} \cap \bar{B} = \overline{A \cup B}$$

In general, these equalities are valid. They are illustrated in Figure 2.7. These equalities are called **DeMorgan's laws.**

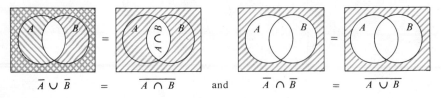

$$\overline{A \cup B} \quad = \quad \overline{A} \cap \overline{B} \quad \text{and} \quad \overline{A} \cap \overline{B} \quad = \quad \overline{A \cup B}$$

Figure 2.7

8. EXTENSION TO THREE SETS

The Venn diagram that is used to illustrate a discussion involving three sets is shown in Figure 2.8. Note that the area inside the rectangle is

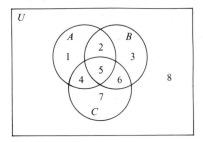

Figure 2.8

divided into eight compartments. These compartments are each assigned a numeral to help identify them. Thus set A consists of compartments 1, 2, 4, and 5.

Observe that $A \cap B$ consists of compartments 2 and 5 and $A \cup B$ consists of compartments 1, 2, 3, 4, 5, and 6.

In addition to the operations involving only two sets, the basic operations may be applied to three sets. For example,

$(A \cup B) \cup C$ consists of compartments 1, 2, 3, 4, 5, 6, 7
$(A \cap B) \cap C$ consists of compartment 5
$(A \cup B) \cap \overline{C}$ consists of compartments 1, 2, 3

These sets are shown in Figure 2.9.

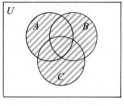

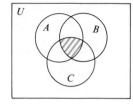

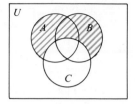

$(A \cup B) \cup C$, shaded $(A \cap B) \cap C$, shaded $(A \cup B) \cap \overline{C}$, shaded

Figure 2.9

9. APPLICATIONS TO SURVEY PROBLEMS

An example illustrating the application of set theory to a survey problem is given next.

EXAMPLE. In a survey of 100 students, the numbers of students studying various subjects was found to be as follows:

English, 56   English and history, 14   all three subjects, 5
history, 38   English and mathematics, 12
mathematics, 30   history and mathematics, 9

    a. How many students were studying none of these subjects?
    b. How many students had English as the only one of these subjects?
    c. How many studied English and history but not mathematics?

Solution. We shall let $E, H,$ and M represent the sets of students studying English, history, and mathematics, respectively. Then we draw the Venn diagram of Figure 2.10 and write the number of students in each of the sets of the eight basic compartments. We begin with the intersection of all three sets, those studying all three subjects. Then, by subtracting this number, 5, from the numbers in the intersections of two sets, we obtain the numbers for three more compartments. Continuing in this manner, we obtain the numbers for each of the eight compartments.

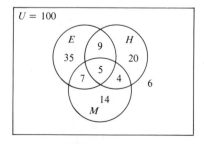

Figure 2.10

a. Now, $(E \cup H) \cup M$, the set of students studying at least one of these subjects, has $35 + 9 + 20 + 7 + 5 + 4 + 14 = 94$ students. Thus the number of students studying none of these subjects, $\overline{(E \cup H) \cup M}$, is $100 - 94 = 6$.
b. The number of students studying English only is 35.
c. The number of students studying English and history but not mathematics is 9.

10. NUMBER

10:1 Cardinal Numbers

Definition: *A* **cardinal number** *is that property of a set which it has in common with all sets that are equivalent to it.*[3] In other words, two sets that are in one-to-one correspondence are said to have the same cardinal number. The cardinal number of a set is often referred to as the "count" of the set. In symbols, we write $n(S)$ to indicate the cardinal number of set S. Thus, if $S = \{a, b, c, d\}$, then $n(S) = 4$. If $S = \varnothing$, then $n(S) = 0$. Thus we see that the cardinal numbers are the number zero and the counting numbers we know as $1, 2, 3, 4, 5, \cdots$.

Note that if $A \leftrightarrow B$, then $n(A) = n(B)$.

It is interesting to observe that this definition is in agreement with the most probable evolution of the abstract number words.

In accordance with the definition above, Figure 2.11 illustrates the cardinal number three. Note that the property that all the different sets have in common is their "threeness" or cardinal number three. The broken line at the right of the figure means that the figure continues in the same manner.

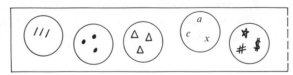

Three

Figure 2.11

---

[3]The first satisfactory definition of number was given by Bertrand Russell in *Introduction to Mathematical Philosophy* (see Newman, *The World of Mathematics*, pp. 537–543), published in 1919. Russell wrote this while in jail, imprisoned for having written a pamphlet accusing the American Army of "intimidating strikes at home." This was regarded as "likely to prejudice His Majesty's relations with the United States." This book put a great burden on the Governor of the prison, who was required to read the manuscript for possible seditious tendencies, even though he was unable to understand the work.

10:2 Counting

In preparation for counting, we shall now assign names to the cardinal numbers of sets by the following process.

Let *A* be the set of a thumb; *B* the set of a thumb and an index finger; *C* the set of a thumb, index finger, and middle finger; and *D* the set of a thumb, index finger, middle finger, and ring finger. Continue in this way to form larger sets by adding one element at a time.

Now let us assign names to the cardinal numbers of these sets. We shall let $n(A)$ be 1, $n(B)$ be 2, $n(C)$ be 3, $n(D)$ be 4, and so on. Now we shall arrange these numbers in order from left to right according to the position their sets occupy in the chain of subsets $A \subset B \subset C \subset D \cdots$.

Continuing this process indefinitely, we obtain an unending *ordered* set of cardinal numbers,

$$N = [1, 2, 3, 4, 5, 6, \cdots]$$

Brackets [ ] are used to enclose the elements of an ordered set to distinguish it from a general set whose elements are not necessarily ordered.

The ordered subsets of *N*,

$$[1], [1, 2], [1, 2, 3], [1, 2, 3, 4], \cdots$$

are called the **counting sets.**

Definition: Counting *is a one-to-one correspondence of the elements of a set of objects with the elements of an appropriate counting set.*

For example, to count the letters in the word "table," a number from a counting set is matched to each letter in the word. The counting set used is the one necessary to establish the one-to-one correspondence.

Set to be counted: {T, A, B, L, E}

Counting set: [1, 2, 3, 4, 5]

Thus the number of the set { T, A, B, L, E } is 5, the *last* cardinal number in the counting set.

10:3 Ordinal Numbers

A cardinal number tells us how many objects are in a set. An **ordinal number** tells us the position of an element in a set according to a particular arrangement.

Very often, but not always, the ordinal numbers are written "1st, 2nd, 3rd, 4th, 5th, $\cdots$" and read "first, second, third, fourth, fifth, $\cdots$" instead of "one, two, three, four, five, $\cdots$."

The process of "matching" is a cardinal concept, whereas the process of "counting" is an ordinal concept. However, the two processes are related when they are used. When we count 1, 2, 3, · · ·, the numbers named are considered ordinal numbers. When we reach the end of the count, having determined the size of the set, the last ordinal number named is identified as the number of the counted set, or as a cardinal number.

Study the examples in Table 2.1 and note the difference between a cardinal number (how many?) and an ordinal number (in what position?). In each example, the numeral in the first statement names a cardinal number while the numeral in the second statement names an ordinal number.

TABLE 2.1 CARDINAL AND ORDINAL NUMBERS

CARDINAL	ORDINAL
a.1. This book has 250 pages.	2. The map is on page 250.
b.1. The cost is 30 cents.	2. I live in apartment 30.
c.1. Over 100 people were there.	2. He was the 100th person to come.
d.1. The store sold 1850 books today.	2. He was born in 1850.
e.1. Today he worked 8 hours.	2. The time is 8 o'clock.

EXERCISES

1. Which of the following collections are sets; that is, which are well defined?
   a. The states in the United States bordering on Canada.
   b. The large states in the United States.
   c. The students at your college over 200 years old.
   d. The students at your college enrolled in a mathematics course.
   e. The happy students at your college.
   f. The stars in the universe.
   g. The counting numbers; 1, 2, 3, 4, · · ·.
2. List the elements in each of the following sets, using the pattern $S = \{a, b, c, \cdots \}$.
   a. The states in the United States bordering on the Pacific Ocean.
   b. The different letters in the word "letter."
   c. The counting numbers that exactly divide 60.
   d. The planets of our solar system.
   e. The former presidents of the United States alive today.
   f. All fractions having 1 for a numerator.
   g. The women who have been presidents of the United States.

3. Describe the following sets by stating a property that determines membership in the set.
   a. {penny, nickel, dime, quarter, half-dollar, dollar}
   b. {April, June, September, November}
   c. {c, o, l, e, g}
   d. {5, 10, 15, 20, 25, · · ·}
   e. { }

4. Which of the following describes the empty set?
   a. The set of humans who are 15 feet tall.
   b. The set of humans who have been to the moon.
   c. The set whose only element is the number zero.
   d. The set of birds who cannot fly.
   e. The set of customers in the post office on Sunday.

5. Name a set that will serve as the universal set for both sets in each of the following pairs.
   a. A = {red, white, blue} B = {green, yellow}
   b. A = the set of vowels B = the letters in "defined"
   c. A = {pie, cake, pudding} B = {coffee, tea, milk}
   d. A = {cat, dog, cow} B = {horse, pig}
   e. A = {orange, apple} B = {peas, carrots, onions}

6. List all the subsets of the set {bird, cat, dog}.

7. Using symbols, write as many proper subset relations as possible among the following sets.
   a. A = set of all letters of the English alphabet.
   b. B = set of all different letters in the word "pneumonia."
   c. C = set of vowels in the English alphabet.
   d. D = set of different letters used in the sentence "New jackets of your next book provide logarithms and a quiz."

8. In how many ways can the set {O, W, N} be placed in one-to-one correspondence with itself? Indicate these ways. In how many of these ways does the new arrangement of letters spell a word?

9. Determine which of the following sets are equal and which are equivalent.
   A = the set of letters in the word "tent"
   B = {10}
   C = {N, E, T}
   D = {3, 5, 7}
   E = {5 + 5}
   F = { }
   G = {0}

10. Determine each of the following sets described in questions a, b, c, and d by selecting a set from those defined as follows:
    A = {5}, B = {F, I, V, E}, C = {5, 10, 15, 20}, D = {V, I, E, F}
    E is the set of different letters in the word "repeat."

    a. A set whose number is 5.
    b. A set equal to set *B*.
    c. A set equivalent to *B* but not equal to *B*.
    d. A proper subset of another set above.

11. Determine each of the following sets described in questions a, b, c, and d by selecting a set or sets from those defined as follows:
    A = the set of different letters in the expression "numeral systems"
    B = the set of numbers which are finger-counting number bases
    $C = \{5, 10, 20\}$
    $D = \{T, E, N\}$
    a. A set whose number is 10.
    b. A proper subset of one of the sets listed above.
    c. A pair of equal sets.
    d. A pair of equivalent sets that are not equal.

12. Let
    N = the set of baseball teams in the National League
    G = the Giants
    D = the Dodgers
    F = the Giant outfielders
    a. Illustrate how these sets are related by drawing a diagram.
    b. Write an English sentence for each of the following and then determine whether each statement has meaning or not. (That is, can you decide whether the statement is true or false?)

      1. $G \subset N$ 7. $N \in D$
      2. $D \subset N$ 8. $F \in N$
      3. $D \subset G$ 9. $F \subset N$
      4. $G \cap D = \varnothing$ 10. $G \not\subset D$
      5. $G \cap N = \varnothing$ 11. $G \leftrightarrow D$
      6. $G \in N$ 12. $G = D$

13. Draw a diagram to illustrate each of the following.
    a. $A \subset B$ and $B \subset C$.
    b. $A \subset B$ and $B \cap C = \varnothing$.
    c. $A \subset B$ and $C \subset B$ (four cases).
    d. $A \subset B$ and $A \cap C = \varnothing$ (three cases).
    e. $A \cap B = \varnothing, A \cap C \neq \varnothing, B \cap C \neq \varnothing$, and no set is a subset of the other two.

14. Let $U = \{a, b, c, d, e, f\}$, $A = \{a, b, c, e\}$, $B = \{a, b, c, d\}$
    Describe each of the following sets by listing its members.
    a. $\bar{A}$ c. $A \cup B$ e. $\bar{A} \cup B$ g. $\overline{A \cup B}$ i. $\bar{A} \cup \bar{B}$
    b. $\bar{B}$ d. $A \cap B$ f. $A \cap \bar{B}$ h. $\overline{A \cap B}$ j. $\bar{A} \cap \bar{B}$

15. Draw a Venn diagram to illustrate each of the sets in Exercise 14.

16. List each of the following sets and draw a Venn diagram for each.
    $U = \{s, t, o, n, e\}$ and $A = \{o, n, e\}$ and $B = \{n, e, t\}$
    a. $A \cap B$ b. $\bar{A} \cup B$ c. $A \cup \bar{B}$ d. $\overline{\bar{A} \cup B}$ e. $\bar{A} \cap B$
    Which of these sets are equal?

17. Let $U = \{1, 2, 3, 4, 5, 6, 7\}$ and $A = \{1, 2, 3, 4\}$ and $B = \{1, 2, 5, 6\}$ and $C = \{1, 3, 5, 7\}$. List the members of each of the following sets and draw a Venn diagram for each.

   a. $(A \cap B) \cap C$ d. $A \cap (B \cup C)$ g. $\overline{A \cup B} \cap C$
   b. $(A \cup B) \cup C$ e. $(A \cup B) \cap C$ h. $(A \cap B) \cup \overline{C}$
   c. $(A \cap B) \cup C$ f. $A \cup (B \cap C)$

18. Let $U = \{f, i, l, t, e, r\}$ and $A = \{f, i, l, e\}$, $B = \{l, i, f, t\}$, and $C = \{r, i, t, e\}$. By listing the members of each of the following sets and by drawing a Venn diagram for each, determine whether each of the following statements is true or false for this special case.

   a. $(A \cup B) \cup C = A \cup (B \cup C)$ d. $\overline{A \cup B \cup C} = \overline{A} \cap \overline{B} \cap \overline{C}$
   b. $(A \cap B) \cap C = A \cap (B \cap C)$ e. $\overline{A \cap B \cap C} = \overline{A} \cup \overline{B} \cup \overline{C}$
   c. $(A \cup B) \cap C = A \cup (B \cap C)$

19. In a certain survey of dining habits, the following information was established:

50 ordered salad	15 ordered salad and soup
65 ordered dessert	25 ordered dessert and soup
50 ordered soup	10 ordered salad, dessert, and soup
20 ordered salad and dessert	20 ordered none of the three

   a. How many people were in the survey?
   b. How many people ordered salad and dessert but not soup?
   c. How many people ordered salad but not dessert?
   d. How many people ordered salad only?

20. A survey of college students revealed the following information about their dates:

44 were beautiful	8 were beautiful and intelligent
30 were intelligent	11 were beautiful and personable
51 were personable	9 were intelligent and personable
	3 were beautiful, intelligent, and personable

   Using a Venn diagram to obtain your answers, answer each of the following.
   a. How many girls were included in the survey? (least number possible)
   b. How many girls were beautiful but not personable?
   c. How many girls were intelligent or personable but not beautiful?

21. A survey of 150 persons revealed the following information:

55 liked classical music	15 liked classical music and jazz
65 liked jazz	25 liked jazz and light opera
75 liked light opera	20 liked classical music and light opera
	5 liked all three

   a. How many liked jazz and light opera?
   b. How many liked classical music but did not like jazz?
   c. How many liked neither classical music nor jazz?
   d. How many liked only classical music?
   e. How many people did not like any of the three?

22. Determine whether each numeral in the following statements refers to a cardinal number or an ordinal number.

    a. The picture is on page 43.

    b. Read 43 pages.

    c. There are 7 days in a week.

    d. The date is May 7.

    e. Number 35 made the touchdown.

    f. They have 35 players on their squad.

    g. The address is 10 Main Street.

    h. Man has 10 fingers.

23. Let S = the set of all months of the year having exactly 30 days.

    a. What is the cardinal number of S?

    b. If the months in S are arranged in calendar order, what is the ordinal number of June?

24. Let Q = the set of all months of the year not having the letter "r" in their name.

    a. What is the cardinal number of Q?

    b. If the months of Q are arranged in alphabetical order, what is the ordinal number of June?

25. Venn suggests using four ellipses such as those shown to illustrate four sets. If the numerals on the diagram are used to identify the compartments, use these numerals to identify each of the following.

    a. $A \cup B$

    b. $A \cap B$

    c. $A \cap B \cap C$
       $A \cap B \cap \bar{C} \cap \bar{D}$

    d. $A \cap B \cap \bar{C} \cap \bar{D}$

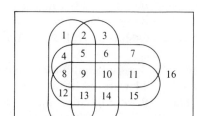

THE ANCIENT
ORIENTAL
PERIOD

During the period from 5000 to 3000 B.C., the well-established Neolithic communities of the prehistoric period gradually evolved into the more advanced societies of the historic period. The communities were located along the fertile river valleys of warm regions in Asia and Africa. The rivers were the Nile in Egypt; the Tigris and Euphrates in the country now called Iraq, formerly Persia, and even earlier Babylonia; the Indus and later the Ganges in India; and the Hoang-ho and later the Yangtse in China.

Our historical sources are from Egypt and Babylonia. The people of China and India wrote on bark or bamboo, which are very perishable, and the Chinese used paper around 200 A.D., also very perishable. We have no records preserved from these areas before 400 A.D. On the other hand, the Babylonians wrote on granite and on clay tablets that were later baked. Both of these materials are almost indestructible. There are over 400 mathematical tablets in museums in Europe and the United States. The Egyptians wrote on papyrus, the inner bark of a vegetable, and this material was preserved due to the dry climate.

The religion of these early people can be described as one that identifies nature and the universe with a set of gods. Unlike the Greeks, who had a temple for each of their gods, each of their deities was accompanied by a group of companion gods.

Socially, the ancient Orientals were divided into two classes. The upper or ruling class consisted of the royalty and governmental and religious officials. These included priests, military generals, architects and master builders, agricultural overseers, judges, treasurers, and scribes. The lower class consisted of shepherds and slaves, both native and captured in war. Later, probably around 1300 B.C., a middle class emerged. These were merchants, traders, artisans, free workmen, weavers, potters, carpenters, and so forth.

The Oriental philosophy was a practical one, answering the question "How?" by stating the rule, "Do thus and so." Their mathematics was more algebraic in character than it was geometric; that is, it was more concerned with number relations. The Egyptian papyri and the Babylonian tablets are essentially handbooks containing mathematical tables and various practical problems together with their solutions. Their documents show these early people to be excellent table makers and computers of great skill. However, there is no evidence of any attempt to give a reason or supply a proof. This philosophy, a concern for answering the question "Why?," was developed later by the Greeks.

Historical records indicate that the early Oriental mathematics developed as a practical science to solve the problems of agriculture and engineering. This involved the computations of the calendar and the solution of problems related to irrigation, surveying, harvesting, food storage, the collection of taxes, the administration of public works, and commercial accounts. In most ancient societies, the priests were the mathematicians and teachers, and the students came from the upper class.

As we enter the period of recorded history, we find in existence the calendar and a primitive astronomy, well-developed numeral systems and systems of weights and measures and a practical arithmetic, and problems with solutions from which the subjects of algebra and geometry evolved.

HISTORICAL CHRONOLOGY

4700 B.C.   Babylonians had a calendar and arithmetic. Tablets dated around 2100 B.C. show their year started with the vernal equinox and the first month was named after Taurus. The constellation of Taurus was in this appropriate position of the sky around 4700 B.C.

4241 B.C.   Introduction of the Egyptian calendar of 12 months of 30 days each and 5 feast days. (Breasted, J. H., *Ancient Times*, Boston, 1916, p. 45.)

3100 B.C.   Royal Egyptian mace in museum at Oxford. On the mace are several numbers in the millions and hundred-thousands written in Egyptian hieroglyphs, recording results of a successful military campaign.

3000 B.C.   Ruins of the city Mohenjo Daro on the Indus River in India show that they had systems of writing; brick dwellings; apartment houses with tiled bathrooms; covered city drains; community swimming pools; systems of counting, weighing, and measuring; irrigation canals; and wide streets.

2900 B.C.   Great pyramid of Gizeh erected. The pyramid age,
or   2900–2200 B.C.
2700 B.C.

2200 B.C.   Over 400 Babylonian mathematical tablets, now
to   in museums in Europe and at Yale, Columbia, and the
1600 B.C.   University of Pennsylvania. Each tablet is about the size of a hand. The age of a tablet is inferred from the stratum of the mound where it was found, or from the style of the handwriting.

1850 B.C.   Moscow papyrus from Egypt. Discovered in 1890 and acquired by the Moscow Museum of Fine Arts in 1912. Contains 25 problems, published 1930 A.D.

1650 B.C.   Rhind papyrus from Egypt. Most of it is in the British museum in London, but some fragments are in the New York Historical Museum. Contains 85 problems, published 1927 A.D. Written by the Egyptian scribe, Ahmes, who wrote that he copied it from an earlier one. Named after Henry Rhind, an Egyptologist from Scotland, who found it in Egypt in 1858 A.D.

REFERENCES FOR
ANCIENT ORIENTAL PERIOD

Aaboe, *Episodes from the Early History of Mathematics*, pp. 1–33.

Eves, *An Introduction to the History of Mathematics*, pp. 7–51.

Midonick, *The Treasury of Mathematics:*
    "The Babylonians," pp. 45–90.
    "The Moscow Papyrus," pp. 507–521.

"The Rhind Papyrus," pp. 706–732.
"The Maya Civilization," pp. 465–495.
"The Sun-Tsu Suan-ching," pp. 751–758.

Newman, *The World of Mathematics*, Vol. 1:
"The Rhind Papyrus," pp. 169–178.
"From Numbers to Numerals," pp. 442–464.

Struik, *A Concise History of Mathematics*, pp. 13–38.

Swain, *Understanding Arithmetic*, pp. 1–26 and pp. 97–112.

CHAPTER III

Numeral Systems

(The Egyptians) calculate with pebbles by moving
the hand from right to left, while the Hellenes
(Greeks) move it from left to right.

Herodotus, Greek historian
(about 450 B.C.)

1. SIMPLE GROUPING NUMERAL SYSTEMS

A simple grouping numeral system is a system for writing numerals in
which symbols are invented to indicate the number of objects in the
different basic groups into which the objects are arranged for counting.
The sizes of the different groups are determined by whatever number is
selected as the **base** of the system. The numeral that is used to name a
particular number is obtained by writing in juxtaposition (side by side)
the symbols that are required to produce that particular number when
the numbers indicated by the symbols are added.

An important feature of a simple grouping numeral system is the
addition principle; that is, the values of the written symbols are added to
produce the number represented. A feature of unciphered systems is the
repetition principle; that is, symbols are repeated when necessary.

Examination and study of various historical examples of simple
grouping systems will illustrate the principles of this type of numeral
system.

1:1 Egyptian Hieroglyphic Numerals

The Egyptian **hieroglyphic numerals** were developed before 3000 B.C.
and were used by the Egyptians to inscribe numerals on stone. Hiero-

glyphic means "sacred picture writing." For writing on papyrus, the priests used a script notation called **hieratic** (priestly). Another type of writing, called **demotic** (popular), was for general use.

The hieroglyphic symbols are illustrated in Figure 3.1 together with a probable interpretation of each symbol. As the numerals indicate, the base of their system was 10. The Egyptians generally wrote from right to left, the opposite of the way we are accustomed to writing. Occasionally they wrote from left to right and also from top to bottom.

1	10	100	1,000	10,000	100,000	1,000,000	10,000,000
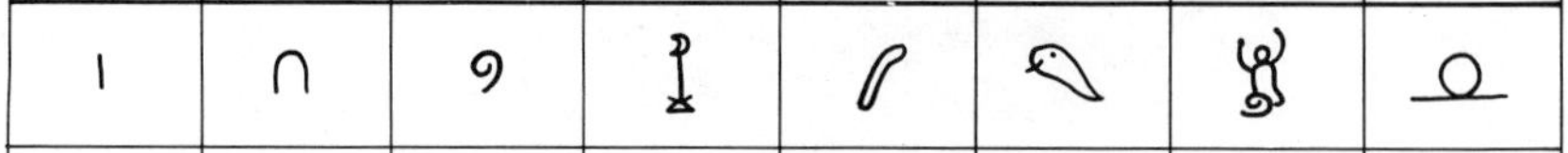 |	∩	ᕼ	𐦜	ℓ	ᕦ	ⵛ	ⵙ
vertical staff	heel bone	rope coil, scroll	lotus flower	pointing finger	burbot (fish)	astonished man	sun?

Figure 3.1

The ancient Egyptian numerals for the numbers from 1 to 20 are shown in Figure 3.2. Repeated symbols were usually written in groups of three or four for clarity in reading.

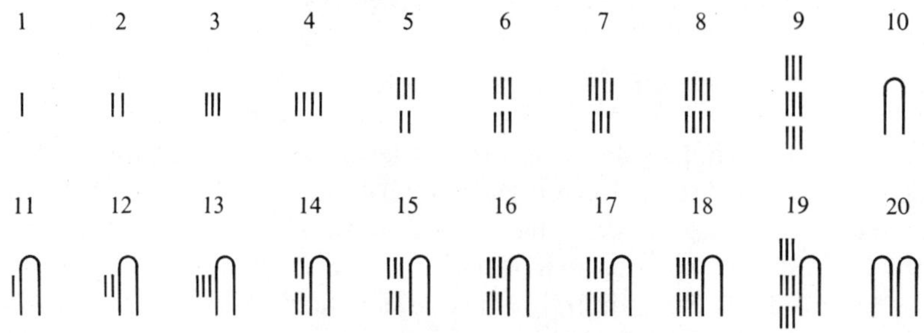

1	2	3	4	5	6	7	8	9	10

11	12	13	14	15	16	17	18	19	20

Figure 3.2

The number 2,345,678 could have been written by the Egyptians as

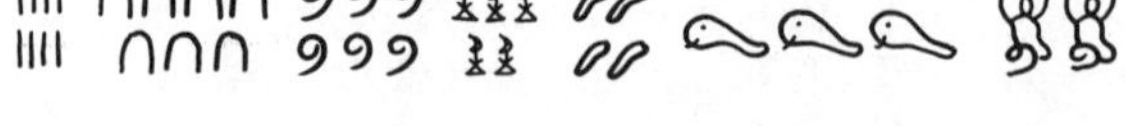

Usually the numerals would be written in a symmetric pattern to achieve a pleasing appearance. However, note that the order or position of the different symbols has no effect on the value of the number being represented. No matter how the symbols were arranged, the sum of the values of the written symbols would always be the same number.

For example, the number 234 *could* have been written in any of the ways shown in Figure 3.3.

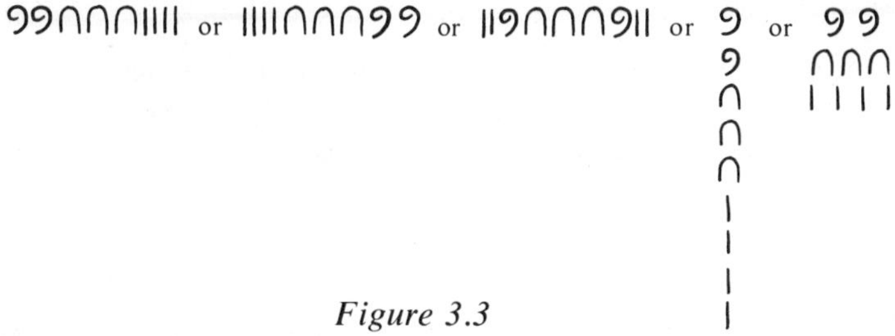

99∩∩∩IIII or IIII∩∩∩99 or II9∩∩∩9II or 9 or 99
                                     9 ∩∩∩
                                     ∩ I I I I
                                     ∩
                                     ∩
                                     I
                                     I
                                     I
                                     I

Figure 3.3

1:2 Babylonian Cuneiform Numerals

Babylonian numerals found on tablets dated around 2000 B.C. developed from those used by the Sumerians before 3000 B.C. The Babylonians were able to express all their numerals as combinations of two **cuneiform** (wedge-shaped) symbols. One was a vertical wedge produced by pressing a prism-shaped stylus or rod into wet clay. The other was a corner wedge that was written horizontally.

∇ represented 1 and ⟨ represented 10

One authority[1] believes that the symbol for 10 was originally the picture of two hands, held in prayer, the palms pressed together, the fingers close to each other, and the thumbs thrust out. These symbols are simplified in Figure 3.4 for convenience in writing.

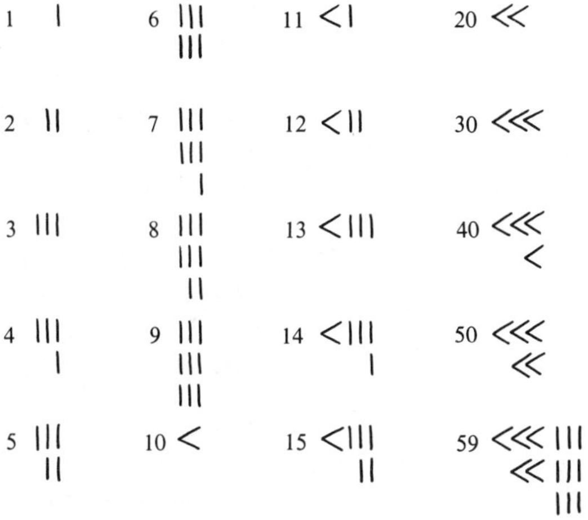

1 I	6 III III	11 <I	20 ≪
2 II	7 III III I	12 <II	30 ≪≪
3 III	8 III III II	13 <III	40 ≪≪ <
4 III I	9 III III III	14 <III I	50 ≪≪ ≪
5 III II	10 <	15 <III II	59 ≪≪ III ≪ III III

Figure 3.4

———

[1] Cajori, *A History of Mathematics*.

Some of the tablets from Nippur indicate the use of the **subtractive principle** similar to that used in writing the Roman numeral XXIX instead of XXVIIII for 29. For example, the Babylonians sometimes wrote ≪≪ ⊓ for 29, meaning 30 − 1.

To represent numbers larger than 59, the Babylonians used a positional numeral system with base 60. The 59 digits used in this system were those for the numbers from 1 to 59 obtained by the simple grouping method explained above. Their complete system will be studied later.

1:3 Attic Greek Numerals

Before 300 B.C., perhaps around 600 B.C., the Greeks used letters of their alphabet for numerals just as the Romans did several centuries later. The numerals for 5 and the powers of 10 (10, 100, 1000, and 10,000) were the initial letters of the names of these numbers. This system is a simple grouping one similar to the Egyptian except that the Greeks combined numerals to obtain symbols for the numbers 50, 500, 5000, and 50,000.

These numerals were described by the grammarian Herodianus in the second century of our era and thus are also called **Herodianic numerals.** However, they are more properly called **Attic numerals,** because they are the ones that are always found in Attic inscriptions[2] (Figure 3.5).

1	5	10	50	100	500	1,000	5,000	10,000	50,000
I	⌐	△	⌐ᴬ⌐	H	⌐ᴴ⌐	X	⌐ˣ⌐	M	⌐ᴹ⌐

Figure 3.5

⌐, pi, an old form of π, initial letter of "pente," meaning "five."
△, delta, initial letter of "deka," meaning "ten."
H, initial letter of "hekaton," meaning "hundred."
X, chi, initial letter of "kilo," or "chilo," meaning "thousand."
M, mu, initial letter for "myriad," meaning "ten thousand."

As an example, the number 24,789 would be written in this system as

$$MMXXXX⌐ᴴ⌐HH⌐ᴬ⌐△△△⌐IIII$$

A vase in a museum at Naples has a decoration that refers to the Persian wars of the time of Darius, about 500 B.C. One picture shows a man seated at a table on which the Attic numerals for 5, 10, 100, 1000, and 10,000 appear.[3]

---

[2] "Attic" pertains to Attica, a territory in Greece surrounding Athens and unified under the control of Athens about 700 B.C.
[3] Newman, *The World of Mathematics*, Vol. 1, p. 447.

1:4 Roman Numerals

Early Roman Numerals. Roman numerals were derived from certain Greek letters not adopted in the Etruscan and early Latin alphabets. There is a monument in Rome, dated 260 B.C., which commemorates the victory over the Carthaginians. On this monument is the numeral for 100,000 repeated 23 times, thus representing the number 2,300,000. The forms of the Roman numerals used as late as 1582 A.D. are shown in a work by a Swiss scholar, Freigius, published in that year.[4] These forms are shown in Figure 3.6.

1	I	100	C	10,000	CCIƆƆ
5	V	500	D or IƆ	50,000	IƆƆƆ
10	X	1000	CIƆ, ⅭⅮ, ⅭⅠⅠⅠ, M	100,000	CCCIƆƆƆ
50	L or ⊥ or ↓	5000	IƆƆ	500,000	IƆƆƆƆ

Figure 3.6

The probable origins of Roman numerals are summarized below.

I,   II, III, and IIII, a stroke or strokes to represent fingers or tally marks.

V,   half an X, or perhaps a simplified picture of an open hand.

X,   picture of two crossed arms, or the tally ⧻⧻⧻⧻⧻, or a double V.

L,   and ⊥ and ↓, old forms of the Greek letter chi.

C,   from the Greek letter theta, Θ, an old form being ⊙. This became ⊂ and finally C. The choice of C was influenced by the fact that it is the initial letter of the Latin word "centum," meaning "hundred."

M,   from the Greek letter phi, Φ, modified to CIƆ and M. The choice of M was influenced by the fact that it is the initial letter of the Latin word "mille," meaning "thousand."

D,   half of ⅭⅮ, just as IƆ is half of CIƆ.

Late Roman Numerals. In Europe Roman numerals were used in bookkeeping until as late as the eighteenth century. Certain European cities forbade the use of our modern Hindu-Arabic numerals in 1300 because they were easier to forge or falsify. The "0" could be easily changed into a "6" or a "9," for example. Also, addition and subtraction were much more easily performed using Roman numerals.

After the invention of the printing press in 1438 A.D., both the Hindu-Arabic and the Roman numerals became *standardized*. The Roman numerals for 50, 100, and 1000 were standardized as L, C, and M, respectively.

---

[4] Newman, *The World of Mathematics*, Vol. 1, pp. 448–450.

The subtraction principle was seldom used until quite recently. It was not popular because it could not be placed on the abacus, the instrument used for computing. The principle of subtraction was used in writing "fours" and "nines." A symbol for a smaller unit placed before a symbol for a larger unit indicates that the smaller is to be subtracted from the larger. For example,

$$\begin{array}{ll} \text{IV is written for IIII} \\ \quad \text{IX} \qquad \text{for VIIII} \\ \quad \text{XL} \qquad \text{for XXXX} \\ \quad \text{XC} \qquad \text{for LXXXX, and so on} \end{array}$$

The use of a bar over a numeral to indicate a multiplication by 1000 was seen occasionally, as in Pliny (1st century A.D.), but it was not common because the bar was also used to distinguish a numeral from a word. The favorite method for writing numerals for large numbers was that already shown for 100,000. Thus the number 1,000,000 was written

$$\text{CCCC|}\mathfrak{DDD}$$

EXAMPLE. $\overline{\text{X}}$ was written to represent 10,000, $\overline{\text{XXV}}$ to represent 25,000.

1:5 Aztec Numerals (Optional)

The Aztec numerals[5] furnish an interesting example of a simple grouping numeral system that does not use 10 as its base (see Figure 3.7). The

AZTEC NUMERALS

1	10	20	400	8000
a dot or finger		flag	feather	bag with tassels

Figure 3.7

base of this system is 20. For example, 404 is written on the Codex Mendocino as

---

[5] Peterson, Frederick, *Ancient Mexico*, New York: G. P. Putnam's Sons (Capricorn Books), 1962, p. 184.

The number 93 could have been written

2. CIPHERED NUMERAL SYSTEMS

2:1 General Discussion

A ciphered numeral system is one in which different symbols are created for each of the digits. In a ciphered simple grouping numeral system, different symbols are also created for basic multiples of the digits. Advantages of cipherization are the elimination of the repetition of symbols and the reduction in the number of symbols required to write most numerals.

To illustrate this principle, let us use our English alphabet with the symbol "#" included to make a total of 27 different symbols. Then we can cipher or code our numerals for the numbers from 1 through 999 in the following manner:

1	a	10	j	100	s	6	f	60	o	600	x
2	b	20	k	200	t	7	g	70	p	700	y
3	c	30	l	300	u	8	h	80	q	800	z
4	d	40	m	400	v	9	i	90	r	900	#
5	e	50	n	500	w						

The number 265 would be written "toe"; that is, $t + o + e = 200 + 60 + 5$.

More symbols would be needed to represent numbers larger than 999 if the pattern is to be extended. Disadvantages of this system are the increase in memory work required to learn all the different symbols and the confusion arising because some numerals look like words.

The Egyptian hieratic numerals, developed from the hieroglyphic numerals, furnish an example of a ciphered system that was not alphabetic (Figure 3.8).

Figure 3.8

The early Hindu Brahmi system used before 300 B.C. is another example of a ciphered system. The special Egyptian hieratic symbols for

5, 7, 8, and 9 indicate a step toward the later Hindu system from which our modern numerals are derived.

2:2 Ionic Greek Numerals

Around the fourth century B.C., the Greeks began to use the letters of their alphabet supplemented by three old Phoenician letters (used for 6, 90, and 900) to cipher their numerals. Capital letters were first used. The use of small letters, shown in Figure 3.9, is a relatively modern invention.

1	α	alpha	10	ι	iota	100	ρ	rho
2	β	beta	20	κ	kappa	200	σ	sigma
3.	γ	gamma	30	λ	lambda	300	τ	tau
4	δ	delta	40	μ	mu	400	υ	upsilon
5	ϵ	epsilon	50	ν	nu	500	ϕ	phi
6	ζ	vau	60	ξ	xi	600	χ	chi
7	ζ	zeta	70	o	omicron	700	ψ	psi
8	η	eta	80	π	pi	800	ω	omega
9	θ	theta	90	ϱ	koph (our Q)	900	λ	sampi

Figure 3.9

The numbers 1000, 2000, $\cdots$, 9000 were written as $/\alpha, /\beta, \cdots, /\theta$. The numbers 10,000, 20,000, $\cdots$, 90,000 were written as $M, \beta M$ or $\overset{\beta}{M}, \cdots, \theta M$ or $\overset{\theta}{M}$. For example, the number 234 was written as $\sigma\lambda\delta$ and the number 50,312 was written as

$$\overset{\epsilon}{M}\tau\iota\beta$$

By using this system, the Greeks were able to write all the numbers less than 1000 with at most three symbols. However, the confusion arising between words and numerals led to numerology and superstitions associated with numbers. For example, the word "amen" is "$\alpha\mu\eta\nu$" in Greek, which is also $1 + 40 + 8 + 50 = 99$. The number 99 appears as a substitute for "amen" in many old editions of the Bible.

Also in the Bible, in the book of Revelations, the number 666 is used as the "number of the beast." Much later 666 was used to refer to certain prominent persons who were disliked.

Plato said that the odd numbers were given to the gods, and Shakespeare wrote "There is divinity in odd numbers" (*The Merry Wives of Windsor*).

3. MULTIPLICATIVE GROUPING NUMERAL SYSTEMS

3:1 General Discussion

A logical development of a simple grouping numeral system is a multiplicative system. Two sets of symbols are used in this system. One set consists of the symbols for the basic digits and the other set consists of the symbols for the powers of the base. For example, in a base 10 system there would be different symbols for the digits (1, 2, 3, 4, 5, 6, 7, 8, 9) and the powers of 10 (10, 100, 1000, $\cdots$).

To represent a number the symbols are written alternately, one symbol indicating the number of groups of the size indicated by the next symbol. For example, if we let I, X, C, and M represent 1, 10, 100, and 1000, respectively, then our decimal numeral 3456 would be written 3M 4C 5X 6I in a multiplicative grouping system. The symbol for the 1s group, I, may be omitted, because it is not necessary. In this example the numeral is written horizontally. If it were written vertically, it would be written

$$
\begin{array}{c}
3 \\
M \\
4 \\
C \\
5 \\
X \\
6
\end{array}
$$

An important feature of the multiplicative grouping system is the **multiplication** principle. The symbols of a numeral are separated into pairs and the numbers represented in each pair are multiplied. Then these products are added to determine the number that the numeral represents. For example, 3M   4C   5X   6I   means

$$(3 \times 1000) + (4 \times 100) + (5 \times 10) + (6 \times 1) = 3456$$

When we read 3456 as "*three* thousand *four* hundred *fifty-six*," we are using the multiplicative grouping principle.

3:2 Traditional Chinese Numerals

The traditional Chinese numeral system is an example of a vertically written multiplicative grouping system with base 10 (Figure 3.10). The type of symbols used reflects the fact that the Chinese wrote with brush and ink on bark, bamboo, silk, and paper.

Note that the digits are ciphered in this system, thus avoiding repetition of symbols. Also the memorization of 27 or more different symbols is eliminated by the use of the multiplication principle.

1	2	3	4	5	6	7	8	9
一	二	三	四	五	六	七	八	九

10	100	1000	10,000	100,000
十	百	千	萬	億

Figure 3.10

EXAMPLE. The decimal numeral 3456 would be written

3:3 Tamil Numerals[6] (Optional)

Tamil is a branch of the Dravidian stock to which the original inhabitants of India belonged. These people inhabit the extreme south of India and have remained comparatively free of admixture with the Sanskrit-speaking Indo-Europeans and other invading races. They adopted and developed the civilization of their conquerors but retained their own language. The Tamil language is still spoken in the extreme south of India, in Ceylon, and in other places farther east. The language dates to the beginning of the Christian era and their earliest literature to the ninth century A.D.

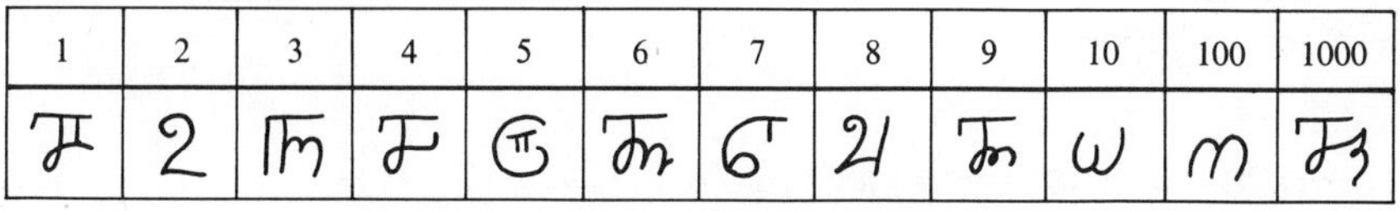

1	2	3	4	5	6	7	8	9	10	100	1000
乐	2	ﬁ	于	⑤	丞	6	21	丞	ω	⑰	丞3

Figure 3.11

The Tamil numeral system is a multiplicative grouping system, base 10, written horizontally (Figure 3.11).

EXAMPLE. The decimal numeral 3456 would be written

$$\text{ﬁ 丞3 于 ⑰ ⑤ ω 丞}$$

It is probable that these numerals of Ceylon are the old, imperfect numerals of India.

Around 300 A.D. the Indian culture was transplanted to Ceylon, where it remained stationary while on the continent the same culture progressed.

The symbols are probably the initial letters of the corresponding numeral adjectives.

4. POSITIONAL NUMERAL SYSTEMS

The most advanced type of numeral system is the **positional system.** In a completely developed positional numeral system, a number is selected as the base; then symbols are selected for each number from 1 to the number that is one less than the base; and, finally, a symbol is selected

---

[6] *Encyclopaedia Britannica.*

for zero. The number of symbols is then the same as the number of the base. A number is represented by placing these symbols in a specified order, the position that a symbol occupies determining the value of the number the symbol represents. The value of each position is obtained by multiplying the base by the value of the position immediately preceding it, with the first position assigned the value 1.

Our Hindu-Arabic numeral system is a positional, base 10, numeral system, referred to as a **decimal system.** For example, 567 represents the sum of five 100s and six 10s and seven 1s. Each position has a value 10 times that of the one on its right. Since 10 is being used as the multiplier to determine positional value, the base is 10.

The important characteristics of a completely developed positional numeral system are:

1. The base, b.
2. Symbols for the digits $1, 2, 3, \cdots, b - 1$.
3. A symbol for zero, the number of the empty set.
4. The principle of place value.
5. The principle of cipherization (a different symbol for each digit).
6. A separation symbol, such as our decimal point, to represent fractions.

Our modern decimal system has all the above features. However, not all these features need to be present in a particular positional system. In fact, our Hindu-Arabic system is the only one in which the digits are ciphered. The other historical examples we shall examine all exhibit the simple grouping technique for forming the numerals for the basic digits. We have seen that the principle of cipherization can be traced to the Greeks and the Egyptians and the use of the positional principle to the ancient Babylonians. Thus we should probably call our modern decimal system the Egyptian-Babylonian-Greek-Hindu-Arabic numeral system.

4:1 Babylonian Numerals

The Babylonian numeral system was a **sexagesimal** (base 60) positional **system** superimposed on a simple grouping decimal system. It was not widely adopted by later civilizations because it did not have a symbol for zero. Around 300 B.C. a symbol similar to a punctuation mark was introduced to serve as a placeholder. However, it was not used consistently and was used only to denote an empty space inside a numeral. Earlier an open space was left occasionally, but often not even this was done.

The choice of 60 as a base rather than 10 is believed to have been influenced by an attempt to unify systems of measure and the fact that

60 has many divisors, making division and computations with fractions easier. Our division of the hour into 60 minutes and the minute into 60 seconds dates back to the Sumerians, as does our division of the circle into 360 degrees, each degree into 60 minutes, and each minute into 60 seconds. Their calendar consisted of 12 months of 30 days each plus 5 feast days.

A simplified version of a Babylonian tablet, dated about 1600 B.C., containing a multiplication table for 10, is shown in Figure 3.12. A transcription of the Babylonian symbols is also shown. The notation 1, 10 means $60 + 10 = 70$; 1, 20 means $60 + 20 = 80$; 2, 10 means $120 + 10 = 130$. This is sexagesimal, or base 60, because 60 units of one kind are written as one of the next higher position. The commas are used to separate the positions so that we can use our decimal numerals for the 59 digits of this base 60 system.

tablet		transcription		tablet		transcription	
I	<	1	10	III III II	I<<	8	1,20
II	<<	2	20	III III III	*	9	1,30
III	<<<	3	30	<	*	10	1,40
III I	<<< <	4	40	<I	*	11	1,50
III II	<<< <<	5	50	<II	II	12	2
III III	I	6	1	<III	II<	13	2,10
III III I	I<	7	1,10				

* This part of the tablet is broken off.

Figure 3.12

EXAMPLE. The decimal number 9314 would have been written by the Babylonians as II <<< II < I (with III above), which can be transcribed as 2, 35, 14. Thus $(2 \times 3600) + (35 \times 60) + 14 = 7200 + 2100 + 14 = 9314$.

Since the Babylonian system did not have an absence symbol, such as our zero, some Babylonian numerals can be interpreted in a variety of ways. |||

For example, ||| ≪ || could indicate

$$(3 \times 60) + 25 = 180 + 25 = 205$$
or $\quad (3 \times 3600) + (25 \times 60) = 10{,}800 + 1500 = 12{,}300$
or $\quad (3 \times 3600) + (0 \times 60) + 25 = 10{,}825$

or other possibilities involving larger positional values.

4:2 Scientific Chinese Numerals

In the "Sun-Tsu Suan-ching," a treatise on arithmetic by the ancient mathematician Sun-Tsu dating probably to the first century A.D., appears a description of the use of the Chinese calculating rods (usually made of bamboo) for representing numbers. Around 1000 A.D. the symbol 0 was used for zero.

Sun-Tsu says in his first book, "In making calculations we must first know positions of numbers. Unity is vertical and ten horizontal; the hundred stands while the thousand lies; and the thousand and the ten look equally, and so also the ten thousand and the hundred."

The digits from 1 to 9 are written as follows:

1	2	3	4	5	6	7	8	9
I	II	III	IIII	IIIII	⊤	⊤̇	⊤⊤	⊤⊤⊤

When the digits from 1 to 9 appear in the 10s position, they are written as follows:

1	2	3	4	5	6	7	8	9
—	=	≡	≣	≣	⊥	⊥	⊥	⊥

For example, the decimal number 6728 would be written ⊥⊤=⊤⊤, the number 7777 would be written as ⊥⊤⊥⊤, and the number 80 would be written as ⊥○ .

4:3 Maya Numerals

Around 400 or 300 B.C. it is believed that the Maya priests of Central America (mainly in Mexico and Guatemala) devised a positional system of numeration with a symbol for zero.[7] Their religion inspired the inven-

---

[7] Recent carbon-14 tests on Stelae C from Veracruz, dated 31 B.C., indicate that this numeral system may have been invented by the Olmecs.

tion of their writing, mathematics, calendar, and the precise stone work found in their pyramids.

The Maya system is **vigesimal** (base 20) superimposed on a **quinary** (base 5) system. In a true vigesimal system, the value of the third position should be 400, or 20 × 20. However, in counting time only, the Maya introduced a variation and used 360, or 20 × 18, as the value of the third position. The number 360 is an approximation to the length of a calendar year, which consisted of 18 months of 20 days each plus 5 "useless" or "unlucky" days.

The Maya used two different notations for writing numerals: (1) head-variant numerals,[8] similar to a ciphered system, and (2) bar and dot numerals, which are shown in Figure 3.13 using simplifications of the actual symbols. There were several symbols for zero, one of the most common being the conventionalized shell, ⬭. It is interesting to note that some forms of symbols used for 20 were also used for zero. The Maya wrote vertically, the highest position being at the top.

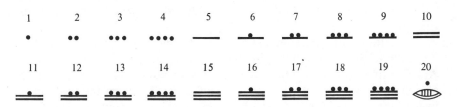

Figure 3.13

Some examples of Maya numerals are illustrated in Figure 3.14.

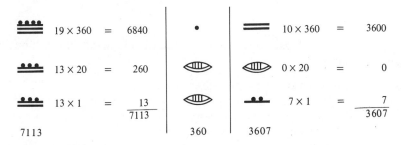

Figure 3.14

[8] Each number from 1 to 13 had a special head to represent it, which was the patron deity of the number. These were probably the 13 gods of the Upper World. The head variant for 10 is the death's head, or skull. The head variants for the numbers from 14 through 19 were formed by combining the lower jaw of the skull (for 10) with the heads of the other numbers from 4 to 9.

4:4 Hindu-Arabic Numerals

Our modern decimal system of numeration is a fully developed positional numeral system with its digits, including zero, ciphered as 0, 1, 2, 3, 4, 5, 6, 7, 8, 9. It is called the **Hindu-Arabic numeral system** because of its historical background. As was mentioned before, it probably should be called the Egyptian-Babylonian-Greek-Hindu-Arabic numeral system, because all these civilizations contributed to its development. The concept of place value is traced to the Babylonians and earlier Sumerians. The concept of cipherization was first evidenced in the Egyptian hieratic numerals and later in the Ionic Greek alphabetical numerals. Alexander the Great invaded India in 326 B.C., and the Greek rule for the next 200 years transmitted the Greek culture into India. The Hindus in Bactria (now Afghanistan) patterned an alphabet after that of the Greeks and used letters of this Bactrian alphabet to represent their digits for 4, 5, 6, 7, 8, and 9. However, until 400 A.D. there is no evidence of the use of a positional notation or of a zero. Later the Hindus *did* develop a positional notation and a symbol for zero. Around 700 A.D. India was invaded by the Arabs and the Arabs later introduced the Hindu numerals to Europe.

The forms of these numerals were standardized shortly after the invention of the printing press in 1438 A.D. Around 1500 A.D. the Hindu-Arabic numerals finally superseded the Roman numerals for the purposes of computation. This marked the end of a battle lasting for 400 years from 1100 A.D. to 1500 A.D., the battle of the Abacists and the Algorists. The Abacists were the proponents of Roman numerals and the use of the abacus for computing. The Algorists were the proponents of the Hindu-Arabic numerals and the use of written calculations using the processes we use today.

Table 3.1 is a capsulized version of the development of our modern decimal numerals.

TABLE 3.1 DEVELOPMENT OF DECIMAL NUMBERS

3000 B.C.	Sumerians in Tigris-Euphrates valley use positional notation. Egyptians use principle of cipherization.
300 B.C.	Babylonians use a separation mark to hold a position within a numeral.

	tally symbols			Letters of Bactrian alphabet									
150 B.C.	−	=	≡	⅄	Γ	⟨	?	⊣	?	∝	○	⊣	₴
	1	2	3	4	5	6	7	8	9	10	20	60	100

Numerals found in a cave at Nana Ghat, near Bombay, inscribed on stone columns about 100 years after the reign of King Asoka.

150 A.D.	Ptolemy, in his *Almagest* (the greatest Greek work on astronomy) uses the Babylonian sexagesimal numerals and the Greek letter *o*, omicron, as a placeholder within numerals.
400 A.D.	Hindu texts use the word "sunya," meaning empty, to indicate the empty column on the abacus. Hindu → Arabic → Latin ⟶ English sunya sifra zephirum zero, cipher
595 A.D.	The date 346 is written on a plate in India in decimal positional notation.
738 A.D.	A dot, ·, is used as a symbol for zero on an Indian land grant.
825 A.D.	The Persian mathematician Al-Khowarizmi developed and improved the decimal positional numeral system with zero. His book was the main source for the transmission into Europe of the numerals and the methods of computations using them.
876 A.D.	Zero on inscription at Gwalior, India.

976 A.D.   Numerals on a cave in Spain

1197 A.D.   The numerals used in

1294 A.D.   Europe

1442 A.D.   became standardized

1500 A.D.	The Algorists (name derived from Al-Khowarizmi) win the battle from the Abacists. The Hindu-Arabic numerals now replace the Roman numerals for computations.

5. DEVELOPMENT OF A NUMERAL SYSTEM

The hypothetical creation of a numeral system is presented below as a summary of the important principles involved in numeral systems and as an account of a logically possible historical development.

1. The **base** is selected. Objects are arranged in groups of powers of the base to facilitate counting. Here the base 5 is chosen. The powers of the base represented below are 1, 5, 25, and 125.

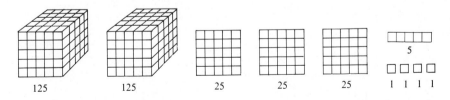

125	125	25	25	25	1 1 1 1

2. **Symbols** are invented for the basic groups and a **simple grouping system** is devised. The number of objects above is recorded as

∞   ∞   ○   ○   ○   ☆ ||||

3. The digits are later **ciphered.**

$$I, II, III, IIII \quad \text{are written as} \quad I, >, \triangle, \square$$

4. The **multiplicative grouping principle** is introduced.

$$\infty \infty \;\; O\,O\,O \;\; \star \;\; IIII \quad \text{is now written as} \quad \begin{array}{c} \infty\,O\,\star\,I \\ >\,\triangle\,I\,\square \end{array}$$

5. The **positional** concept is soon invented. The symbols for the powers of the base are now omitted from the multiplicative grouping notation.

$$\begin{array}{c} \infty\,O\,\star\,I \\ >\,\triangle\,I\,\square \end{array} \quad \text{is now written as} \quad >\,\triangle\,I\,\square$$

6. **Zero** is invented. Here the symbol O is used. Now

$$\triangle\,\square \quad \text{means } (3 \times 5) + 4 = 19$$
$$\triangle\,\square\,O \quad \text{means } (3 \times 25) + (4 \times 5) + 0 = 75 + 20 = 95$$
$$\triangle\,O\,\square \quad \text{means } (3 \times 25) + (0 \times 5) + 4 = 75 + 4 = 79$$

EXERCISES

1 to 8. Express the following numerals in Hindu-Arabic symbols.

1. $\overset{III}{II}$ ∩∩ ⌇ ℓℓℓℓ
2. $\overset{IIII}{III}$ ∩∩ 999 ⌇ ⟑   Egyptian hieroglyphic

3. $\overset{\lll}{\ll}$ $\overset{III}{II}$
4. $\ll$ $\overset{III}{\underset{I}{III}}$ Babylonian

5. XXⲘHHⲘII   6. MⲘ△△△△ IIII   Attic Greek

7. DCCLXXXVIIII   8. MCMXLIV   Roman

9. Write the decimal numerals 56 and 47 in each of the following numeral systems.
   a. Egyptian hieroglyphic.
   b. Babylonian.
   c. Attic Greek.
   d. Early Roman.
   e. Aztec.

10. Write the decimal numerals 3649 and 5780 in each of the following numeral systems.
    a. Egyptian hieroglyphic.
    b. Attic Greek.
    c. Early Roman (no subtraction).
    d. Late Roman (use the subtraction principle).
    e. Aztec.

11. The following Cretan numerals were found on inscriptions dated around 1200 B.C.:

	1	10	100	1000
	1	—	O	▱

Using the fact that their system was a simple grouping system, write the decimal numerals 3649 and 5780 in this system.

12. Express the following Ionic Greek numerals in our decimal system.
    a. $\rho\beta$ b. $/\gamma\phi\pi\theta$ c. $\overset{\epsilon}{M}\rho\epsilon$ d. $\pi M/\mu\kappa\alpha$

13. Write the following decimal numerals in the Ionic Greek system.
    a. 48 b. 737 c. 6555 d. 90,201

14. Write the Hindu-Arabic numerals for each of the following Chinese traditional numerals.

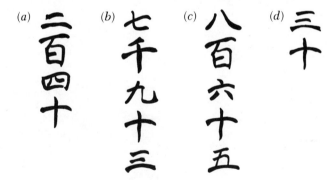

15. Write the decimal numerals 637 and 4219 in Chinese traditional numerals.

16. State some advantages and disadvantages of a ciphered system such as the Ionic Greek as compared to other simple grouping systems.

17. State some advantages and disadvantages of a multiplicative grouping system such as the Chinese traditional as compared to the simple grouping systems.

18. Did any of the above systems need a symbol for zero? Why?

19. Using the symbols 1, ✠, ⊏⊐, ⌀ to represent the Hindu-Arabic
    numerals *1, 5, 25, 125* write decimal 347 in
  a. A simple grouping system.
  b. A multiplicative grouping system, unciphered.
  c. A multiplicative grouping system, ciphered if 1, 11, 111, and 1111
     are ciphered as a, b, c, and d, respectively.
  d. A simple grouping ciphered system using the alphabetic scheme
     below:

1	a	5	e	25	i
2	b	10	f	50	j
3	c	15	g	75	k
4	d	20	h	100	l

20. Using the symbols 1, ⬡, ☐, ○ to represent the Hindu-Arabic
    numerals *1, 6, 36, 216* express the decimal numerals
    58 and 452 in
  a. A simple grouping system.
  b. A multiplicative grouping system, unciphered.
  c. A multiplicative grouping system, with the first five digits ciphered
     as 1, a, b, c, and d.
  d. A simple grouping ciphered system, extending the alphabetic
     cipherization of the previous problem.
21. Express the following numerals in Hindu-Arabic symbols.

a.	b.	Babylonian
c.	d.	Chinese, scientific
e.	f.	Maya

22. Write the numbers "four hundred four" and "seven thousand two
    hundred forty-five" in each of the following systems.
    a. Hindu-Arabic.   c. Babylonian.
    b. Scientific Chinese.   d. Maya.
23. Name at least three important advantages of a positional system as
    contrasted to a simple grouping numeral system.
24. What are some disadvantages of a positional system?

25. Name the principles that the Hindu-Arabic numeral system has in common with the Egyptian hieroglyphic, the Attic Greek, and the Roman numeral systems.
26. In what way or ways does the Hindu-Arabic numeral system differ from each of the following?
    a. Babylonian.   b. Maya.   c. Scientific Chinese.
27. Using the symbols *I, A, B,* and *C* to represent the decimal numerals 1, 4, 16, and 64, respectively, write the decimal numerals 25, 100, and 197 in
    a. A simple grouping system.
    b. A multiplicative grouping system, unciphered.
    c. A multiplicative grouping system with I, II, and III ciphered as 1, 2, and 3.
    d. A positional system, unciphered, no zero.
    e. A positional system, ciphered as in part c, no zero.
    f. A positional system, ciphered as in part c and with 0 used for zero.

CHAPTER IV

Arbitrary Bases

> Four times five is twelve, and four times six is thirteen,
> and four times seven is—oh dear! I shall never get
> to twenty at that rate!
>
> *Alice's Adventures in Wonderland,* Lewis Carroll

The study of arbitrary bases has been included in the elementary mathematics curriculum today for several reasons.

First, it has been included in order to develop mathematical concepts as well as mathematical skills. Studying the topic of arbitrary bases helps the student to understand the basic principles involved in computations; he learns the *why* of computing as well as the *how*. From this beginning he develops an understanding of the structure of mathematics.

Second, it has been included in order to study content matter which is now an important part of scientific knowledge and which may become an even more important part in the future. Science is growing so rapidly that even the average citizen must prepare for future technological applications. Today base 2 (the binary system) and its companion base, base 8 (the octal system), are widely used with reference to the electronic computer. The internal structure of a computer is concerned with whether an electrical current is on or off, and this is best analyzed in base 2.

There have been many advocates for the duodecimal system (base 12). Some of the famous ones were John Quincy Adams, George Bernard Shaw, and H. G. Wells. Today the Duodecimal Society of America has its headquarters at 20 Carleton Place, Staten Island, New York 10304. It publishes *The Duodecimal Bulletin* and *Manual of the Dozen System.*

The society uses an *X* symbol (called "dek") for 10 and an inverted 3 (called "el") for 11. Its members are supplied with a special base 12 slide rule. Its chief advantage is that it simplifies calculations with certain fractions.

Third, arbitrary bases are studied in order to increase the pleasure of learning and help relieve a feeling of boredom and apathy, resulting from tedious calculations that have little motivation.

1. EXPONENTIAL NOTATION

1:1 Decimal Notation

A decimal system is a positional system that has a base of 10. Each digit in a decimal numeral is understood as multiplied by a power of 10, the power being indicated by the position the digit occupies in the numeral.

To illustrate this concept, the decimal numeral 7856 is written below in what is called **expanded notation**:

$$7856 = (7 \times 1000) + (8 \times 100) + (5 \times 10) + (6 \times 1)$$

This numeral can be also expressed in **exponential notation** by using the properties of exponents.

A counting number is called an **exponent** if its name is written to the right and higher than the name of another number, the base; the exponent indicates how many times the base is used as a factor in a product.

For example, $5^2 = 5 \times 5 = 25$, where 5 is the base and 2 is the exponent.

Similarly, $5^3 = 5 \times 5 \times 5 = 125$, and $10^2 = 100$ and $10^3 = 1000$. Thus, in exponential notation,

$$7856 = (7 \times 10^3) + (8 \times 10^2) + (5 \times 10) + (6 \times 1)$$

It is possible to use 0 and 1 as exponents by defining

$$10^0 = 1 \quad \text{and} \quad 10^1 = 10$$

In general, $b^0 = 1$ and $b^1 = b$, where the letter b is used in a general way to designate any number different from 0.

EXAMPLE 1. Write $(2 \times 10^3) + (5 \times 10^2) + (0 \times 10^1) + (3 \times 10^0)$ in decimal notation.

Solution. 2503.

EXAMPLE 2. Write 5679 in exponential notation.

Solution. $(5 \times 10^3) + (6 \times 10^2) + (7 \times 10^1) + (9 \times 10^0)$.

1:2 Bases Other Than Ten

If a number is expressed in a positional system with a base other than 10, then the values of the positions are powers of this base. The format in Table 4.1 illustrates how these values are determined.

TABLE 4.1 POSITIONAL VALUES

b^4	b^3	b^2	b^1	b^0
10,000	1000	100	10	1
16	8	4	2	1
625	125	25	5	1
20,736	1728	144	12	1

EXAMPLE 1. Write $(1 \times 2^4) + (1 \times 2^2) + (1 \times 1)$ in binary (base 2) notation.

Solution. 10,101.

EXAMPLE 2. Write 1111 base 2 in binary notation, exponential form.

Solution. $(1 \times 2^3) + (1 \times 2^2) + (1 \times 2) + (1 \times 1)$.

EXAMPLE 3. Write $(3 \times 5^2) + (4 \times 5) + (2 \times 1)$ in quinary (base 5) notation.

Solution. 342.

EXAMPLE 4. Write the duodecimal (base 12) numeral 769 in exponential notation.

Solution. $(7 \times 12^2) + (6 \times 12) + (9 \times 1)$.

2. CONVERSION TO AND FROM BASE 5

2:1 Conversion to Base 10

In base 5 there are exactly five digits. These are 0, 1, 2, 3, and 4. In a positional numeral system the number of digits is always equal to the number of the base.

To convert a number to base 10, the powers of 5 must be supplied as the multipliers of the digits.

EXAMPLE. Convert 24,314 base 5 to base 10.

Solution

1. Supply the values of the positions:

625	125	25	5	1
2	4	3	1	4

2. Write the numeral in expanded notation:
    $(2 \times 625) + (4 \times 125) + (3 \times 25) + (1 \times 5) + (4 \times 1)$

3. Perform the calculation (in base 10):

    $$2 \times 625 = 1250$$
    $$4 \times 125 = 500$$
    $$3 \times 25 = 75$$
    $$1 \times 5 = 5$$
    $$4 \times 1 = 4$$
    $$\overline{1834}$$

Thus 24,314 base 5 = 1834 base 10.

2:2 Conversion from Base 10

The conversion to base 5 from base 10 is done most simply by dividing by the powers of 5 smaller than the number to be converted. In other words, one finds out how many of each basic group size is needed, the groups now being arranged as powers of five.

EXAMPLE. Convert 576 base 10 to base 5.

Solution

1. Find the powers of 5 smaller than the number to be converted:
    $5^0 = 1$, $5^1 = 5$, $5^2 = 25$, $5^3 = 125$

2. Divide by these powers of 5 as follows:

    $$
    \begin{array}{cccc}
    4 & 3 & 0 & 1 \\
    125\overline{)576} & 25\overline{)76} & 5\overline{)1} & 1\overline{)1} \\
    500 & 75 & 0 & 1 \\
    \hline
    76 & 1 & 1 & 0
    \end{array}
    $$

3. Write the numeral in exponential notation, using powers of 5:
    $(4 \times 5^3) + (3 \times 5^2) + (0 \times 5) + (1 \times 1)$

4. Write the numeral in positional notation, base 5:
    4301

Thus 576 base 10 = 4301 base 5.

3. CONVERSION OF ARBITRARY BASES

3:1 To Base 10

To convert a number from an arbitrary base to base 10, supply the powers of the base as multipliers, write the number in expanded notation, and then perform the computation in base 10.

EXAMPLE 1. Convert 376 base 8 to base 10.

Solution. The powers of 8 needed are 1, 8, and 64. Then
$$376 \text{ base } 8 = (3 \times 8^2) + (7 \times 8) + (6 \times 1)$$
$$= (3 \times 64) + 56 + 6$$
$$= 192 + 56 + 6 = 254 \text{ base } 10$$

EXAMPLE 2. Convert 101,101 base 2 to base 10.

Solution. Supplying the powers of 2:

32	16	8	4	2	1
1	0	1	1	0	1

Thus 101,101 base 2 = 32 + 8 + 4 + 1 = 45 base 10.

3:2 From Base 10

To convert a number from base 10 to an arbitrary base, divide by the powers of the base in order beginning with the largest power smaller than the number.

EXAMPLE 1. Convert 9783 base 10 to base 8.

Solution. The required powers of 8 are 1, 8, 64, 512, and 4096:

$$
\begin{array}{ccccc}
2 & 3 & 0 & 6 & 7 \\
4096\overline{)9783} & 512\overline{)1591} & 64\overline{)55} & 8\overline{)55} & 1\overline{)7} \\
8192 & 1536 & 0 & 48 & 7 \\
\hline
1591 & 55 & 55 & 7 & 0
\end{array}
$$

Thus 9783 base 10 = 23,067 base 8.

EXAMPLE 2. Convert 75 base 10 to base 2.

Solution. The required powers of 2 are 1, 2, 4, 8, 16, 32, and 64.

$$
\begin{array}{ccccccc}
1 & 0 & 0 & 1 & 0 & 1 & 1 \\
64\overline{)75} & 32\overline{)11} & 16\overline{)11} & 8\overline{)11} & 4\overline{)3} & 2\overline{)3} & 1\overline{)1} \\
64 & & & 8 & 0 & 2 & 1 \\
\hline
11 & & & 3 & 3 & 1 & 0
\end{array}
$$

Thus 75 base 10 = 1,001,011 base 2.

4. COMPUTATION IN ARBITRARY BASES

4:1 Addition and Subtraction in Base 5

To add and subtract in base 5, we must use the facts from the addition table, Table 4.2. To obtain the entries in the table, we used a fundamental principle of the addition process; that is, the number is still the same when we regroup the units.

For example, $1111 + 111 = 11111 + 11 = (1 \times 5) + 2 = 12$ base 5:

$$4 + 3 = 5 + 2 = 12 \text{ base } 5$$

TABLE 4.2 ADDITION TABLE

+	0	1	2	3	4
0	0	1	2	3	4
1	1	2	3	4	10
2	2	3	4	10	11
3	3	4	10	11	12
4	4	10	11	12	13

Sums of larger numbers are obtained by the same process that is used in base 10. The digits in the units' position are added first. The digit in the units' position of the sum is recorded. If the sum has a digit in the next larger position, this digit is added to the others in this position. In other words, this digit is "carried" to the next position. Thus the principle of carry is used in other bases just as it is used in base 10.

EXAMPLE. Add in base 5: $434 + 223$.

Solution

$$
\begin{array}{l}
\overset{1\;1}{434} \\
\underline{223} \\
1212
\end{array}
\qquad
\begin{array}{l}
3 + 4 = 12 \text{ (put down 2 and carry 1)} \\
(2 + 3) + 1 = 10 + 1 = 11 \text{ (put down 1 and carry 1)} \\
(2 + 4) + 1 = 11 + 1 = 12 \text{ (record 12)}
\end{array}
$$

Subtraction is done by using the table of addition facts and the fact that subtraction is the opposite of addition. Thus, in base 10, $8 - 2 = 6$, because $8 = 2 + 6$.

Similarly, in base 5,

$$4 - 3 = 1 \text{ because } 4 = 3 + 1$$
$$12 - 3 = 4 \text{ because } 12 = 3 + 4$$

These statements can be checked by referring to the addition table.

By using the same principle of carrying, or borrowing, that is used in base 10 subtraction, we can subtract larger numbers in base 5.

EXAMPLE. Subtract in base 5: 214 − 132.

Solution

$$
\begin{array}{r}
\overset{\text{\tiny 1 1}}{2}14 \\
132 \\
\hline
32
\end{array}
$$

4 − 2 = 2 from the table
borrow 1 from 2 in 214
11 − 3 = 3 from the table
1 − 1 = 0 (do not record)

Thus 214 − 132 = 32.

Subtraction is **checked** by addition.   For example, to check 214 − 132 = 32, we add 132 + 32:

$$
\begin{array}{r}
132 \\
32 \\
\hline
214
\end{array}
$$

4:2 Multiplication in Base 5

Multiplication is done by using a table of the multiplication facts for the products of the digits (Table 4.3). These products are obtained by using the fact that a product is a repeated addition. Thus $4 \times 3 = 3 + 3 + 3 + 3$. Thus $4 \times 3 = [(3+3)+3]+3 = [11+3]+3 = 14+3 = 22$.

TABLE 4.3   MULTIPLICATION TABLE

×	0	1	2	3	4
0	0	0	0	0	0
1	0	1	2	3	4
2	0	2	4	11	13
3	0	3	11	14	22
4	0	4	13	22	31

The process for multiplying larger numbers is the same as that used in base 10 multiplication. Partial products are arranged according to positions and then they are added.

EXAMPLE 1. Multiply 423 by 4 in base 5.

Solution

$$
\begin{array}{r}
423 \\
\underline{4} \\
22 \\
13 \\
\underline{31} \\
3302
\end{array}
$$

By "carrying" mentally, this can be shortened to

$$
\begin{array}{r}
423 \\
\underline{4} \\
3302
\end{array}
$$

EXAMPLE 2.   Multiply 423 by 34 in base 5.

Solution

$$
\begin{array}{r}
423 \\
\underline{34} \\
3302 \\
\underline{2324} \\
32042
\end{array}
$$

4:3 Division in Base 5 (Optional)

Division is performed in base 5 by using the same process that is used in base 10, that is, by considering division to be the opposite operation to multiplication. For example, $12 \div 3 = 4$ because $12 = 3 \times 4$.

EXAMPLE. Divide 1243 by 3 in base 5.

Solution

$$
\begin{array}{r}
231 \\
3\,)\overline{1243} \\
\underline{11} \\
14 \\
\underline{14} \\
3 \\
3
\end{array}
$$

$3 \times 2 = 11$ from the multiplication table

$3 \times 3 = 14$

$3 \times 1 = 3$

4:4 Computation in Arbitrary Bases

Addition, subtraction, multiplication, and division are performed in arbitrary bases by using the same processes that are used in base 10 and in base 5. The only difference is that each base has its own addition and multiplication tables.

EXAMPLE 1.   Perform the indicated operations in base 2.

Solution

Add:	Subtract:	Multiply:	Divide:
1101	1110	1101	1110
1110	1011	11	11) 101010
11001	11	1101	11
		1101	100
		100111	11
			110
			110

+	0	1
0	0	1
1	1	10

×	0	1
0	0	0
1	0	1

In base 12, we must supply two digits, *t* for ten and *e* for eleven, because 10 in base 12 means twelve and 11 base 12 means twelve plus one or thirteen. The addition and multiplication tables must be constructed as shown in Tables 4.4 and 4.5.

TABLE 4.4   ADDITION TABLE

+	0	1	2	3	4	5	6	7	8	9	*t*	*e*
0	0	1	2	3	4	5	6	7	8	9	*t*	*e*
1	1	2	3	4	5	6	7	8	9	*t*	*e*	10
2	2	3	4	5	6	7	8	9	*t*	*e*	10	11
3	3	4	5	6	7	8	9	*t*	*e*	10	11	12
4	4	5	6	7	8	9	*t*	*e*	10	11	12	13
5	5	6	7	8	9	*t*	*e*	10	11	12	13	14
6	6	7	8	9	*t*	*e*	10	11	12	13	14	15
7	7	8	9	*t*	*e*	10	11	12	13	14	15	16
8	8	9	*t*	*e*	10	11	12	13	14	15	16	17
9	9	*t*	*e*	10	11	12	13	14	15	16	17	18
t	*t*	*e*	10	11	12	13	14	15	16	17	18	19
e	*e*	10	11	12	13	14	15	16	17	18	19	1*t*

TABLE 4.5 MULTIPLICATION TABLE

×	0	1	2	3	4	5	6	7	8	9	t	e
0	0	0	0	0	0	0	0	0	0	0	0	0
1	0	1	2	3	4	5	6	7	8	9	t	e
2	0	2	4	6	8	t	10	12	14	16	18	$1t$
3	0	3	6	9	10	13	16	19	20	23	26	29
4	0	4	8	10	14	18	20	24	28	30	34	38
5	0	5	t	13	18	21	26	$2e$	34	39	42	47
6	0	6	10	16	20	26	30	36	40	46	50	56
7	0	7	12	19	24	$2e$	36	41	48	53	$5t$	65
8	0	8	14	20	28	34	40	48	54	60	68	74
9	0	9	16	23	30	39	46	53	60	69	76	83
t	0	t	18	26	34	42	50	$5t$	68	76	84	92
e	0	e	$1t$	29	38	47	56	65	74	83	92	$t1$

EXAMPLE 2. In base 12, add $7te$ to 896.

Solution

$7te$ $e + 6 = 15$ from the addition table (record 5, carry 1)

  896   $(9 + t) + 1 = 17 + 1 = 18$ (record 8, carry 1)

$\overline{1485}$ $(8 + 7) + 1 = 13 + 1 = 14$ (record 14)

EXAMPLE 3. In base 12, multiply $7t3$ by $e5$.

Solution

$7te$ $e \times 5 = 47$ from the multiplication table (record 7, carry 4)

  $e5$ $(5 \times t) + 4 = 42 + 4 = 46$

 3367 $(5 \times 7) + 4 = 2e + 4 = 33$

$\underline{7301}$ $e \times e = t1$

76377 $(e \times t) + t = 92 + t = t0$

   $(e \times 7) + t = 65 + t = 73$

5. BASIMAL FRACTIONS (OPTIONAL)

5:1 Quinary Fractions

A **quinary fraction** is a number between 0 and 1 represented in a positional base 5 notation. To write fractions as quinary fractions, we must know the values of the positions to the right of the units' position. The mark used to separate the units' position from the next position to its right is called a **quinary point** as contrasted to the decimal point used in a base 10 positional notation. The values of the fractional positions in a quinary system are

$$1. \quad \frac{1}{5} \bigg| \frac{1}{25} \bigg| \frac{1}{125} \bigg| \frac{1}{625}$$

To represent a fraction as a quinary fraction, the fraction must first be changed to one having a power of 5 as the denominator. Then the numerator written in base 5 is the quinary notation for the fraction.

EXAMPLE 1. Convert 0.4 base 10 to a quinary fraction.

Solution. $\frac{4}{10} = \frac{2}{5}$. Thus 0.4 base 10 = 0.2 base 5:

$$0.4 \text{ base } 10 = \frac{4}{10} \text{ base } 10 = \frac{2}{5} \text{ base } 10 = \frac{2}{10} \text{ base } 5 = 0.2 \text{ base } 5$$

EXAMPLE 2. Express $\frac{269}{625}$ base 10 as a quinary fraction.

Solution. Since 625 is a power of 5, $625 = 5^4$, we convert 269 to base 5: 269 base 10 = 2034 base 5:

$$
\begin{array}{cccc}
\dfrac{2}{125 \overline{)\, 269}} & \dfrac{0}{25 \overline{)\, 19}} & \dfrac{3}{5 \overline{)\, 19}} & \dfrac{4}{1 \overline{)\, 4}} \\[2mm]
\underline{250} & & \underline{15} & \\
19 & & 4 &
\end{array}
$$

Thus $\frac{269}{625}$ base 10 = 0.2034 base 5:

$$\frac{269}{625} \text{ base } 10 = \frac{2,034}{10,000} \text{ base } 5 = 0.2034 \text{ base } 5$$

EXAMPLE 3. Express 0.43 base 5 as a decimal fraction.

Solution

$$0.43 \text{ base } 5 = \frac{43}{100} \text{ base } 5 = \frac{23}{25} \text{ base } 10 = \frac{23 \times 4}{25 \times 4} \text{ base } 10$$

$$= \frac{92}{100} \text{ base } 10$$

$$= 0.92 \text{ base } 10$$

5:2 Fractions, Arbitrary Bases

Basimal fractions is a general term used to describe the expression of fractions in positional notation.

To change a common fraction (one having any integer or counting number as its denominator) to a basimal fraction (the denominators, unwritten, being understood as powers of the base), the fraction is changed to one having a power of the base for its denominator. When the new numerator is converted to this base, the digits in order preceded by a basimal point constitute the basimal fraction.

EXAMPLE 1.   Change $\frac{1}{2}$ base 10 to a basimal fraction in each of the bases 6, 8, 10, and 60.

Solution

$$\text{In base } 10, \frac{1}{2} = \frac{1 \times 3}{2 \times 3} = \frac{3}{6} \text{ ; thus } \frac{3}{6} \text{ base } 10 = \frac{3}{10} \text{ base } 6$$

$$= 0.3 \text{ base } 6$$

$$\text{In base } 10, \frac{1}{2} = \frac{1 \times 4}{2 \times 4} = \frac{4}{8} \text{ ; thus } \frac{4}{8} \text{ base } 10 = \frac{4}{10} \text{ base } 8$$

$$= 0.4 \text{ base } 8$$

$$\text{In base } 10, \frac{1}{2} = \frac{1 \times 5}{2 \times 5} = \frac{5}{10} \text{ base } 10 = 0.5 \text{ base } 10$$

$$\text{In base } 10, \frac{1}{2} = \frac{1 \times 30}{2 \times 30} = \frac{30}{60} \text{ ; thus } \frac{30}{60} \text{ base } 10 = \frac{30,}{1,0} \text{ base } 60$$

$$= 0.30, \text{ base } 60$$

(Commas are used to separate positions in base 60 so that our decimal numerals can be used for the 60 digits.)

EXAMPLE 2.   Change 0.625 base 10 to base 2.

Solution. In base 10,

$$\frac{625}{1000} = \frac{125}{200} = \frac{25}{40} = \frac{5}{8}$$

$$\frac{5}{8} \text{ base } 10 = \frac{101}{1000} \text{ base } 2 = 0.101 \text{ base } 2$$

EXERCISES

1. Write each of the following in decimal notation.
   a. $(4 \times 10^3) + (7 \times 10^2) + (3 \times 10) + (5 \times 1)$.
   b. $(5 \times 10^3) + (6 \times 10^2) + (2 \times 1)$.
   c. $(9 \times 10^2) + (8 \times 10^1)$.
   d. $(2 \times 10^4) + (3 \times 10^2) + (4 \times 10) + (5 \times 1)$.
   e. $(9 \times 10^4) + (1 \times 10^2) + (6 \times 10)$.
2. Write each of the following in exponential notation, as in Exercise 1.
   a. 4567   b. 304   c. 34,000   d. 70,903   e. 32,010
3. Convert each of the following numerals to base 10.
   a. 110101 base 2   b. 1234 base 5   c. 567 base 8
   d. t5e base 12   e. 2,20 base 60   f. 123 base 4
   g. 305 base 7   h. 1221 base 3   i. 357 base 9
   j. 2,12,17 base 20

Commas are used to separate positions in bases 20 and 60 so that the decimal numerals can be used as the digits. This notation was introduced by O. Neugebauer, the leading authority on the decipherization of the Babylonian mathematical clay tablets. See "The Exact Sciences in Antiquity" in Midonick, *The Treasury of Mathematics*.

4. Convert 200 base 10 and 345 base 10 to each of the following bases.
   a. base 2   b. base 3   c. base 4   d. base 5
   e. base 6   f. base 7   g. base 8   h. base 9
   i. base 12   j. base 20   k. base 60
5. Convert each of the following decimal numerals to base 2 and base 8. What relationship can you discover between base 2 and base 8?
   a. 45   b. 125   c. 234   d. 207   e. 64   f. 256
6. Compute in base 2:
   a. Add 1001   b. Add 1111   c. Subtract 10101
           1111   1011   1111

   d. Multiply 1011   e. Multiply 1101   f. Divide 11)100111
               11   101

7. Compute in base 5:
   a. Add 134   b. Add 423   c. Subtract 412   d. Multiply 312
          223   443   234   4

   e. Multiply 234   f. Divide 24)14043
               43

8. Compute in base 12:
   a. Add t57   b. Subtract e64   c. Multiply 27   d. Divide 27)14107
          3e8   985   e5

9. The Dekto system is positional and uses

the symbols	O	I	<	△	□	✶	✶̄	⧫	⧫	✶
for our	0	1	2	3	4	5	6	7	8	9

Make the addition and multiplication tables for this system and then compute below.

a. add

$$< ✶ ✶$$
$$□ ⧫ △$$

b. subtract

$$⧫ ✶̄ I$$
$$< O ✶$$

c. multiply

$$□ △ ✶$$
$$< ✶$$

d. divide

$$✶△\overline{)□I△□}$$

10. Does the process used in the calculations in base 5, in base 10, and in the Dekto system depend on
    a. The base used?
    b. The kind of symbols used?
    c. The kind of numeral system (whether positional or not)?

11. In *Alice's Adventures in Wonderland* by Lewis Carroll, Alice says, "Let me see: four times five is twelve, and four times six is thirteen, and four times seven is—oh dear! I shall never get to twenty at that rate!" Assuming that the calculations below are each correct in *some* base (different for each case), find this base for each of the following.
    a. $4 \times 5 = 12$ b. $4 \times 6 = 13$ c. $4 \times 7 = 14$
    d. $4 \times 8 = 15$ e. $4 \times 9 = 16$
    Why can't Alice get to 20 at this rate?

12. Convert the base 10 common fractions below to basimal fractions:
    a. $\frac{1}{2}, \frac{3}{4}, \frac{7}{8}$ each to base 2.
    b. $\frac{4}{5}, \frac{7}{25}$ each to base 5.
    c. $\frac{1}{2}, \frac{2}{3}, \frac{3}{4}, \frac{4}{5}, \frac{5}{6}$ each to base 10.
    d. $\frac{1}{2}, \frac{2}{3}, \frac{3}{4}, \frac{5}{6}$ each to base 12.
    e. $\frac{1}{2}, \frac{2}{3}, \frac{3}{4}, \frac{4}{5}, \frac{5}{6}$ each to base 60.

13. Convert each of the following to common fractions whose numerators and denominators are base 10 numerals.
    a. 0.111 base 2   b. 0.101 base 5   c. 0.875 base 10
    d. 0.*t*6 base 12   e. 0.20,30 base 60

14. In a true base 2 coinage system, the denominations of the coins are 1¢, 2¢, 4¢, 8¢, 16¢, 32¢, 64¢, 128¢, and so on. In a true base 5 coinage system, the denominations of the coins are 1¢, 5¢, 25¢, 125¢, and so on. In a true base 10 coinage system, the denominations of the coins are 1¢, 10¢, 100¢, and so on.
    a. In each of the above systems, what is the least number of coins required to make each of the following sums: 63¢, 124¢, and 99¢?

   b. What is the base of the currency of the United States? Why?
   c. What would be the best base for a coinage system? Why?
   d. What would be the best base for a system of weights and measures? Why?
15. Compare the advantages and disadvantages of small-number bases such as 2 and 3 versus large-number bases such as 20 and 60. Consider each of the following:
   a. The length of the numerals.
   b. The number of *different* symbols required.
   c. The amount of memory required for computation (addition and multiplication tables).
   d. Difficulty of division or computation with fractions.
   e. The applications as coinage bases or bases of systems of weights and measures.

CHAPTER V

Early Computations

Accurate reckoning of entering into things, knowledge
of existing things all, mysteries . . . secrets all.

A translation of the title page of the Rhind
papyrus written by the Egyptian scribe Ahmes
around 1650 B.C.

Prealgebra

1. ABACUS

Today the electronic computer and the electric desk calculator help us
to perform the laborious operations of arithmetic. The oldest computing
machine known to man is the abacus. The Greek historian Herodotus,
around 450 B.C., wrote that the Egyptians calculated with pebbles. The
fact that pebbles were used for counters in Roman time is suggested by
our word "calculate," which is derived from the Latin "calculus," which
means "pebble."

On an ancient bronze abacus used by the Romans, the pebbles or
counters were moved along grooves or slots. Figure 5.1 is a simplified
representation of such an abacus, with the number 357 recorded on it.

Addition and subtraction were done by moving the pebbles along
the grooves toward the center and exchanging five 1s for a V, two Vs for
an X, and so on. In subtraction it was sometimes necessary to exchange in
reverse or to "borrow."

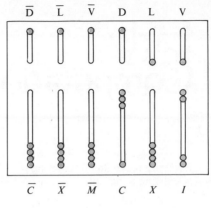

Figure 5.1

Multiplication was done by repeated additions and division by repeated subtractions.

Today the abacus is still used in different forms. Figure 5.2 shows the Russian *s'choty*, the Chinese *suan pan*, and the Japanese *soroban*.

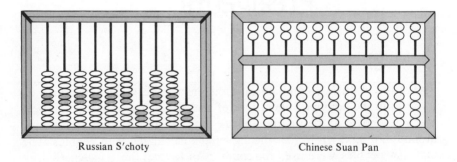

Russian S'choty   Chinese Suan Pan

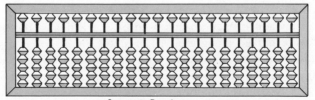

Japanese Soroban

Figure 5.2

2. EGYPTIAN ADDITION AND SUBTRACTION

Egyptian addition and subtraction were performed by using the principles of "regrouping" and "exchange." This was also the method that was used with Roman numerals, so addition and subtraction using both numeral systems is shown below.

Roman Numerals

Facts to remember: IIIII = V and VV = X
XXXXX = L and LL = C
CCCCC = D and DD = M

EXAMPLE. Add

CCC L XX V IIII
 CCXXXX V III
─────────────────
CCCCC L XXXXX X VV IIII II   (regrouping)
    D   L L   X X V II   (exchanging)
    D   C   XX V II   (exchanging again)

Thus the sum is DCXXVII.

EXAMPLE. Subtract

CC XX III   exchange by   C L XXXXX XX III
 CLXXXI   borrowing to   C L   XXX   I
─────────   ──────────────────
                              XX   XX II or XXXXII

Egyptian Numerals

Facts to remember:

$$| \; | \; | \quad | \; | \; | \quad | \; | \; | \quad | = \cap$$
$$\cap\cap\cap \quad \cap\cap\cap \quad \cap\cap\cap \quad \cap = 9$$
$$999 \quad 999 \quad 999 \quad 9 = \mathrm{\mathfrak{f}}$$

EXAMPLE. Add

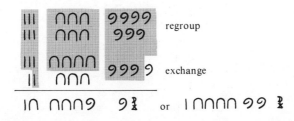

EXAMPLE. Subtract

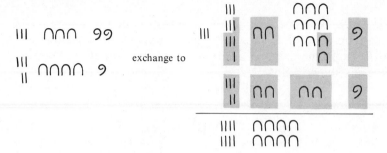

3. MULTIPLICATION BY DUPLATION

The Egyptians multiplied by a process called **duplation,** which means doubling and summing. Since every number can be expressed as the sum of powers of 2, the product of any two numbers is obtained by multiplying one number by the different powers of 2 necessary to express the other, and then the partial products are added.

For example, multiply 35 by 19 by duplation:

$$19 = 16 + 2 + 1$$

⟍ 1	35 ⟋
⟍ 2	70 ⟋
4	140
8	280
⟍ 16	560 ⟋

Total 19   665

The following is an example from the Rhind papyrus.

EXAMPLE. "Make thou the multiplication ⦀⦀ ∪ by ⦀⦀ ." The doing, as it occurs, is shown in Figure 5.3.

Figure 5.3

4. FRACTIONS, DIVISION

4:1 Egyptian Unit Fractions

The Egyptians performed division by repeated subtractions of the "doubles" of the divisor. When the division was not exact, unit fractions were used to express the remainder. The mathematical principle involved is the fact that division by a counting number is the same as multiplication by the reciprocal of the counting number. Thus

$$12 \div 2 = 12 \times \frac{1}{2} = 6$$

$$16 \div 3 = 16 \times \frac{1}{3} = 5\frac{1}{3}$$

With the exception of the fraction $\frac{2}{3}$, the Egyptians had symbols for unit fractions only. Some examples are shown in Figure 5.4.

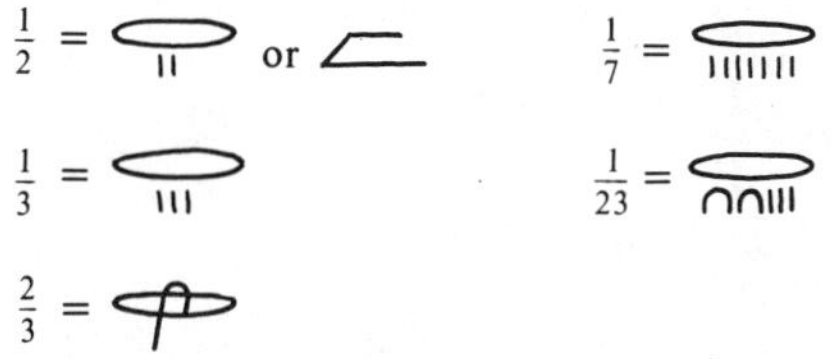

Figure 5.4

The Rhind papyrus contains tables for the reduction of fractions of the form $2/n$ to unit fractions. Since the Egyptians multiplied by doubling, this was the only decomposition that was needed. Using our notation, some entries in their tables are

$$2 \div 5 = \frac{1}{3} + \frac{1}{15} \quad \text{and} \quad 2 \div 7 = \frac{1}{4} + \frac{1}{28}$$

The table continues in this manner for all odd denominators from 5 to 331. Even denominators were not necessary, since

$$\frac{2}{2n} = \frac{1}{n}, \frac{2}{6} = \frac{1}{3}, \frac{2}{8} = \frac{1}{4}, \frac{2}{10} = \frac{1}{5}, \cdots$$

An example of a division is given below.

EXAMPLE. Divide 100 by 7.

Solution. $100 = 64 + 32 + 4$ (the representation by powers of 2). Now multiply 100 by $\frac{1}{7}$.

$$1 \quad \frac{1}{7}$$

$$2 \quad \frac{1}{4} + \frac{1}{28} \left(\text{from the table, } 2 \div 7 = \frac{2}{7} = \frac{1}{4} + \frac{1}{28} \right)$$

$$\diagdown 4 \quad \frac{1}{2} + \frac{1}{14} \left(\text{that is, } \frac{2}{4} = \frac{1}{2} \text{ and } \frac{2}{28} = \frac{1}{14} \right)$$

$$8 \quad 1 + \frac{1}{7}$$

$$16 \quad 2 + \frac{1}{4} + \frac{1}{28}$$

$$\diagdown 32 \quad 4 + \frac{1}{2} + \frac{1}{14}$$

$$\diagdown 64 \quad 9 + \frac{1}{7}$$

$$\overline{}$$

$$\text{Total } 100 \quad 14 + \frac{1}{4} + \frac{1}{28}$$

Thus $100 \div 7 = 14 + \frac{1}{4} + \frac{1}{28}$, or $14\frac{2}{7}$, as we would write this number.

4:2 Babylonian Sexagesimal Fractions

The Babylonians were more advanced in their computations than the Egyptians. The Babylonians used a base 60 positional system of numerals instead of the more primitive simple grouping system of the Egyptians.

Thus the Babylonians used sexagesimal (base 60) positional fractions similar to our decimal fractions. Instead of limiting the *numerator* as the Egyptians did with their unit fractions, the Babylonians limited the *denominators* of their fractions to be powers of 60, that is, 60, 3600, 216,000, and so on.

EXAMPLE 1. $\frac{1}{2}$ would have been written as 30, using our symbols, or as ⋘, using Babylonian symbols. The denominator 60 was not written but was to be understood $\left(\frac{1}{2} = \frac{30}{60} \right)$.

EXAMPLE 2. Since $\frac{1}{3} = \frac{20}{60}$, the Babylonians wrote $\frac{1}{3}$ as $\ll(20)$. This sexagesimal system of fractions is still used in our measurements of time and angles. For example, 3 hours, 15 minutes, 36 seconds = 3; 15, 36, using the semicolon for the sexagesimal point and commas to separate the positions.

$$3 + \frac{15}{60} + \frac{36}{3600} = 3 + \frac{1}{4} + \frac{1}{100} = 3\frac{26}{100} = 3.26 \text{ decimal}$$

or

Sexagesimal 3; 15, 36 = decimal 3.26

It is very probable that one of the reasons the Babylonians chose base 60 was the fact that 60 has many divisors. The divisors of 60 are 1, 2, 3, 4, 5, 6, 10, 12, 15, 20, 30, and 60. Thus more fractions can be written in a simple manner (that is, as a terminating positional fraction) in base 60 than in other bases. Compare Table 5.1.

TABLE 5.1 COMPARISON OF FRACTIONS

COMMON FRACTION	DECIMAL FRACTION	SEXAGESIMAL FRACTION
$\frac{1}{3}$	$0.33333\cdots$	0; 20
$\frac{1}{6}$	$0.16666\cdots$	0; 10
$\frac{1}{9}$	$0.1111\cdots$	0; 6, 40
$\frac{1}{12}$	$0.08333\cdots$	0; 5
$\frac{1}{15}$	$0.06666\cdots$	0; 4
$\frac{1}{30}$	$0.03333\cdots$	0; 2

Tables of Reciprocals. A **table of reciprocals** is a list of numbers, b and $1/b$, with the property that $b \times 1/b = 1$. The reciprocal number is used to change a division problem into a multiplication. For example, division by 2 is equivalent to multiplication by $\frac{1}{2}$, or 0.5, the reciprocal of 2, in base 10.

$$\frac{1}{2} = 0.5; \qquad 12 \div 2 = 12 \times 0.5 = 6$$

The following is a translation of part of a Babylonian table of reciprocals, written as sexagesimal fractions.

2	30
3	20
4	15
5	12
6	10
8	7, 30
9	6, 40
10	6
12	5
15	4
16	3, 45
18	3, 20
20	3

Note that

$$2 \times 30 \quad = 1, 0 \quad \text{just as} \quad 2 \times 5 \quad = 10 \text{ in base } 10$$
$$2 \times 0; 30 = 1 \qquad\qquad\qquad 2 \times 0.5 = 1$$
$$0; 2 \times 30 \quad = 1 \qquad\qquad\qquad 0.2 \times 5 \quad = 1$$
$$0; 2 \times 0; 30 = 0; 1 \qquad\qquad 0.2 \times 0.5 = 0.1$$

Thus it is not necessary to supply a sexagesimal (or decimal) point in the table. This can always be supplied when it is needed for a particular problem.

Note also that there are no entries for the reciprocals of 7, 11, 13, 14, and so on.

In decimal notation, $\frac{1}{7} = 0.142857142857 \cdots$

In sexagesimal notation, $\frac{1}{7} = 0; 8, 34, 17, 8, 34, 17, \cdots$

Both expressions for $\frac{1}{7}$ are repeating fractions. In fact, some Babylonian tablets state "7 does not divide," "11 does not divide," and so on. However, there are other tablets that explain the division process to be used in these cases.

5. MISCELLANEOUS PROBLEMS

5:1 Rule of False Position

It is most probable that methods for solving problems evolved from satisfactory results obtained by a trial and error process. This is illustrated by the **rule of false position** as applied to certain linear equations (Table 5.2).

TABLE 5.2

PROBLEM 24 FROM THE RHIND PAPYRUS	OUR MODERN TRANSCRIPTION

"A quantity and its seventh, added together, become 24. What is the quantity?
$$N + \frac{N}{7} = 24$$

Do it thus: Add 7 to the seventh of 7.
Try $N = 7$

Then the result will be 8.
Then $7 + \frac{7}{7} = 7 + 1 = 8$

As many times as is necessary to multiply 8 to make 24, so many times must thou multiply 7.
$24 \div 8 = 3$
Thus $N = 7 \times 3 = 21$

The result is 21.

See, it is 21. You will find it right."
Check: $21 + \frac{21}{7} = 21 + 3 = 24$

5:2 Special Quadratic and Cubic Equations (Optional)

The Babylonians solved some special quadratic and cubic equations by using tables of squares and cubes and a trial and error process.

EXAMPLE. Solve $N^3 + N^2 = 810$.

Solution. Construct Table 5.3, continuing until the solution is found. We see from the table that our solution is $N = 9$ because $81 + 729 = 810$. (A Babylonian tablet similar to the one below runs from $N = 1$ to $N = 60$.)

TABLE 5.3

N	1	2	3	4	5	6	7	8	9
N^2	1	4	9	16	25	36	49	64	81
N^3	1	8	27	64	125	216	343	512	729
$N^3 + N^2$	2	12	36	80	150	252	392	576	810

5:3 Compound Interest Problems (Optional)

A problem appearing on a Louvre tablet dated about 1700 B.C. asks how long it would take for a sum of money to double itself at a compound annual interest rate of 20 percent. This problem requires the solution of an exponential equation,

$$(1.2)^n = 2$$

Again the problem is solved by using a table. However, this time the process of linear interpolation is used.

n	1	2	3	4
$(1.2)^n$	1.2	1.44	1.728	2.0736

From the table we see that the solution is between 3 and 4 years. Now we find the differences,

$$\begin{array}{cc} 2.0736 & 2.0000 \\ 1.7280 & 1.7280 \\ \hline 0.3456 & 0.2720 \end{array}$$

Then the ratio

$$\frac{2720}{3456} \ (=) \ 0.816 \text{ year, or about 10 months}$$

Thus N is approximately 3 years and 10 months.

5:4 Progressions (Optional)

The Rhind papyrus exhibits problems involving arithmetical progressions and the curious problem, #79, concerned with a geometric progression.

An **arithmetical progression** is a set of numbers arranged in order, each number obtained from the previous one by the *addition* of a fixed amount, called the **common difference.**

Thus $\{3, 7, 11, 15, 19, \cdots\}$ is an arithmetic progression with common difference 4 ($3 + 4 = 7, 7 + 4 = 11, 11 + 4 = 15, 15 + 4 = 19$, and so on).

A **geometric progression** is a set of numbers arranged in order, each number obtained from the previous one by the *multiplication* of a fixed amount, called the **common multiplier** or ratio.

Thus $\{1, 4, 16, 64, \cdots\}$ is a geometric progression with common ratio 4 ($1 \times 4 = 4, 4 \times 4 = 16, 16 \times 4 = 64$, and so on).

Problem 79 of the Rhind Papyrus. "Sum the geometrical progression of five terms, of which the first term is 7 and the multiplier 7.

The sum according to the rule. Multiply 2801 by 7.

$$\begin{array}{rr} 1 & 2,801 \\ 2 & 5,602 \\ 4 & 11,204 \\ \hline \text{Total 7} & 19,607 \end{array}$$

The sum by addition.

houses	7
cats	49
mice	343
spelt	2,401
hekat	16,807
Total	19,607."

(Spelt is grain and a hekat is a unit of measurement, about half a peck.)

There are various interpretations of this problem. Eisenlohr considers the words to be the names of the powers of 7. Another version: In each of 7 houses are 7 cats, each cat kills 7 mice, each mouse would have eaten 7 ears of grain, each ear of grain would have produced 7 hekats of grain; how much grain is saved? But why does the author add all these quantities together? The addition seems absurd.

Around 1202 A.D. there appeared in the book *Liber Abaci,* written by the mathematician Leonardo Fibonacci, the following problem:

> There are seven old women on the road to Rome. Each woman has seven mules; each mule carries seven sacks; each sack contains seven loaves; with each loaf are seven knives; and each knife is in seven sheaths. Women, mules, loaves, knives, and sheaths, how many are there in all on the road to Rome?

This reminds us of the Mother Goose rhyme published at a later date:

> As I was going to Saint Ives,
> I met a man with seven wives;
> Every wife had seven sacks;
> Every sack had seven cats;
> Every cat had seven kits.
> Kits, cats, sacks, and wives,
> How many were going to Saint Ives?

Here there is a joke contained in the first and last lines, the correct answer being "one" or "none," depending on the interpretation.

Did this surprise twist also occur to the ancient Egyptians?

Why has this problem lasted through all the centuries, absurd as it is in its addition?

Pregeometry

> Herodotus writes "They said also that this king (Sesostris) divided the land among all Egyptians so as to give each one a quadrangle of equal size and to draw from each his revenues, by imposing a tax to be levied yearly. But every one from whose part the river tore away anything, had to go to him and notify what had happened; he then sent the overseers, who had to measure out by how much the land had become smaller, in order that the owner might pay on what was left; in proportion to the entire tax imposed. In this way, it appears to me, geometry originated, which passed thence to Hellas."

1. INTRODUCTION TO GEOMETRIC FIGURES

The science of geometry evolved from the practical problems dealing with the measurement of land areas and granary volumes. The Egyptians were noted for making constructions and determining areas and volumes. On the other hand, the Babylonians solved many problems stated in a geometric form, although these problems were usually algebraic in content. In general, Egyptian mathematics was stronger geometrically, whereas Babylonian mathematics was stronger algebraically.

The ancient Orientals were familiar with the geometric figures illustrated below. However, they did not know all the correct modern formulas, which are also shown.

A formula is a pattern indicating what arithmetic computations are to be performed on the numbers designated by the letters of the formula. The algebraic conventions that are used are summarized in Table 5.4. Parentheses are used to indicate that the operation within the parentheses is to be performed before any other operation.

TABLE 5.4 ALGEBRAIC CONVENTIONS

OPERATION	CONVENTION	EXAMPLE, USING $a = 6$ AND $b = 2$
Addition	$a + b$	$6 + 2 = 8$
Subtraction	$a - b$	$6 - 2 = 4$
Multiplication	ab or $a(b)$ or $a \cdot b$	$6 \cdot 2 = 6 \times 2 = 12$
Division	$\dfrac{a}{b}$	$\dfrac{6}{2} = 6 \div 2 = 3$

For example, if $h = 5$, $a = 6$, and $b = 2$, then

$$\frac{h(a + b)}{2} = \frac{5(6 + 2)}{2} = \frac{5(8)}{2} = \frac{40}{2} = 20$$

Measurement — Pregeometry

Areas:

1. Square $A = s^2$

2. Rectangle $A = bh$

3. Right triangle $A = \dfrac{bh}{2}$

4. Isosceles triangle $A = \dfrac{bh}{2}$

5. Isosceles trapezoid $A = \dfrac{h(a + b)}{2}$

6. Right trapezoid $A = \dfrac{h(a + b)}{2}$

7. Circle $A = \pi r^2$, where $\pi \,(=)\, 3.1416$[1]

Volumes:

1. Cube $V = s^3$

2. Rectangular parallelepiped (box) $V = wlh$

3. Square pyramid $V = \dfrac{hb^2}{3}$

4. Truncated pyramid $V = \dfrac{h(a^2 + ab + b^2)}{3}$

5. Cylinder $V = \pi r^2 h$

6. Cone $V = \dfrac{\pi r^2 h}{3}$

7. Sphere $V = \dfrac{4\pi R^3}{3}$

8. Frustrum of a cone $V = \dfrac{\pi h(a^2 + ab + b^2)}{3}$

2. FORMULAS FOR AREAS

2:1 Squares, Rectangles, Right Triangles

Both Egyptians and Babylonians had the correct formulas for the areas of the square, rectangle, and right triangle.

Square $A = s^2$ Example:

$$A = 3^2 = 3 \times 3 = 9 \text{ square units}$$
$$\text{or 9 unit squares}$$

[1]This notation means that 3.1416 is an approximation to the number π whose decimal representation requires infinitely many nonrepeating digits.

Rectangle $\qquad$ h $A = bh$ Example: 3

8

$$A = 3 \times 8 = 24 \text{ square units}$$

Right triangle h $A = \dfrac{bh}{2}$ Example: 3

b 8

$$A = \frac{3 \times 8}{2} = \frac{24}{2} = 12 \text{ square units}$$

Problems indicate that the Orientals knew that the right triangle was half of a rectangle.

2:2 Isosceles Triangles

Problems 56, 57, 58, and 59 of the Rhind papyrus indicate that the Egyptians probably knew the correct way to calculate the area of an isosceles triangle.

However, there are also some examples of the incorrect method, where the side is used instead of the altitude.

Thus the area of 10 10 12 would be calculated incorrectly as

$$\frac{bs}{2} = \frac{12 \times 10}{2} = 60$$

instead of correctly as

$$A = \frac{bh}{2} = \frac{12 \times 8}{2} = 48$$

Problem 57 of the Rhind Papyrus.   "If the seked of a pyramid is 5 palms 1 finger per cubit and the side of its base is 140 cubits, what is its altitude?"

4 fingers = 1 palm and the seked $= \dfrac{b}{2h}$ or the cotangent ratio as used

7 palms = 1 cubit   in trigonometry

"Divide 1 cubit by the seked doubled, which is 10½.

$$h = \frac{b}{2 \times \text{seked}} = \frac{140}{2 \times 5\frac{1}{4}}$$

Multiply 10½ so as to get 7, for this is a cubit.

$$= 140 \times \frac{7}{2 \times 5\frac{1}{4}}$$

7 is $\frac{2}{3}$ of 10½.

$$7 \div 10\frac{1}{2} = \frac{2}{3}$$

Operate on 140, which is the side of the base: $\frac{2}{3}$ of 140 is

$$140 \times \frac{2}{3} = 93\frac{1}{3}$$

93⅓, the altitude."

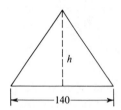

2:3 Trapezoids

Right trapezoid

Both Egyptians and Babylonians knew that the area was obtained by using the calculation $A = \frac{h}{2}(a + b)$.

EXAMPLE. $A = \frac{6}{2}(3 + 5) = 3 \times 8 = 24$

Isosceles trapezoid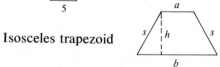

The Babylonians used the incorrect forumla $A = \frac{s}{2}(a + b)$ instead of the correct formula $A = \frac{h}{2}(a + b)$; that is, the side was used for the altitude.

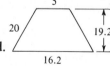

EXAMPLE. Calculate the area of the isosceles trapezoid.

Incorrect method: $A = \frac{20}{2}(5 + 16.2) = 10 \times 21.2 = 212$

Correct method: $A = \frac{19.2}{2}(5 + 16.2) = 9.6 \times 21.2 = 203.52$

2:4 Circles $d = 2r$

The Babylonians approximated the circumference C, and the area A, of the circle by the rules:

$$C = 3d \text{ (the circumference is 3 times the diameter)}$$
$$A = \frac{C^2}{12} \text{ (the area is } \frac{1}{12} \text{ of the square of the circumference)}$$

This is equivalent to using the approximation $\pi = 3$.

The Egyptians used the rule

$$A = \left(\frac{8}{9} d\right)^2 \text{ (the area is the square of } \frac{8}{9} \text{ of the diameter)}$$

This is equivalent to using the approximation $\pi = 3.1604$.

The modern formulas are $C = \pi d$ and $A = \pi r^2$, with the more accurate approximation $\pi = 3.1416$ appropriate for most practical applications.

3. FORMULAS FOR VOLUMES

3:1 Cubes and Boxes

Both Egyptians and Babylonians knew the correct methods for calculating the volumes of the cube and the box. (Mathematicians call a box a "rectangular parallelepiped.")

Cube   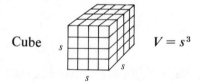 $V = s^3$

EXAMPLE. If the side is 4 units, then the volume is $4 \times 4 \times 4 = 64$, or $V = 4^3 = 64$ cubic units (or 64 unit cubes).

Box   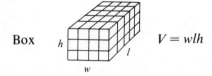 $V = wlh$

EXAMPLE. If the width is 4 units, the length is 5 units, and the height is 3 units, then the volume $V = 3 \times 4 \times 5 = 60$ cubic units.

3:2 Cylinders

Both Egyptians and Babylonians found the volume of a right circular cylinder by multiplying the area of the circular base by the height. This procedure is correct but their answers were in error due to the approximations they used for the area of the circular base.

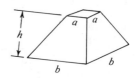

The Babylonians used $\quad V = \frac{3}{4} d^2 h$

the Egyptians used $\quad V = \frac{64}{81} d^2 h$

and we use $\quad V = \frac{\pi}{4} d^2 h$ with $\pi (=) 3.14164$ (or $\pi r^2 h$)

(Cubes, boxes, and cylinders were used as containers of grain.)

3:3 Truncated Pyramid

The correct formula,

$$V = \frac{h}{3} (a^2 + ab + b^2)$$

was known to the Egyptians. Problem 14 of the Moscow papyrus exhibits this correct method for obtaining the volume of a truncated pyramid. This problem illustrates the highest point of Egyptian geometry. E. T. Bell has called this problem "the greatest Egyptian pyramid."

Problem 14 of the Moscow Papyrus. "If you are told: A truncated pyramid of 6 for the vertical height be 4 on the base by 2 on the top:

You are to square this 4; result 16.	$b^2 = 4^2 = 16$
You are to double 4; result 8.	$ab = 2 \times 4 = 8$
You are to square this 2; result 4.	
You are to add the 16 and the 8 and the 4;	$a^2 = 2^2 = \underline{4}$
result 28.	$a^2 + ab + b^2 = 28$ Total
You are to take $\frac{1}{3}$ of 6; result 2.	$\frac{h}{3} = \frac{6}{3} = 2$
You are to take 28 twice; result 56.	$2 \times 28 = 56$

See, it is 56. You will find it right."

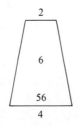

4. PYTHAGOREAN NUMBERS AND THE RIGHT TRIANGLE

Both Egyptians and Babylonians exhibited problems indicating an elementary knowledge of proportions and similar triangles. Egyptian surveyors were known as "rope stretchers" and may have formed a right angle by putting 11 equidistant knots on a rope 12 units in length and then forming a triangle having sides 3 units, 4 units, and 5 units, respectively. However, there is no documentary evidence supporting this.

The sides of a right triangle have the special property that the sum of the squares of two sides is equal to the square of the largest side, called the **hypotenuse.** Thus $3^2 + 4^2 = 9 + 16 = 25 = 5^2$. In general, for the right triangle whose sides are a, b, and c units, respectively, we find that $a^2 + b^2 = c^2$.

This statement is called the **theorem of Pythagoras** (about 540 B.C.) after the Greek mathematician, who is credited with giving the first proof of this statement. Here again, there is no documentary proof that Pythagoras did supply the first proof.

Numbers a, b, and c, having the property that $a^2 + b^2 = c^2$, are called **Pythagorean triplets.** For example, the numbers 3, 4, and 5 are a Pythagorean triplet.

Amazingly enough, a Babylonian tablet dated around 1900 B.C. to 1600 B.C. and called Plimpton 322 deals with Pythagorean triplets. This tablet indicates that the Babylonians not only knew about Pythagorean triplets but also knew rules for producing them. This, indeed, is a high point in Babylonian mathematics. Here the fundamental properties of the numbers themselves are being investigated.

Plimpton 322 (a part of it):   *Transcription:*

b	c	a	b	c	a	$a^2 + b^2 = c^2$
1,59	2,49	2,0	119	169	120	
56,7	1,20,25	57,36	3367	4825	3456	
1,5	1,37	1,12	65	97	72	
5,19	8,1	6,0	319	481	360	

√2 and the Diagonal of a Square.[2] An old Babylonian tablet in the collection at Yale University indicates that the Babylonians knew the special case of the theorem of Pythagoras: that the diagonal of a square is √2 times its side:

$$s^2 + s^2 = d^2 \quad \text{or} \quad 2s^2 = d^2 \quad \text{or} \quad \sqrt{2}s = d$$

A copy of the tablet and a transcription (in Babylonian base 60) is shown in Figure 5.5. Note that the tablet exhibits a very good approximation to the irrational[3] number √2.

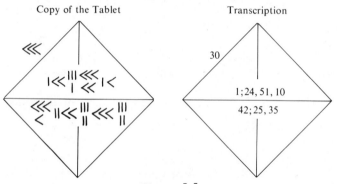

Copy of the Tablet

Transcription

30

1;24, 51, 10

42;25, 35

Figure 5.5

$$\sqrt{2} \ (=) \ 1; \ 24, \ 51, \ 10 \ \text{base} \ 60 = 1 + \frac{24}{60} + \frac{51}{3600} + \frac{10}{216,000}$$

$$(=)1.414213 \ \text{base} \ 10$$

√2 = 1.414213 base 10 is correct to the sixth decimal place

The diagonal

$$d = \sqrt{2} \times 30 \ (=) \ 42; \ 25, \ 35 = 42 + \frac{25}{60} + \frac{35}{3600}$$

Thus √2 × 30 = 42.42639 base 10, which is correct to the fifth decimal place.

---

[2] √2 designates the number that when multiplied by itself produces the number 2; that is, √2 × √2 = 2. Similarly, √9 = 3 because √9 × √9 = 9; that is, 3 × 3 = 9.

[3] An irrational number is a number that cannot be expressed as the ratio of two counting numbers. Fractions such as $\frac{3}{4}, \frac{5}{17},$ and $\frac{1,234}{56,789}$ are rational because they are expressed as the ratio of two counting numbers. The number √2 cannot be expressed as the ratio of two counting numbers and can only be approximated using fractions.

EXERCISES

1. Add by regrouping. Check by converting to Hindu-Arabic numerals.

   a. XXXVIIII
      XXVIII

   b. MMDCLXXVII
      MDCCCXXIII

   c. |||
      ||| ∩∩∩ 9999

      ||| ∩∩∩ 9999
      || ∩∩∩ 999

2. Subtract by regrouping. Check by converting to Hindu-Arabic numerals.

   a. C X III
      L XXX

   b. MMDCLX
      MDCCXXIII

   c. |||| 999
      ||| ∩9

3. Multiply by duplation, the Egyptian method of doubling.

   a. XXXVI by XVII   b. CCXXXV by XXVI   c. |||| ∩∩∩
                                            |||| ∩∩ by ||| ∩∩

4. a. Divide 34 by 9; that is, multiply 34 by $\frac{1}{9}$ using $2 \times \frac{1}{9} = \frac{1}{6} + \frac{1}{18}$.

   b. Divide 68 by 5, Egyptian style; that is, use the duplation method to multiply 68 by $\frac{1}{5}$ using the fact that $2 \times \frac{1}{5} = \frac{1}{3} + \frac{1}{15}$ and $2 \times \frac{1}{15} = \frac{1}{8} + \frac{1}{120}$.

5. Solve the following problems by using the Egyptian rule of false position.

   a. "A quantity and its ninth, added together, becomes 30. What is the quantity?"

   b. "Go down I, $\frac{2}{3}$ of me, $\frac{1}{2}$ of me, $\frac{1}{7}$ of me are added to me, we become 33. What is the quantity saying it?"

   $$N + \frac{2N}{3} + \frac{N}{2} + \frac{N}{7} = 33$$

6. Solve the following equations, Babylonian style, that is, by making a table of N, N^2, N^3, and computing until the desired result is obtained.
   a. $N^3 + 2N^2 = 441$.   b. $4N^3 - 2N^2 = 450$.   c. $4N^3 - 2N^2 = 605$.

7. How long would it take for a sum of money to double itself at 10 percent compound annual interest? Solve this problem Babylonian style. Make a table of n and $(1.1)^n$ until an entry is reached such that $(1.1)^n$ is larger than 2. Now solve $(1.1)^n = 2$; use linear interpolation.

8. On a piece of graph paper draw a right triangle with sides 6, 8, and 10 units. Also draw an isosceles triangle, sides 25 units, 25 units, and

14 units ($h = 24$). Determine the areas of the two triangles above by

a. Counting squares.

b. The incorrect method, $A = \dfrac{bs}{2}$.

c. The correct method, $A = \dfrac{bh}{2}$.

9. On a piece of graph paper draw (1) a right trapezoid, lower base 14, upper base 4, height 12; and (2) an isosceles trapezoid, lower base 14, upper base 4, sides 13 ($h = 12$). Determine the areas of the two trapezoids above by

a. Counting squares.

b. The incorrect method, $A = \dfrac{(a + b)s}{2}$.

c. The correct method, $A = \dfrac{(a + b)h}{2}$.

10. Compute the area of a circle with diameter d, 18 units (radius r, 9 units) by using the

a. Babylonian method, $A = 3 \times r^2$.

b. Egyptian method, $A = \left(\dfrac{8}{9} \text{ of } d\right)^2$.

c. Modern method, $A = \pi r^2$ and $\pi = 3.1416$.

11. Compute the volume of a truncated square pyramid of vertical height 9 units, upper base 3 units, and lower base 5 units by using the correct Egyptian method,

$$V = \frac{h}{3} (a^2 + ab + b^2)$$

12. Theorem of Pythagoras (in a right triangle, $a^2 + b^2 = c^2$)

a. On a sheet of graph paper, draw a right triangle having sides 3 units, 4 units, and 5 units. Draw squares upon each of the three sides. Show that the areas of the squares on two sides is equal to the area of the square on the hypotenuse (the 5-units side).

b. Complete the following table of Pythagorean numbers, similar to a table on a Babylonian tablet, Plimpton 322.

$$a = p^2 - q^2, \qquad b = 2pq, \qquad c = p^2 + q^2$$

	p	q	a	b	c	$a^2 + b^2 =$	c^2
	2	1	3	4	5	$9 + 16 =$	25
(1)	3	2					
(2)	4	3					
(3)	4	1					

c. Select any two numbers you wish for p and q. Find a, b, and c by the rule above. Verify that $a^2 + b^2 = c^2$.

PART III

THE GREEK PERIOD

The Formative Years

From 1200 to 600 B.C., the Mediterranean was the scene of violent social change. This period was marked by mass migrations and by innumerable wars. The most important single factor in this change was probably the introduction of a technology based on iron; the changeover from bronze to iron occurred about 1200 B.C. Bronze was, and is, an expensive metal to produce. It is an alloy of copper and tin, metals that are quite scarce and are rarely found together. By contrast, iron is abundant and easy to mine. Iron weapons and tools were not only better than bronze ones, they were cheaper. Agriculture was improved by the use of iron, and trade was stimulated. Where the production of bronze had required the unification of many areas by commerce or by conquest, the increasingly widespread use of iron resulted in the decentralization of economic units. For six centuries the trend was toward small, self-sufficient, and politically autonomous units.

From a mathematical point of view, the period 900 to 600 B.C. was transitional. We know of no great or sudden developments in mathematics at this time, yet the evidence suggests that there was a gradual change of outlook; a slow transition from the practical viewpoint of the Egyptians and Babylonians to the logical viewpoint of the Greeks. Furthermore, there was probably wide dissemination of the already existing knowledge.

Merchants and conquerors, traveling to new lands, carried their knowledge with them. At this time the power of Egypt and Babylonia was greatly reduced. Many new peoples appeared in the Mediterranean world, notably the Jews, the Greeks, and the Phoenicians. It was during this time that the alphabet was invented and coined money was introduced. Asia meanwhile was the scene of the religious reforms of Gautama the Buddha in India and Confucius in China.

Our principal interest here is with the Greeks, among whom there were two important social developments at this time. The first of these was the rise of a new class, a class of economically powerful and politically conscious merchants. These men enjoyed and valued the freedom they had so recently won from the land-owning aristocracy. They enjoyed also sufficient leisure time to engage in philosophical investigations.

The second development among the Greeks was the rise of the "polis," or self-governing city-states. Perhaps the most famous *polis* was Athens on the Greek mainland. Around 594 B.C., the law-giver Solon set down a code of law in Athens. This marked a change from rule of custom to rule of law that had far-reaching social consequences. One of Solon's most famous laws made it illegal for a man to sell himself into slavery (formerly common practice among debtors). This may be said to mark the first glimmerings of the idea that slavery is inconsistent with human dignity. The Greeks saw man's value as residing in his rationality. They thought of man as a rational being living in a rational world, a world operating by precise laws that were waiting only to be discovered. The prevalence of this point of view among the Greeks certainly contributed to their development of mathematics as a logical, deductive system.

Thales of Miletus
(ca. 640–548 B.C.)

Thales, the father of Greek mathematics, was a member of the new merchant class. His youth was spent in trading; in the course of his commercial ventures, he probably visited Egypt, Babylonia, Crete, and Asia. Thales brought the mathematical knowledge of the ancient Orientals to the Greeks, but more important than this were his own original contributions to mathematics. For it was Thales who introduced the concept of proof into geometry. Thus he was the first to exhibit the main concern of early Greek mathematicians, that is, *to understand man's place in the universe according to a rational scheme.* The "How?" of the Egyptians was no longer enough. The Greek man also wanted to know "Why?"

There are many stories concerning Thales and even if they are not true, they are certainly appropriate.

Thales was known as one of the seven wise men of ancient Greece. Herodotus states that he predicted an eclipse, probably the year of the solar eclipse of May 28, 585 B.C. The story is told of his falling into a ditch while contemplating the stars during an evening walk. An old woman attending him asked, "How can you know what is happening in the heavens when you can't see what is at your feet?"

Aristotle writes that Thales, during a good season of olives, obtained control of all the oil presses in Miletus and Chios. Thus he "cornered" the market and could set his own terms. However, instead of taking advantage of his buyers, he sold the fruit very reasonably. His purpose had been accomplished, because he had *proved* what could be done.

Plutarch tells of how Solon went to Thales in Miletus and asked him why he never married and had children. Thales did not answer immediately, but several days later he sent a runner, who, pretending he had just come from Athens, told Solon that Solon's son had been killed in an accident. Thales consoled the grief-stricken Solon by revealing that the report was fiction and had been invented only to explain why he, Thales, had never married.

Pythagoras

(ca. 580–501 B.C.)

Although there are many stories about the life of Pythagoras, little is known for certain. He was probably born on the island of Samos, probably traveled to Egypt and Babylonia, and is known to have settled in Crotona on the Italian coast. In Crotona he founded a brotherhood composed of some 300 wealthy young aristocrats. This group, known as the Pythagoreans, became the prototype of all the secret societies of Europe and America. Their motto, "Number rules the universe," expressed the combination of mathematics and mysticism in which they believed. Shakespeare refers to the Pythagorean belief in immortality and transmigration of the soul in *The Merchant of Venice:*

Thou almost mak'st me waver in my faith,
To hold opinion with Pythagoras,
That souls of animals infuse themselves
Into the trunks of men.

The Pythagoreans considered the universe to be ordered by means of the counting numbers and the person who fully understood the harmony of numerical ratios would become divine and immortal.

The name of Pythagoras is most famous in connection with the relationship of the squares of the sides of a right triangle. While Pythagoras did not discover this property (it was already known to the Babylonians), he may have offered the first proof of this statement.

Most significant among the contributions of the Pythagoreans was the discovery that $\sqrt{2}$ (the length of the diagonal of a square whose sides are each 1 unit in length) is an irrational number; that is, $\sqrt{2}$ cannot be expressed as the ratio of two counting numbers. This discovery caused a temporary crisis in mathematics. Not only did it upset the Pythagorean belief that everything was based on the counting numbers, but it exposed logical defects in their theory of proportion. The Pythagoreans based their theory on the assumption that a common unit of measurement could be found for any two lengths. Yet $\sqrt{2}$ and 1 do *not* have a common unit of measurement. The story is told of how the Pythagorean, Hippasus, was drowned in a shipwreck because he revealed to outsiders the secret that $\sqrt{2}$ is irrational.

The Pythagoreans were noted for their study of the properties of numbers, which study they called *arithmetic,* as distinguished from *logistic,* the name they gave to the practical art of computing with numbers (what is now called "arithmetic" in the United States).

The word *mathematics* was also originated by this secret society. To them it meant the four subjects of geometry, arithmetic, music, and astronomy—the famous "quadrivium" of the Middle Ages.

The Birth and Development of Mathematics

Beginning around 546 B.C., the Greeks were attacked and invaded by the Persians (led, in turn, by Cyrus, Darius, and Xerxes), who had arisen on the ruins of the Assyrian Empire. Eventually the Persians were defeated and the democratic elements in Greece became more and more influential. Finally, Athens, under Pericles (461–429 B.C.), emerged as the center of a new and remarkable civilization, the Golden Age of Greece.

The year 431 B.C. marked the beginning of the Peloponnesian War between Athens and Sparta. As a result, Athens was reduced to a minor political power but she regained her cultural leadership. It was the end of a slave-owning democracy and the start of a new period of aristocratic supremacy. The ruling classes had more wealth, more slaves, and thus more time to cultivate art and science. This was the period that witnessed the birth of the professional scientist, a man who devoted his life to the pursuit of knowledge and was paid for doing so.

The schools of Socrates (400 B.C.), Plato (380 B.C.), and Aristotle (340 B.C.) developed the disciplines of mathematics and the methods of deductive logic. Theaetetos (369 B.C.) developed the theory of irrational numbers, later to be written in the tenth book of Euclid. Eudoxes (408–355 B.C.) developed the "exhaustion" method and the theory of proportion as presented in the fifth book of Euclid. The "crisis" that was introduced by the Pythagoreans was finally resolved.

Athens was defeated by King Philip of Macedonia in 338 B.C. Four years later, his son, Alexander the Great, began his reign and conquests. Alexander founded the city of Alexandria in Egypt as his new capital, an intellectual center and an economic center. In time, all the Near East fell to the Greeks. Upon Alexander's death in 323 B.C., his conquests were divided among his generals; Egypt under the Ptolemies, Mesopotamia and Syria under the Seleucids, and Macedonia under Antigones. The Indus valley in India also had its Greek princes.

Around 300 B.C. the University of Alexandria opened its doors. This was the first institution of its kind and it was similar to our modern universities. It was famous for its library, which contained over 600,000 papyrus rolls. To this university came Euclid, probably from Athens, to head the mathematics department.

Euclid

(ca. 300 B.C.)

Mathematics was born with the appearance of the *Elements,* written by Euclid. Euclid's texts are the first Greek texts that have been fully preserved. Next to the Bible, *Elements* has been reproduced and studied more than any other book. Our elementary high school geometry is taken almost literally from the first six of these thirteen books.

Elements is a collection of the works of earlier writers, arranged in a strictly logical order according to the methods of deductive reasoning. The logical structure of these books, in addition to their content, has influenced scientific thinking more than any other publication.

Very little is known about the life of Euclid. Pappus wrote in his *Collections* that Apollonius (ca. 225 B.C.) lived for a long time in Alexandria with the pupils of Euclid. Proclus, in his *Commentaries,* wrote that Euclid was younger than the pupils of Plato (who died around 347 B.C.) but older than Archimedes (born 287 B.C.). Proclus also wrote that Euclid lived in the time of the first Ptolemy (who reigned 306–283 B.C.) to whom he said, "There is no royal road to geometry," when Ptolemy asked him if there wasn't an easier way to learn geometry. This information places Euclid around 300 B.C., and this is about all that is known.

Euclid has been pictured as a mathematician noted for his modesty and fairness and as a teacher noted for his kindness and patience. Stobaeus relates that a student who had just learned the first theorem of geometry asked Euclid, "But what advantage shall I get by learning these things?" Euclid directed his slave by saying "Give him threepence, since he must make profit out of what he learns."

Archimedes

(287–212 B.C.)

Archimedes, the immortal Syracusan, ranks as one of the three greatest mathematicians of all times; the other two are Sir Isaac Newton (1643–1727 A.D.) of England and Carl Freidrich Gauss (1777–1855 A.D.) of Germany.

The amazing genius of Archimedes is seen in his many creative works, ranging from pure geometry to applied mechanics. So powerful was his insight that his original contributions included investigations into the subject that was later called "calculus."

Plutarch wrote in his life of Marcellus that although Archimedes had acquired fame and a reputation for divine rather than human intelligence because of his mechanical inventions, he would not deign to leave any writings about them. He regarded mechanics and utilitarian art as ignoble and vulgar, and preferred to devote himself to subjects "whose elegance and subtlety are untrammeled by the necessities of life." Discussing the works of Archimedes, Plutarch said "It is not possible to find in geometry more difficult and weighty questions treated in simpler and purer terms. Some attribute this to the natural endowments of the man, others think it was the result of exceeding labor that everything done by him appeared to have been done without labor and with ease."

Little is known of the life of Archimedes. In the preface of his book, *The Sand-Reckoner*, he mentioned his father Pheidias, the astronomer. Tzetzes, the Byzantine grammarian, stated that Archimedes died when he was 75. Plutarch wrote that Archimedes was slain by a Roman soldier during the seige of Syracuse in 212 B.C. Thus it is inferred that Archimedes was born in 287 B.C.

Plutarch also stated that Archimedes was a kinsman and friend of King Hiero of Syracuse (260–216 B.C.) in response to whose requests many of Archimedes' physical and mechanical discoveries were made.

Vitrivius has related the familiar story of how Archimedes discovered the law of buoyancy while bathing. Excited, he ran naked through the streets of Syracuse, shouting "Heureka, heureka," which means "I have found it, I have found it." This discovery enabled Archimedes to confirm King Hiero's suspicion that a goldsmith had substituted silver for gold in making a crown for him.

Pappus attributed to Archimedes the famous saying "Give me a place to stand, and I shall move the earth." Another version of this saying is found in Plutarch in the description of the compound pulley invented by Archimedes. Writing to King Hiero, he stated that if there were another earth, by going into it, he could move this one. Hiero asked him to make good this statement and accordingly Archimedes loaded a ship to full capacity with passengers and freight so that it could be drawn out of dock only by many men and with great labor. Then, "sitting himself the while far off, with no great endeavor, by only holding the head of the pulley in his hand and drawing the cords by degrees, he drew the ship in a straight line, as smoothly and evenly as if she had been in the sea."

From the prefaces to his works, it is known that Archimedes had friends among the Alexandrian mathematicians, and the Greek historian Diodorus stated that Archimedes studied mathematics at Alexandria. Most of his life, however, was spent in Syracuse.

The "war machines" of Archimedes, in which he applied his discoveries of pulleys, levers, cranes, burning mirrors, and other devices, were chiefly responsible for the delay of the fall of Syracuse to Rome. "The Romans became so filled with fear that, if they saw a little piece of rope or of wood projecting over the wall, they cried, 'There it is! Archimedes is training some engine upon us,' and fled."

Eventually, Marcellus took the city and Archimedes was slain by a blundering soldier. Plutarch gave three versions of his death, one of which stated that Archimedes was so intent in his contemplation of a mathematical diagram that, when a soldier came up to him and commanded him to follow him to Marcellus, he refused to go until after he had completed the proof to his problem. The soldier, enraged, drew his sword and killed him.

Another account in Tzetzes stated that Archimedes told the Roman soldier who came too close "Stand away, fellow, from my diagram." The infuriated soldier killed him. From this remark is probably derived the expression "Don't disturb my circles."

The Roman general Marcellus was deeply afflicted by the death of Archimedes and "ever after regarded the one that killed him as a murderer, and sought out the relatives of Archimedes to do them honor."

It is significant that we are informed about the death of Archimedes because of Plutarch's interest in Marcellus. Almost everyone today knows of Archimedes, but Marcellus is chiefly remembered only as the Roman general one of whose soldiers murdered Archimedes.

Alfred North Whitehead regarded the death of Archimedes at the hands of a Roman soldier as symbolic of a world change of the first magnitude. "The Romans were a great race, but they were cursed by the sterility which waits upon practicality. They were not dreamers enough to arrive at new points of view, which could give more fundamental control over the forces of nature. No Roman lost his life because he was absorbed in the contemplation of a mathematical diagram."

Apollonius and Eratosthenes

Other important contributions were made by Apollonius (225 B.C.) in his work on conics, which constituted the beginnings of analytic geometry, and by Eratosthenes (230 B.C.), who is noted for his measurement of the circumference of the earth and for his work in number theory.

Old Age and Death

Alexandrian Greece and the Age of Hellenism soon gave way to the might of the Roman Empire. In short order, between 212 B.C. and 30 B.C., Syracuse, Carthage, Corinth, Mesopotamia, and Egypt all fell to Rome. These were the times of the conquests of Pompey and Julius Caesar. Augustus became emperor in 1 A.D. and Christ was born in 7 A.D. Christianity was carried into western Europe and Rome conquered England. By 100 A.D., the Roman Empire ruled the world.

The peace that followed helped to spread the knowledge of the Greeks from Rome and Athens and Alexandria to Babylonia, China, and India. However, the spread of a slave economy was fatal to original scientific development. The Romans disdained that which did not have an immediate material value. The lack of interest and the lack of financial support spelled the doom of mathematics.

Between 200 and 300 A.D., the barbarians attacked the Roman Empire. In 400 A.D. the western part of the Roman Empire fell and the

Papacy began. The Greek masterpieces were lost or destroyed and Europe sank into the Dark Ages. For 1000 years there was a dearth of scientific development in the western world.

Late Contributions

Some mathematical contributions were made during the last days of the Roman Empire. Most of these were compilations of earlier works, and then, finally, only histories or commentaries were written. The most significant contributions were made by Ptolemy, Diophantos, and Pappus.

Ptolemy, about 150 A.D., wrote the *Almagest,* which deals with astronomy and trigonometry.

Diophantos, about 250 A.D., developed number theory and exhibited the first systematic use of symbols in algebra.

Pappus, about 300 A.D., provided developments that later became a part of projective geometry. His commentaries provide us with valuable information about the early Greek mathematicians.

Our most important source of the history of Greek mathematics is from the *Commentaries* of Proclus, written about 450 A.D. He used as a source *The History of Greek Mathematics,* written by Eudemus about 335 B.C., but which is now lost. This work of Eudemus is also called the "Eudemian Summary."

SOURCES OF
GREEK MATHEMATICS

There are no primary sources. Classical scholars have restored the original texts from the Arabic and Latin translations of the original manuscripts and from commentaries.

430–349 B.C. Plato	*Republic:* philosophy and logic
384–322 B.C. Aristotle	*Analytica posteriora; Organon:* systematizing deductive logic
ca. 300 B.C. Euclid	*Elements:* plane and solid geometry; first deductive system
ca. 225 B.C. Apollonius	*Conic Sections:* preanalytic and projective geometry

287–212 B.C. Archimedes   *Measurement of a Circle; Quadrature of the Parabola; On Spirals:* plane geometry

On the Sphere and Cylinder; On Conoids and Spheroids: solid geometry

The Sand-Reckoner: arithmetic of large numbers

On Plane Equilibriums; On Floating Bodies; On Levers: applied mathematics (physics)

Method: integral calculus

ca. 230 B.C. Eratosthenes   *On Means:* measurement of the earth

ca. 150 A.D. Ptolemy   *Almagest:* astronomy; trigonometry

ca. 250 A.D. Diophantos   *Arithmetica; On Polygonal Numbers:* algebra; number theory

ca. 300 A.D. Pappus   *Collections:* projective geometry; history

ca. 450 A.D. Proclus   *Commentaries:* history

REFERENCES FOR GREEK MATHEMATICS

Eves, *An Introduction to the History of Mathematics,* Chaps. 3–6.

Heath, *History of Greek Mathematics.*

Midonick, *The Treasury of Mathematics:*
    "Appollonius," pp. 1–12.
    "Archimedes," pp. 13–36.
    "Diophantus," pp. 309–327.
    "Euclid," pp. 349–360.
    "Hippocrates of Chios," pp. 406–413.
    "Metrodorus," pp. 496–506.
    "Pappus," pp. 599–609.
    "Plato," pp. 660–680.
    "Proclus," pp. 681–688.

Newman, *The World of Mathematics,* Vol. 1:
    "The Great Mathematicians," pp. 74–117.

"Archimedes," pp. 179–187.
"Greek Mathematics," pp. 188–209.

Struik, *A Concise History of Mathematics*, Chap. 3.

FROM HOW TO WHY: A Mathematical Example of "A Way of Thinking"

How? How do you make a right triangle?

1. The Egyptians probably knew that lengths of 3, 4, and 5 made a right triangle.

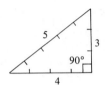

2. The Babylonians knew that $3^2 + 4^2 = 5^2$ (or that $9 + 16 = 25$). The Babylonians generalized this property of numbers and made a table of Pythagorian triplets (Plimpton 322).

$$A^2 + B^2 = C^2$$

5, 12, 13	$5^2 + 12^2 = 13^2$
7, 24, 25	$7^2 + 24^2 = 25^2$

Why? Why in a right triangle does $A^2 + B^2 = C^2$? The Greek Pythagoras may have given a "dissection" proof:

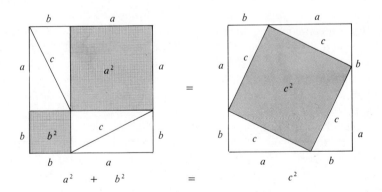

The theorem of Pythagoras: In a right triangle, the square upon the hypothenuse is equal to the sum of the squares upon the two legs.

CHAPTER VI

Logic

"Then you should say what you mean," the March
     Hare went on.
"I do," Alice hastily replied; "at least—at least I mean
     what I say—that's the same thing, you know."
"Not the same thing a bit!" said the Hatter.
"Why, you might just as well say that 'I see what I eat'
     is the same thing as 'I eat what I see'!"
"You might just as well say," added the March Hare,
     "that 'I like what I get' is the same thing as 'I get
     what I like'!"
"You might just as well say," added the Dormouse,
     which seemed to be talking in its sleep, "that 'I
     breathe when I sleep' is the same thing as 'I sleep
     when I breathe'!"
"It is the same thing with you," said the Hatter.

Alice's Adventures in Wonderland, Lewis Carroll

1. SHORT HISTORY OF LOGIC

The processes that man uses to think or to reason were first analyzed by
the ancient Greeks. These principles were systematized by *Aristotle*
(ca. 384–322 B.C.) in his work *Organon.* Aristotelian syllogistic reasoning
was the logic that was taught and studied for over 2000 years.

The German mathematician, *Gottfried Wilhelm Leibniz* (1646–1716)
was the first serious student of symbolic logic, although his works did
not immediately motivate the development of the subject. However, they
did stimulate interest and were significant because of his feeling that all
mathematical and scientific concepts can be derived from the principles
of logic.

The founder of the modern study of symbolic logic was *George
Boole* (1815–1864), a self-educated English mathematician. For the first
time, in his works *The Mathematical Analysis of Logic* (1847) and *An
Investigation of the Laws of Thought* (1854), algebraic operations are
systematically and successfully applied to logic.

The next developments were related to the goal stated by Leibniz.
The three large volumes of *Principia Mathematica* (1910–1913), written
by the English mathematicians *Alfred North Whitehead* and *Bertrand*

Russell, present a detailed development of arithmetic, starting with only the undefined concepts and the assumptions of logic.

In 1932, the Austrian mathematician *Kurt Goedel* (1906–), now at the Institute for Advanced Study at Princeton, proved that in any axiomatic system, consisting of a finite set of axioms free of contradiction, there always exists a statement that can be neither proved nor disproved. Thus no axiomatic system can be both consistent and complete.

Developments in logic continue. The goal of Leibniz remains unrealized but we are beginning to understand better the nature of logical truth.

REFERENCES

Midonick, *The Treasury of Mathematics:*
George Boole, "The Mathematical Analysis of Logic" and "The Laws of Thought," pp. 147–165.

Newman, *The World of Mathematics,* Vol. 3:
George Boole, "Mathematical Analysis of Logic," pp. 1856–1858.
Lewis and Langford,"History of Symbolic Logic," pp. 1859–1877.
Alfred Tarski, "Symbolic Logic," pp. 1901–1931.
Ernest Nagel and James R. Newman, "Goedel's Proof," pp. 1668–1695.

Nidditch, P. H., *The Development of Mathematical Logic,* The Free Press, New York, 1962.

2. ARISTOTELIAN LOGIC

2:1 Syllogisms

The logic of Aristotle was concerned with only four kinds of statements. These were the statements having the structures:

> 1. All *S* is *P*.
> 2. No *S* is *P*.
> 3. Some *S* is *P*.
> 4. Some *S* is not *P*.

In the above statements, the letter *S* represents the subject and the letter *P* the predicate. (The patterns of the above statements were designated by the letters *A, E, I,* and *O,* respectively.)

Reasoning, then, was the application of different syllogistic patterns involving the above statements.

An ancient example of a **syllogism** is the following:

> All men are mortal.
> Socrates is a man.
> Therefore, Socrates is mortal.

Another example of a syllogism, called the **hypothetical syllogism:**

> All residents of Paris are residents of France.
> All residents of France are residents of Europe.
> Therefore, all residents of Paris are residents of Europe.

2:2 Difficulties

The logic of Aristotle was incomplete and inexact. There were no compound or complex statements, no attention being paid to connectives such as "or" and "and." Also, there was no systemized order or algebra for quickly deducing conclusions. With the work of Boole, the syllogistic logic of Aristotle was transformed into our modern symbolic logic.

3. SYMBOLIC LOGIC

3:1 tf Statements

Symbolic logic is concerned with only those statements that can be classified as true or false. Such sentences are called tf statements.

Definition: *A* **tf statement** *is a declarative sentence to which it is meaningful to assign a truth value of "true" or "false," but not both.*

Some examples of tf statements are the following:
  a. Bronze is made of copper and tin.
  b. San Francisco is in California.
  c. If an arrow is shot into the air, it will fall to the ground.
  d. Either London or Berlin is the capital of France.
  e. Ostriches do not fly and a whale is not a fish.
  f. Paris is the capital of Italy.
Sentences that are *not* tf statements include questions, exclamations, and expressions of opinions. Some example of these are given below.
  a. Come in!
  b. What are you doing?
  c. Brahms wrote better music than Bach.
  d. Watch the camera!
  e. 13 is an unlucky number.
  f. This statement you are reading is false.

3:2 Connectives

The use of certain words in our language determines the structure or pattern of a statement. Such words are called **connectives.** Summarized in Table 6.1 are the connectives that are most common, symbols[1] that are used as substitutes for these words, and the names of the statements obtained by using these connectives.

TABLE 6.1

CONNECTIVE	SYMBOL	NAME
NOT	−	Negation
AND	∧	Conjunction
OR	∨	Disjunction
IF · · · , THEN · · ·	→	Implication
IF AND ONLY IF	↔	Equivalence

In symbolic logic, tf statements are represented by symbols such as P, Q, and R. By using these capital letters and the symbols for the connectives, the logical structure of a statement can be expressed completely in symbols. This is illustrated in Table 6.2, where P = "fish swim" and Q = "birds have wings."

TABLE 6.2

NAME OF PATTERN	ENGLISH STATEMENT	SYMBOLIC STATEMENT
Negation	Fish do not swim.	$\overline{P}$
Conjunction	Fish swim and birds have wings.	$P \wedge Q$
Disjunction	Fish swim or birds have wings.	$P \vee Q$
Implication	If fish swim, then birds have wings.	$P \rightarrow Q$
Equivalence	Fish swim if and only if birds have wings.	$P \leftrightarrow Q$

3:3 Truth Tables and Set Diagrams

The truth of a statement[2] obtained by using one or more of the connectives depends on the truth of each component statement. A table indicat-

---

[1] Other symbols in current usage are:

$$\text{Negation, } P', \tilde{P}, \sim P, -P$$
$$\text{Conjunction, } P \cdot Q, PQ$$
$$\text{Disjunction, } P + Q$$
$$\text{Implication, } P \supset Q$$
$$\text{Equivalence, } P \equiv Q$$

[2] From now on, unless it is indicated otherwise, the term "statement" will mean "tf statement."

ing this dependence is called a **truth table.** The truth table also defines the connective, that is, explains its meaning. Set diagrams illustrated below serve to clarify these meanings.

Negation, $\bar{P}$.   The word "not" is used to change the truth value of a statement. If P is true, then $\bar{P}$ is false. If P is false, then $\bar{P}$ is true.

TRUTH TABLE

P	$\bar{P}$
T	F
F	T

Set diagram

EXAMPLE.   If $P =$ fish swim, then $\bar{P} =$ fish do not swim. If $P =$ fish have wings, then $\bar{P} =$ fish do not have wings.

Conjunction, $P \wedge Q$.   The word "and" is used with the meaning that P and Q is true only when both P and Q are each true.

TRUTH TABLE

P	Q	$P \wedge Q$
T	T	T
T	F	F
F	T	F
F	F	F

Set diagram

EXAMPLE.   I know that story. I read the book and I saw the movie.

Disjunction, $P \vee Q$.   The word "or" is used in mathematical logic with the meaning that P *or* Q is false only when both P and Q are false.

TRUTH TABLE

P	Q	$P \vee Q$
T	T	T
T	F	T
F	T	T
F	F	F

Set diagram

EXAMPLE.   That story sounds familiar. I read the book or I saw the movie.

Implication, $P \rightarrow Q$. The implication is considered false when the "if" statement, P, is true and the "then" statement, Q, is false. This definition is consistent with the set relationship, P is a subset of Q, $P \subset Q$. The statement "All P is Q" is considered as having the same meaning as the statement "If P, then Q."

TRUTH TABLE

P	Q	$P \rightarrow Q$
T	T	T
T	F	F
F	T	T
F	F	T

Set diagram

All P is Q. $P \subset Q$
If P, then Q. $P \rightarrow Q$

The example below should help to clarify the meaning of an implication. Each of the four possible cases is illustrated. Note that case 2, the case in which the implication is false, is the only one that cannot be illustrated on the figure following the example.

EXAMPLE. Let P = An animal is a bird. Let Q = An animal has wings. Then $P \rightarrow Q$ can be translated as "All birds have wings" or as "If an animal is a bird, then it has wings." or as "The set of all birds is a subset of the set of animals with wings" (see Figure 6.1).

Case 1. TT If a robin is a bird, then a robin has wings. True.
Case 2. TF If a robin is a bird, then a robin does not have wings. False.
Case 3. FT If a bee is a bird, then a bee has wings. True.
Case 4. FF If a cow were a bird, then a cow would have wings. True.

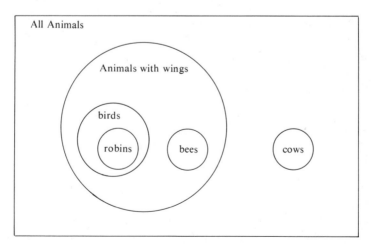

Figure 6.1

Equivalence, $P \leftrightarrow Q$. The compound statement "*P* if and only if *Q*" is considered true only when both *P* and *Q* are true or when both *P* and *Q* are false.

If *P* and *Q* are interpreted as sets, then the equivalence of *P* and *Q* would mean that *P* and *Q* were equal sets.

TRUTH TABLE

P	*Q*	$P \leftrightarrow Q$
T	T	T
T	F	F
F	T	F
F	F	T

Set diagram

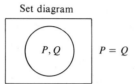

$P = Q$

Whenever two statements are equivalent, one can be substituted for the other in a given statement without changing the truth value of the statement.

3:4 Word Translations

A summary of common sentence structures is given in Table 6.3 together with translations into the language of symbolic logic.

TABLE 6.3

$P \rightarrow Q$	$P \wedge Q$	$\bar{P} \rightarrow Q$
1. If *P*, then *Q*.	1. *P* and *Q*.	1. Unless *P*, then *Q*.
2. All *P* is *Q*.	2. *P* but *Q*.	2. If not *P*, then *Q*.
3. *Q* if *P*.	3. *P* although *Q*.	
4. *P* only if *Q*.		
5. *P* implies *Q*.		
6. *P* causes *Q*.	$P \vee Q$	$P \rightarrow \bar{Q}$
7. When *P*, then *Q*.		
8. Those who are *P* are *Q*.	1. *P* or *Q*.	1. No *P* is *Q*.
9. *Q* is necessary for *P*.	2. *P* unless *Q*.	2. If *P*, then not *Q*.
10. *P* is sufficient for *Q*.		

4. TAUTOLOGIES

4:1 Definition and Examples

Definition: *A* **tautology** *is a symbolic statement that is true for every case of its pattern.* The truth follows from the structure of the statement and has nothing to do with its subject matter.

The Trivial Tautology, $P \leftrightarrow P$

EXAMPLE. "Fish swim" is equivalent to "Fish swim." "A rose is a rose" means "A rose is a rose."

The Law of the Double Negative, $P \leftrightarrow \overline{\overline{P}}$

P	$\overline{P}$	$\overline{\overline{P}}$	$P \leftrightarrow \overline{\overline{P}}$
T	F	T	T
F	T	F	T

EXAMPLE. "It was not impossible" means "It was not (not possible)" means "It was possible." "He was not guilty" means "He was not (not innocent)" means "He was innocent."

The Law of the Excluded Middle, $P \vee \overline{P}$

P	$\overline{P}$	$P \vee \overline{P}$
T	F	T
F	T	T

EXAMPLE. He was guilty or he was not guilty.

4:2 Statement, Converse, Inverse, Contrapositive

Related to an implication, $P \rightarrow Q$, are three other statements defined below.

Statement. If P, then Q. $P \rightarrow Q$ If one is in Paris, then one is in France.

Converse. If Q, then P. $Q \rightarrow P$ If one is in France, then one is in Paris.

Inverse. If not P, then not Q. $\overline{P} \rightarrow \overline{Q}$ If one is not in Paris, then one is not in France.

Contrapositive. If not Q, then not P. $\bar{Q} \to \bar{P}$ If one is not in France, then one is not in Paris.

All these statements are *not* equivalent in meaning. For example, a statement may be true while its converse is false, as illustrated in the example above. However, the statement *is* equivalent to its contrapositive and the converse *is* equivalent to the inverse as Table 6.4 shows. Thus $(\bar{Q} \to \bar{P}) \leftrightarrow (P \to Q)$ and also $(\bar{P} \to \bar{Q}) \leftrightarrow (Q \to P)$.

TABLE 6.4

P	Q	STATEMENT $P \to Q$	CONTRAPOSITIVE $\bar{Q} \to \bar{P}$	CONVERSE $Q \to P$	INVERSE $\bar{P} \to \bar{Q}$
T	T	T	T	T	T
T	F	F	F	T	T
F	T	T	T	F	F
F	F	T	T	T	T

The Law of the Contrapositive, $(\bar{Q} \to \bar{P}) \leftrightarrow (P \to Q)$.   The law of the contrapositive is a tautology, as the truth table above indicates.

4:3 DeMorgan's Laws, $\overline{P \wedge Q} \leftrightarrow \bar{P} \vee \bar{Q}$ and $\overline{P \vee Q} \leftrightarrow \bar{P} \wedge \bar{Q}$

DeMorgan's laws tell us how to distribute a negation over a conjunction or disjunction. They are verified by constructing their truth tables. Note the relationship to the complementation of an intersection or union of two sets.

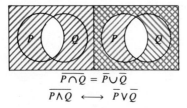

$$\overline{P \cap Q} = \bar{P} \cup \bar{Q}$$
$$\overline{P \wedge Q} \longleftrightarrow \bar{P} \vee \bar{Q}$$

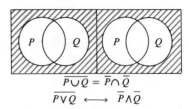

$$\overline{P \cup Q} = \bar{P} \cap \bar{Q}$$
$$\overline{P \vee Q} \longleftrightarrow \bar{P} \wedge \bar{Q}$$

Figure 6.2

EXAMPLE. "It is *not* the case that he lived in Paris *and* in London" is equivalent to "He did *not* live in Paris *or* he did *not* live in London."

EXAMPLE. "It is *not* the case that it rained *or* it snowed" is equivalent to "It did *not* rain *and* it did *not* snow."
[*Rule:* To distribute a "not" change the "and" to an "or" (or the "or" to an "and").]

4:4 Other Tautologies (Optional)

Other tautologies that are important for the principles of argument and proof are stated below.

Modus Ponens or Direct Reasoning, $[(P \to Q) \land P] \to Q$

Modus Tollens or Indirect Reasoning (Law of the Contrapositive), $[(P \to Q) \land \overline{Q}] \to \overline{P}$

Hypothetical Syllogism or Chain Reasoning (Law of Transitivity), $[(P \to Q) \land (Q \to R)] \to (P \to R)$

    The truth table for the law of hypothetical syllogism is given as Table 6.5.

TABLE 6.5

P	Q	R	$[P \to Q$	$\land$	$Q \to R]$	$\to$	$(P \to R)$
T	T	T	T	T	T	T	T
T	T	F	T	F	F	T	F
T	F	T	F	F	T	T	T
T	F	F	F	F	T	T	F
F	T	T	T	T	T	T	T
F	T	F	T	F	F	T	T
F	F	T	T	T	T	T	T
F	F	F	T	T	T	T	T

5. METHODS OF PROOF

5:1 Proof Patterns

To reason, or more technically, to derive conclusions, a rule for reasoning is needed. A rule for reasoning is referred to as a **rule of inference.**

    The basic rule of inference that is used is called the **rule of detachment,** or **modus ponens,** and it is based on the tautology

$$[P \land (P \to Q)] \to Q$$

The truth table for this tautology is exhibited as Table 6.6. Examining the column for $P \to Q$ in the table, we observe that whenever P is true *and $P \to Q$ is also true,* there is only one possibility for Q and that is for Q to be true.

TABLE 6.6

P	Q	$P \rightarrow Q$	$P \wedge (P \rightarrow Q)$	Q	$[P \wedge (P \rightarrow Q)] \rightarrow Q$
T	T	T	T	T	T
T	F	F	F	F	T
F	T	T	F	T	T
F	F	T	F	F	T

Thus we state that we can *conclude* statement Q to be true whenever we know that both statements P and $P \rightarrow Q$ are true.

This reasoning can be written in the form of either one of these patterns:

1. $P \rightarrow Q$ 1. P
2. P 2. $P \rightarrow Q$
3. Therefore, Q 3. Therefore, Q

In mathematics, a **proof** is an ordered set of tf statements, the order being justified by one or more tautologies and a rule of inference. The most basic or elementary proofs are summarized in Table 6.7 as **proof patterns,** followed by an example illustrating each.

TABLE 6.7 PROOF PATTERNS

DIRECT	INDIRECT (CONTRAPOSITIVE)	CHAIN (HYPOTHETICAL SYLLOGISM)	INDIRECT CHAIN (CONTRAPOSITIVE AND HYPOTHETICAL SYLLOGISM)
$P \rightarrow Q$	$P \rightarrow Q$	$P \rightarrow Q$	$P \rightarrow Q$
P	$\overline{Q}$	$Q \rightarrow R$	$Q \rightarrow R$
Thus Q	Thus $\overline{P}$	Thus $P \rightarrow R$	Thus $\overline{R} \rightarrow \overline{P}$

EXAMPLES

DIRECT   1. If an object is an art object, then it is expensive.
              2. This painting is an art object.
              3. Therefore, this painting is expensive.

INDIRECT   1. If an object is an art object, then it is expensive.
              2. This bracelet is not expensive.
              3. Therefore, this bracelet is not an art object.

CHAIN   1. If an object is an art object, then it is expensive.
              2. If an object is expensive, then it is valuable.
              3. Therefore, If an object is an art object, then it is valuable. (Or we could say, "All art objects are valuable.")

CHAIN
INDIRECT   1. All art objects are expensive.
              2. All expensive objects are valuable.
              3. Therefore, objects of no value are not art objects.

5:2 Validity

In each of the above patterns, it is important to note that the order of the statements numbered 1 and 2, called the **premises,** can be interchanged. However, the statement numbered 3, called the **conclusion,** must follow the other two; that is, it is a logical consequence of the first two statements.

Each of the examples stated above is called a **valid argument.** This means the final statement or conclusion follows logically from the preceding statements according to a tautology. More specifically, the final statement or conclusion must be a consequent (a "then" statement) of a tautological implication and the antecedent (the "if" statement) must be assumed or previously concluded true.

There are many valid argument patterns, since any tautology can be used. We are especially concerned with the tautologies listed below, which justify our previously stated proof patterns.

DIRECT $[P \wedge (P \rightarrow Q)] \rightarrow Q$
INDIRECT $[\bar{Q} \wedge (P \rightarrow Q)] \rightarrow \bar{P}$
CHAIN $[(P \rightarrow Q) \wedge (Q \rightarrow R)] \rightarrow (P \rightarrow R)$
INDIRECT CHAIN $[(P \rightarrow Q) \wedge (Q \rightarrow R)] \rightarrow (\bar{R} \rightarrow \bar{P})$

Sometimes an argument is given that is not valid. This means that the argument *cannot* be justified by a tautology, and a counterexample for the pattern can be found, that is, a case where the conclusion does not follow from the premises. Such an argument is called an **invalid argument.** Some common examples of these reasoning errors or invalid arguments are illustrated below.

Invalid-Converse Pattern

1. $P \rightarrow Q$ If a person lives in San Francisco, then he lives in California.
2. Q This person lives in California.
3. Thus P This person lives in San Francisco.

Counterexample: Joe Alpha lives in Los Angeles, California.

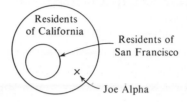

Invalid-Inverse Pattern
1. $P \rightarrow Q$ If a person lives in San Francisco, then he lives in California.
2. $\overline{P}$ This person does not live in San Francisco.
3. Thus Q This person does not live in California.
    Counterexample: Joe Alpha lives in Los Angeles, California.

Invalid−False Chain Pattern
1. $P \rightarrow Q$ If an animal is a dog, then it is a mammal.
2. $P \rightarrow R$ If an animal is a dog, then it has four legs.
3. Thus $Q \rightarrow R$ If an animal is a mammal, then it has four legs.
    Counterexample: A whale is a mammal and it does *not* have four legs.

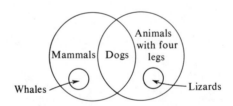

In this last example, it would also be invalid to conclude $R \rightarrow Q$. The counterexample is a lizard, which has four legs but is a reptile, *not* a mammal.

5:3 Combination of Patterns

Once a conclusion has been obtained by a logical argument or, in other words, a valid argument, this conclusion may become the premise of another argument. Thus an ordered set or chain of valid arguments is produced. This chain is again a valid argument and is called the proof of the final conclusion.

EXAMPLE 1. Form a valid conclusion using all the following statements.
    1. If demand is greater than supply, then prices increase.

2. If prices increase, then salaries increase.

3. If salaries increase, then inflation results.

The pattern can be written

1. $A \rightarrow B$ where A = Demand is greater than supply.

2. $B \rightarrow C$ B = Prices increase.

    Thus $A \rightarrow C$ C = Salaries increase.

3. $C \rightarrow D$ D = Inflation results.

Thus the *conclusion* using all the given statements is: $A \rightarrow D$, or If demand is greater than supply, then inflation results. For convenience, the above pattern can be expressed as a chain:

$$A \rightarrow B \rightarrow C \rightarrow D. \quad \text{Thus } A \rightarrow D.$$

EXAMPLE 2. Form a valid conclusion using all the statements below.

1. If there is a storm, then the duck hunting is good.

2. If they don't get their limit, then the duck hunting is bad.

3. They did not get their limit.

Let A = There was a storm.

    B = Duck hunting is good.

    C = They did not get their limit.

Then

1. $A \rightarrow B$ or $\bar{B} \rightarrow \bar{A}$, the contrapositive

2. $C \rightarrow \bar{B}$

3. C

Then we have the chain $C \rightarrow \bar{B} \rightarrow \bar{A}$. Thus $C \rightarrow \bar{A}$. Now, since C is assumed true, we conclude $\bar{A}$ is true by valid, direct reasoning.

Conclusion. $\bar{A}$, or There was no storm.

EXERCISES

1. Determine which of the following are tf statements.

    a. San Francisco is in California.

    b. London is in Africa.

    c. Open the window.

    d. Look out!

    e. If wishes were horses, beggars would ride.

    f. Paris is in France or Berlin is in England.

    g. Can you read this?

    h. If an object is lighter than water, then it floats.

    i. I like apple pie.

    j. All animals can fly.

    k. This sentence you are reading is false.

    l. Absence makes the heart grow fonder.

    m. Out of sight, out of mind.

n. If you do not work, then you will not succeed.

o. There is divinity in odd numbers.

p. The moon is made of green cheese.

q. I am the Queen of England and 1 equals 2.

r. You succeed if and only if you fail.

2. Separate each of the following statements into simple tf statements P, Q, R, and so on, and write the statement in symbolic form using the logical symbols for the connectives.

   a. He is studying French or Spanish.

   b. Ostriches cannot fly.

   c. If you are a good citizen, then you vote at election time.

   d. All lemons are sour.

   e. To be or not to be: that is the question.

   f. You cannot be a Senator if you are not 30 years old.

   g. It is raining and the wind is blowing.

   h. He is on time if and only if he catches the bus.

   i. It is not true that Mary was not invited.

   j. If he gets a scholarship and a job, then he will go to college.

   k. If it is cloudy or if it rains, then the sun does not shine.

   l. No diligent student fails.

   m. When it rains, it pours.

   n. Everyone who likes music appreciates Beethoven.

   o. Unless he hears from you, he will sell.

   p. He is here but he is busy.

   q. Smith came although his wife is ill.

   r. Higher salaries cause higher prices.

   s. No circles are squares.

   t. Good grades imply good study habits.

3. Write in English the following symbolic statements and determine their truth values, given that P = "Paris is in Italy" is false and Q = "London is in England" is true.

   a. $\overline{P}$ e. $\overline{P} \wedge Q$ i. $P \rightarrow \overline{Q}$ m. $\overline{P} \vee \overline{Q}$

   b. $\overline{Q}$ f. $P \wedge \overline{Q}$ j. $\overline{P} \rightarrow Q$ n. $\overline{P \wedge Q}$

   c. $P \wedge Q$ g. $P \rightarrow Q$ k. $P \vee \overline{Q}$ o. $\overline{P \vee Q}$

   d. $P \vee Q$ h. $Q \rightarrow P$ l. $\overline{P} \vee Q$ p. $\overline{\overline{Q}}$

4. a. Make a truth table for $P \times Q$ meaning "Either P or Q, but not both." This is called the **exclusive or**, as contrasted with the **inclusive or**, as defined in the text.

   b. In each of the following, determine whether the word "or" is used with the inclusive meaning, "P or Q, or both" or with the exclusive meaning, "P or Q, but not both."

   (1) When I go to New York, I shall either fly or take the train.

   (2) Mary is either in the library or she is in the cafeteria.

   (3) The story sounds familiar. I saw the movie or I read the book.

(4) According to the menu, you may have pie or you may have cake.

(5) You can use the charge account or your husband can.

(6) Her mother was born in England or in Australia.

(7) Either the demands are met or there will be a strike.

(8) You qualify for the job if you read French or if you read German.

5. a. Make a truth table for $P * Q$ meaning "Neither P nor Q."

    b. Verify the tautology: $(P * Q) \leftrightarrow (\overline{P} \wedge \overline{Q})$.

    c. Express the above tautology in English by replacing P by "Roses are red" and Q by "Snow is white."

6. Make truth tables for each of the following and verify that they are tautologies.

    a. DeMorgan's laws: $\overline{P \wedge Q} \leftrightarrow (\overline{P} \vee \overline{Q})$ and $\overline{P \vee Q} \leftrightarrow (\overline{P} \wedge \overline{Q})$.

    b. Law of contradiction: $\overline{P \wedge \overline{P}}$.

    c. Law of implication and disjunction: $(P \rightarrow Q) \leftrightarrow (\overline{P} \vee Q)$.

    d. $(\overline{P} \rightarrow Q) \leftrightarrow (\overline{Q} \rightarrow P)$.

7. Write the contrapositive of each of the following. Use DeMorgan's laws when they apply.

    a. If I study, then I will pass.

    b. If it rains, then I will not go.

    c. If I am not invited, then I will be unhappy.

    d. If I get a loan or a scholarship, then I will go to college.

    e. If Jane comes and John does not, then we will have trouble.

    f. If that is John's coffee, then it has cream and no sugar in it.

    g. If the baby cries, then he is hungry or he is not well.

    h. If you buy a dress and it does not fit, then you may exchange it.

    i. If I don't go by boat, then I will fly.

    j. No one who is not at least 30 years old or who has not been a citizen for at least 9 years can be a United States Senator.

8. Construct the truth tables for each of the following and then determine which of the following are equivalent.

    a. $P \rightarrow \overline{Q}$ b. $\overline{P} \wedge \overline{Q}$ c. $\overline{P \vee Q}$ d. $\overline{P} \vee \overline{Q}$

9. The Sheffer stroke, written P / Q, means "not P or not Q."

    a. Write the truth table for P / Q.

    b. Show that P / P defines $\overline{P}$ (that is, show they both have the same truth tables).

    c. Show that $(P / P) / (Q / Q)$ defines $P \vee Q$.

    [In 1913, H. M. Sheffer showed that the five basic connectives (not, and, or, implication, and equivalence) could each be defined by starting with just one connective, the Sheffer stroke.]

10. Determine whether each of the following arguments are valid or invalid. If valid, determine which of the proof patterns is being used. If invalid, determine the error in reasoning.

a to d. "If a girl is a blonde, then she is beautiful."

a. Mary is a blonde. Therefore, Mary is beautiful.
b. Jane is beautiful. Therefore, Jane is a blonde.
c. Betty is a brunette. Therefore, Betty is not beautiful.
d. Janice is homely. Therefore, Janice is not a blonde.

e to h. "If an object is lighter than water, then it floats on water."

e. Cork is lighter than water. Therefore, cork floats.
f. Water is heavier than oil. Therefore, oil floats on water.
g. Iron will not float on water. Therefore, iron is heavier than water.
h. A needle can be made to float on water. Therefore, a needle is lighter than water.

i to l. "Drinking coffee in the evening prevents me from sleeping."

i. I slept last night. Therefore, I did not drink coffee.
j. I did not drink coffee last night. Therefore, I slept last night.
k. I did not sleep last night. Therefore, I drank coffee last night.
l. I drank coffee last night. Therefore, I did not sleep last night.

m to p. "If a person was not at the scene of the crime, then he is innocent."

m. Mr. *A* was at the scene of the crime. Therefore, Mr. *A* is guilty.
n. Mr. *B* is not guilty. Therefore, Mr. *B* was not at the scene of the crime.
o. Mr. *C* was not at the scene of the crime. Therefore, Mr. *C* is innocent.
p. Mr. *D* was guilty. Therefore, Mr. *D* was at the scene of the crime.

q to v. "If you study mathematics, then you learn logic."

q. If you are able to vote intelligently, then you learn logic. Therefore, if you study mathematics, then you are able to vote intelligently.
r. If you learn logic, then you are able to vote intelligently. Therefore, if you study mathematics, then you are able to vote intelligently.
s. If you study mathematics, then you are able to vote intelligently. Therefore, if you learn logic, then you are able to vote intelligently.

    t. If you are unable to vote intelligently, then you did not learn logic. Therefore, if you study mathematics, then you are unable to vote intelligently.

    u. If you learn logic, then you are able to vote intelligently. Therefore, if you are unable to vote intelligently, then you did not study mathematics.

    v. If you do not study mathematics, then you are able to vote intelligently. Therefore, if you are unable to vote intelligently, then you learn logic.

11. Indicate whether the following argument patterns are valid or invalid. If valid, state a tautology justifying the pattern. If invalid, produce a counterexample.

a. $\bar{S}$
$R \to Q$
$Q \to S$
Thus $\bar{R}$

b. $\bar{R}$
$R \to Q$
$Q \to S$
Thus $\bar{S}$

c. $P \vee Q$
$\bar{P}$
Thus Q

d. $P \wedge Q$
Thus P

e. $P \to Q$
$Q \to R$
$R \to S$
Thus S

f. $P \to (Q \to R)$
$\bar{Q} \to \bar{P}$
P
Thus R

g. $P \to Q$
$R \to \bar{Q}$
$\bar{R}$
Thus P

h. $P \to Q$
$R \to \bar{Q}$
R
Thus $\bar{P}$

i. $P \to \bar{Q}$
$S \to P$
$\bar{R} \to Q$
Thus $S \to R$

j. $\bar{Q}$
Thus $\overline{P \wedge Q}$

12. For each of the following, determine whether a logical conclusion is possible. If so, state the conclusion. Illustrate each with a set diagram.

    a. If a man is successful, then he is wealthy.
       If a man is wealthy, then he is happy.

    b. If a student is diligent, then he does not fail.
       If a student is intelligent, then he is diligent.

    c. All art objects are valuable.
       All expensive objects are valuable.

    d. If it rains, then the fishing is good.
       When the night is starless, then it rains.

    e. No animal without wings can fly.
       All birds can fly.

    f. All sour fruit contains acid.
       All lemons are sour.

    g. All fruits containing acid are sour.
       All lemons are sour.

    h. If the book is blue, then it is mine.
       My books are attractive.

    i. None of my books is green.
       Red books are attractive.

    j. Well-informed people are good company.
       People who talk about themselves are bad company.

    k. If food is not sweet, then it is wholesome.
       If food is fattening, then it is unwholesome.
    l. If I eat pickles and ice cream, then I get sick.
       I am not sick.
    m. If I go Friday, then I can't go Saturday or I can't go Sunday.
       I went Saturday.
    n. If I go Friday, then I can't go Saturday or I can't go Sunday.
       I went Saturday and Sunday.
    o. If I park overtime or in a red zone, then I get a ticket.
       I did not get a ticket.
    p. If I park overtime or in a red zone, then I get a ticket.
       I did not park overtime and I did not park in a red zone.
    q. Either I saw the movie or I read the book.
       If I read the book, then I know the author.
       I did not see the movie.
    r. If I don't eat lunch, then I have dessert with my dinner.
       If I eat potatoes, then I don't have dessert with my dinner.
       If I get up early, then I eat potatoes.
       Either I get up early or I miss the morning news.
       I did not miss the morning news.
    s. If I go to the Orient, then I'll stop in Hawaii if I go by plane.
       If I can't go by plane, then I won't go to the Orient.
       I went to the Orient.

13.[3] Translate each of the following into symbolic implications. Form a syllogism containing all the implications in one chain. Translate the conclusion and its contrapositive into English.

EXAMPLE. 1. All hummingbirds are richly colored.
          2. No large birds live on honey.
          3. Birds that do not live on honey are dull in color.

Let U = birds; A = hummingbirds; B = richly colored birds; C = large birds; D = birds that live on honey. Then the above statements are translated as follows:

$$1.\ A \to B \qquad 2.\ C \to \overline{D} \qquad 3.\ \overline{D} \to \overline{B}$$

The symbolic chain: $C \to \overline{D} \to \overline{B} \to \overline{A}$ (using the contrapositive of 1).
The conclusion is $C \to \overline{A}$ or its contrapositive $A \to \overline{C}$, which may be translated as: Large birds are not hummingbirds,
               or Hummingbirds are not large birds.

---

[3] Examples adapted from Lewis Carroll, *Symbolic Logic*, New York: Dover Publications, Inc., 1958.

a. No ducks waltz.
   No officers refuse to waltz.
   All my poultry are ducks.
b. All puddings are nice.
   This dish is a pudding.
   No nice things are wholesome.
c. All unripe fruit is unwholesome.
   All these apples are wholesome.
   No fruit, grown in the shade, is ripe.
d. Every one who is sane can do logic.
   No lunatics are fit to serve on a jury.
   None of your sons can do logic.
e. Things sold in the street are of no great value.
   Nothing but rubbish can be had for a song.
   Eggs of the Great Auk are very valuable.
   It is only what is sold in the streets that is really rubbish.
f. No interesting poems are unpopular among people of real taste.
   No modern poetry is free of affectation.
   All your poems are on the subject of soap bubbles.
   No affected poetry is popular among people of real taste.
   No ancient poem is on the subject of soap bubbles.

CHAPTER VII

Mathematical Systems

> "I don't know what you mean by 'glory'," Alice said.
> Humpty Dumpty smiled contemptuously. "Of course
> you don't—till I tell you. I meant 'there's a nice
> knock-down argument for you!'"
> "But 'glory' doesn't mean 'a nice knock-down
> argument,'" Alice objected.
> "When I use a word," Humpty Dumpty said, in
> rather a scornful tone, "it means just what I
> choose it to mean—neither more nor less."
>
> *Through the Looking-Glass,* Lewis Carroll

1. GENERAL DISCUSSION

1:1 Undefined Concepts and Definitions

Definitions are agreements to use words, phrases, or symbols as substitutes for other words, phrases, or symbols.

If we are to avoid errors in our reasoning and if we are to obtain exactness in meaning, the words we use must be carefully defined. Try to detect the error in the example below.

1. A drug is a dope.
2. A dope is a foolish person.
3. Therefore, a drug is a foolish person.

Here the word "dope" is used with two different meanings. Thus we may use valid reasoning and still reach a conclusion that we are unwilling to accept if we are careless in defining our words.

In defining a word, other words must be used. Obviously we cannot define every word that we use. Some words must be left **undefined.** For example, suppose we look up the word "happy" in a dictionary. We would find that "happy" means "content" or "glad." If we looked up the meanings of these two words, we would find that they mean "happy." To avoid this circular process, we state at the beginning what our undefined words shall be and then define the rest of our words in order, using only the undefined words or words that have already been defined.

In selecting the words that are to be undefined, we try to select those that are simplest or most elementary in meaning. The undefined concepts are also called the **primitive terms.**

Example of a set of definitions from the subject of elementary plane geometry:

Undefined concepts: point, line, plane; on, between, equal

Definition: *A* **line segment** *is a set of two points on a line, called the* **end points** *of the line segment, and all the points on this line between the two end points.*

Definition: *A* **triangle** *is a set of three points not all on the same line, and the three line segments determined by these points used as end points of the line segments.*

In addition to maintaining an order in the list of definitions, each definition is carefully worded by following the criteria listed.

Criteria for definitions:
1. Use only undefined words or words already defined.
2. Place the word being defined in a *general* category.
3. *Specialize* the general category.
4. Avoid redundancy; that is, do not state more than is necessary.

1:2 Assumptions and Theorems

The deductive reasoning process involves the addition of a third statement, the conclusion, to two other given statements. Thus any argument or logical theory must begin with at least two general statements that are assumed true. These statements that are assumed true are called **assumptions,** or **axioms,** or **postulates.** Today in mathematics, all these words are equivalent in meaning.

The statements that are obtained from the assumptions as conclusions of deductive reasoning are called **theorems.** Thus a theorem is a statement that is proved by deductive reasoning.

Example of a set of three axioms and a theorem from the subject of elementary plane geometry:

Transitive axiom: If x, y, and z are counting numbers, then if $x = y$ and $y = z$, then $x = z$.

Subtraction axiom: If x, y, and z are counting numbers, then if $x + z = y + z$, then $x = y$.

Axiom (on "supplementary angles"): If two straight lines intersect, then the sum of the measures of two angles on one side of one of the lines is 180°.

Theorem ("Vertical angles are equal."): If straight line AB and straight line CD intersect at P, then $a = b$.

Proof

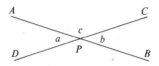

STATEMENTS	REASONS	LOGIC
1. If line AB and line CD intersect at P, then $a + c = 180°$ and $b + c = 180°$.	1. Axiom (on supplementary angles)	$P \to Q$
2. If $a + c = 180°$ and $b + c = 180°$, then $a + c = b + c$.	2. Transitive axiom	$Q \to R$
3. If $a + c = b + c$, then $a = b$.	3. Subtraction axiom	$R \to S$
		Thus $P \to S$

1:3 Formal Systems

A **mathematical system** is an ordered set of undefined concepts, definitions, assumptions, and theorems.

To understand the world in which he lives, man makes observations and measurements. Then he arranges his results and searches for relationships. He generalizes by finding a pattern that is shared by his different results, and by ignoring special differences. The general pattern that he obtains is not identical with any of its special cases but it is an abstraction of all of them.

Next a system is developed in the realm of mathematics, beginning with the abstract concepts and assumptions about them. Theorems are then obtained by deductive logic. The formal mathematical system is then ready for interpretation in the real world.

One advantage of a mathematical system is that many essentially different interpretations of it may be possible in the real world. Then the scientist, for example, can use the same results or theorems in many different applications. As long as the axioms are true for a particular interpretation, all the theorems must be true.

Another advantage of the mathematical system is that the theorems may serve as predictions that can be tested in the real world. If a prediction is false, then it follows logically that one or more of the axioms must be false. A new theory can be advanced to serve this special subject area by changing one or more of the axioms.

Historically, this has happened both in mathematics and in physics. Non-Euclidean geometry was developed by changing only the parallel postulate of Euclid. Newtonian physics developed into that of Einstein by changing a basic assumption.

Although most mathematical systems originate from concrete subjects in the real world, this is not always the case. Boolean algebra began as an abstract mathematical system. Now it is also known as the theory of electrical circuits.

Figure 7.1 illustrates the relation between a mathematical system and its interpretations in the real world. The circles are drawn overlapping because it is not always possible to determine exactly where one world ends and the other begins.

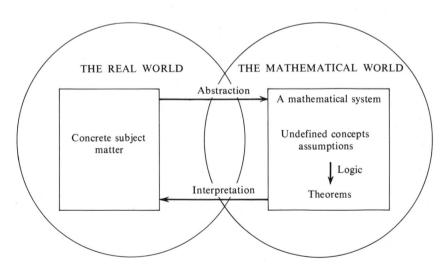

Figure 7.1

2. FINITE ALGEBRAS

2:1 Clock Arithmetic

An example of a finite mathematical system is furnished by the arithmetic of the numbers that appear on the face of a clock. Let us consider a 12-hour clock.

The sum of 6 and 9, $6 + 9$, shall mean 9 hours past 6. Since 9 hours past 6 o'clock is 3 o'clock, $6 + 9 = 3$. The table of the addition facts in this system is given as Table 7.2. Note that $12 + N = N + 12 = N$, or N hours after 12 o'clock is N o'clock, the same time as 12 hours after N o'clock, when the hands of the clock return to the position from which they started.

TABLE 7.2

+	1	2	3	4	5	6	7	8	9	10	11	12
1	2	3	4	5	6	7	8	9	10	11	12	1
2	3	4	5	6	7	8	9	10	11	12	1	2
3	4	5	6	7	8	9	10	11	12	1	2	3
4	5	6	7	8	9	10	11	12	1	2	3	4
5	6	7	8	9	10	11	12	1	2	3	4	5
6	7	8	9	10	11	12	1	2	3	4	5	6
7	8	9	10	11	12	1	2	3	4	5	6	7
8	9	10	11	12	1	2	3	4	5	6	7	8
9	10	11	12	1	2	3	4	5	6	7	8	9
10	11	12	1	2	3	4	5	6	7	8	9	10
11	12	1	2	3	4	5	6	7	8	9	10	11
12	1	2	3	4	5	6	7	8	9	10	11	12

Subtraction, multiplication, and division may be defined as they are in ordinary arithmetic; subtraction as the inverse or opposite of addition, multiplication as repeated addition, and division as the inverse or opposite of multiplication.

EXAMPLE 1. Find $5 - 8$. This means find the number that when added to 8 produces 5. Thus solve $5 = 8 + N$. From the table, $N = 9$.

EXAMPLE 2. Find 5×8. This means find $8 + 8 + 8 + 8 + 8 = 4$.

EXAMPLE 3. Find $4 \div 5$. This means find the number that when multiplied by 5 produces 4. Thus solve $4 = 5 \times N$. Since $5 \times 8 = 4$, $4 \div 5 = 8$.

Clock arithmetic is also called **modular arithmetic.** The above example is called modulo-12 arithmetic. Numbers other than 12 may also be used as a modulus. Modulo-4 arithmetic is illustrated below.

Modulo-4 Arithmetic. Addition in this system is based on a clock having 4 hours, or 4 units of time. The addition and multiplication tables are given below as Tables 7.3 and 7.4 with the modulus 4 replaced by 0.

TABLE 7.3

+	0	1	2	3
0	0	1	2	3
1	1	2	3	0
2	2	3	0	1
3	3	0	1	2

TABLE 7.4

×	0	1	2	3
0	0	0	0	0
1	0	1	2	3
2	0	2	0	2
3	0	3	2	1

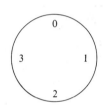

Definition of subtraction: $a - b = N$ *if and only if* $a = b + N$.

Definition of division: $a \div b = N$ *if and only if* $a = b \times N$.

The mathematical system consisting of the set $S = \{0, 1, 2, 3\}$ and the operation of addition, $+$, has some very interesting properties.

Closure. The set S is closed with respect to the operation $+$. This means that the sum of any two numbers or elements of the set S is again a member of set S.

From the table, we observe closure by noting that every entry in the table is an element of set S.

Commutativity. $a + b = b + a$, where a and b are any two elements of S. In other words, the order of addition does not affect the sum.

For example, $2 + 3 = 3 + 2 = 1$.

From the table, we observe commutativity by noting that the table is symmetrical about its principal diagonal (in this case, a line beginning in the upper left corner with the symbol "$+$" and ending in the lower right corner with the symbol "2").

Identity. There exists an element, I, so that $a + I = a$ for *every* a in S. In this case, we see that the identity element is 0:

$$0 + 0 = 0, \ 1 + 0 = 1, \ 2 + 0 = 2, \text{ and } 3 + 0 = 3$$

From the table, we observe the identity element by finding a column identical to the first column of the table. The heading of this column is the identity.

Inverse. For *every* element a in S, there exists an inverse element, $\bar{a}$, in S so that $a + \bar{a} = I$. Since 0 is our identity element in this case, $a + \bar{a} = 0$.

> The inverse of 0, $\bar{0}$, is 0 because $0 + 0 = 0$
> The inverse of 1, $\bar{1}$, is 3 because $1 + 3 = 0$
> The inverse of 2, $\bar{2}$, is 2 because $2 + 2 = 0$
> The inverse of 3, $\bar{3}$, is 1 because $3 + 1 = 0$

From the table, we observe the inverse property by noting that the identity element appears in each row.

Associativity. $(a + b) + c = a + (b + c)$ for all elements a, b, and c in S. In other words, when addition is repeated, the manner in which the numbers are grouped does not affect the sum.

For example, $(1 + 2) + 3 = 3 + 3 = 2$ and $1 + (2 + 3) = 1 + 1 = 2$. Thus $(1 + 2) + 3 = 1 + (2 + 3)$.

There is no general method for easily detecting the associativity of a system from its table. However, if the set S has 5 or fewer than 5 elements and if it is known that the system *has* the closure, commutative, identity, and inverse properties, then the system is associative if and only if there are no repeats in a row or column. When a system has 6 or more than 6 elements, it may not be associative even when it has no repeats in a row or column.

In general, the mathematical system consisting of a set and an operation that satisfies the properties of closure, commutativity, identity, inverse, and associativity is called a **commutative group.**

Now let us examine the properties of the system consisting of the set $\{0, 1, 2, 3\}$ and the operation $\times$, as observed from the multiplication table.

This system is **closed.** Every entry in the table belongs to the set S. $a \times b \in S$.

This system is **commutative.** The table is symmetric about its main diagonal. $a \times b = b \times a$.

The number 1 is the multiplication **identity.** We see that $a \times 1 = a$ for every $a \in S$.

The system is **associative.** $(a \times b) \times c = a \times (b \times c)$. This has to be verified for every special case.

However, the **inverse property** is not satisfied. The numbers 1 and 3 have inverses: each is its own inverse. That is, $1 \times 1 = 1$ and $3 \times 3 = 1$. On the other hand, the numbers 0 and 2 do not have inverses. It is impossible to multiply 0 by some number and get 1, and it is impossible to multiply 2 by some number and get 1.

This means that *some* division problems are not possible in this system. In particular, division by 0 or by 2 is impossible. For example, $3 \div 2$ is meaningless because it is impossible to multiply 2 by a number and obtain 3 as the product. On the other hand, $2 \div 3 = 2$ because $2 = 3 \times 2$, as seen in the table.

We have observed that the inverse property is satisfied for the addition operation. This means that every subtraction problem has a solution, a number in S.

Modulo-4 arithmetic has another interesting property that shows the relationship between addition and multiplication. This is called the **distributive property,** which is illustrated below.

Distributive property. $a \times (b + c) = (a \times b) + (a \times c)$ [or $a(b + c) = ab + ac$].

$$2 \times (3 + 1) = (2 \times 3) + (2 \times 1)$$

because

$$2 \times (3 + 1) = 2 \times 0 = 0 \quad \text{and} \quad (2 \times 3) + (2 \times 1) = 2 + 2 = 0$$

Similarly, $3(2 + 3) = (3 \times 2) + (3 \times 3) = 3$.

The subject of elementary algebra is concerned with an infinite set of numbers, the operations of addition, multiplication, subtraction, and division, and the number properties of this system. We shall learn more about this in a later chapter.

Summary of the Commutative Group Properties. Let $\mathscr{S}$ be a mathematical system consisting of the set S and the operation $\oplus$. Then $\mathscr{S}$ is a commutative group if the following properties are satisfied:

Closure. If $a \in S$ and $b \in S$, then $a \oplus b \in S$.

Commutativity. If $a \in S$ and $b \in S$, then $a \oplus b = b \oplus a$.

Identity. There exists an element $I \in S$ so that for all $a \in S$, $a \oplus I = a$.

Inverse. If $a \in S$, then there exists an element $\bar{a} \in S$ so that $a \oplus \bar{a} = I$.

Associativity. If $a \in S$ and $b \in S$ and $c \in S$, then $(a \oplus b) \oplus c = a \oplus (b \oplus c)$.

2:2 Boolean Algebra (Optional)

A Boolean algebra[1] is an abstract mathematical system described as follows.

---

[1] Boolean algebra was originated by the English mathematician George Boole (1815–1864) in his book *An Investigation into the Laws of Thought*, published in 1854.

Undefined concepts

   Set $S = \{a, b, c, \cdots\}$.

   Two binary operations, $+$ and $\times$, used as follows: $a + b$ and $a \times b$ (also written ab).

   A unary operation, $\bar{\ }$, used as follows: $\bar{a}$.

Axioms

1. Closure. $a + b \in S$ and $ab \in S$ for all a and b in S.
2. Commutativity. $a + b = b + a$ and $ab = ba$.
3. Associativity. $(a + b) + c = a + (b + c)$ and $(ab)c = a(bc)$.
4. Distributive properties. $a(b + c) = ab + ac$; $a + bc = (a + b)(a + c)$.
5. Identity elements. There exist two special elements, 0 and 1, so that $a + 0 = a$ for every $a \in S$ and $a \times 1 = a$ for every $a \in S$.
6. Complementation. For each $a \in S$ there exists an element $\bar{a} \in S$ so that $a + \bar{a} = 1$ and $a \times \bar{a} = 0$.

Theorems

1. $a^2 = a$
2. $a + a = a$ } idempotent properties
3. $\bar{\bar{a}} = a$ law of double negative
4. $a + ab = a$
5. $a(a + b) = a$ } reduction or absorption laws
6. $\overline{a + b} = \bar{a} \times \bar{b}$
7. $\overline{a \times b} = \bar{a} + \bar{b}$ } DeMorgan's laws

   This abstract theory was motivated by the subject matter of logic. It can be shown that it can be interpreted as symbolic logic and also as the algebra of sets.

   A simple model of a Boolean algebra is obtained by selecting the set S to be $\{0, 1\}$, and the binary operations as defined by the tables

$+$	0	1
0	0	1
1	1	1

$\times$	0	1
0	0	0
1	0	1

   The interpretations of Boolean algebra as symbolic logic and set algebra are illustrated by Table 7.5.

TABLE 7.5

BOOLEAN ALGEBRA	SET ALGEBRA	SYMBOLIC LOGIC
1. Set $S = \{a, b, c, \cdots\}$	Set of all subsets of some universal set, U	Set of all tf-statements
2. Binary operation, $+$	Set union, $\cup$	Connective, "or"
3. Binary operation, $\times$	Set intersection, $\cap$	Connective, "and"
4. Unary operation, $\bar{a}$	Set complementation, $\bar{A}$	Connective, "not"
5. Special element, 1	Universal set, U	A tautology (always true)
6. Special element, 0	Empty set, $\varnothing$	An absurdity (always false)

The interpretations of the axioms and the idempotent theorems of Boolean algebra are shown in Table 7.6.

TABLE 7.6

BOOLEAN ALGEBRA	SET ALGEBRA	SYMBOLIC LOGIC
Closure:		
$a + b \in S, ab \in S$	$A \cup B \subset U, A \cap B \subset U$	P or Q is a tf statement
		P and Q is a tf statement
Commutativity:		
$a + b = b + a$	$A \cup B = B \cup A$	P or $Q \leftrightarrow Q$ or P
$ab = ba$	$A \cap B = B \cap A$	P and $Q \leftrightarrow Q$ and P
Associativity:		
$(a + b) + c = a + (b + c)$	$(A \cup B) \cup C = A \cup (B \cup C)$	$(P$ or $Q)$ or $R \leftrightarrow P$ or $(Q$ or $R)$
$(ab)c = a(bc)$	$(A \cap B) \cap C = A \cap (B \cap C)$	$(P$ and $Q)$ and $R \leftrightarrow P$ and $(Q$ and $R)$
Distributivity:		
$a(b + c) = ab + ac$	$A \cap (B \cup C) = (A \cap B) \cup (A \cap C)$	P and $(Q$ or $R) \leftrightarrow (P$ and $Q)$ or $(P$ and $R)$
$a + bc = (a + b)(a + c)$	$A \cup (B \cap C) = (A \cup B) \cap (A \cup C)$	P or $(Q$ and $R) \leftrightarrow (P$ or $Q)$ and $(P$ or $R)$
Identity:		
$a + 0 = a$	$A \cup \varnothing = A$	P or an absurdity $\leftrightarrow P$
$a \cdot 1 = a$	$A \cap U = A$	P and a tautology $\leftrightarrow P$
Complementation:		
$a + \bar{a} = 1$	$A \cup \bar{A} = U$	P or $\bar{P} \leftrightarrow$ a tautology
$a \cdot \bar{a} = 0$	$A \cap \bar{A} = \varnothing$	P and $\bar{P} \leftrightarrow$ an absurdity
Idempotent theorems:		
$a^2 = a$	$A \cap A = A$	P and $P \leftrightarrow P$
$a + a = a$	$A \cup A = A$	P or $P \leftrightarrow P$

Application of Boolean Algebra to Switching Circuits.[2] **Parallel switches** shall be interpreted as the "or" operation, where we assign the value "1" if the switch is closed and the value "0" if the switch is open.

In → Out $P + Q$ (also P or Q)

Switches in **series** shall be interpreted as the "and" operation.

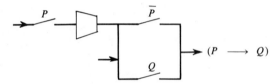

If switches are such that one is open if and only if the other is closed, then if one is P, the other is "not" P.

$P \longrightarrow \boxed{} \longrightarrow \bar{P}$

The implication circuit can be made by using the tautology $(P \rightarrow Q) = (\bar{P} + Q)$.

These circuits may be combined as illustrated in Figure 7.2.

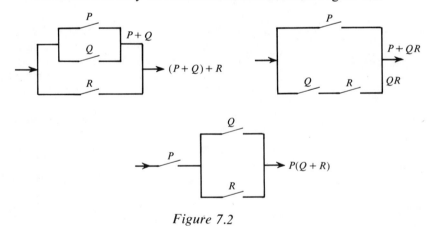

Figure 7.2

---

[2] In 1938 Claude Shannon published his work on the application of Boolean algebra to relay and switching circuits. C. E. Shannon, "A Symbolic Analysis of Relay and Switching Circuits," *Transactions of the American Institute of Electrical Engineers,* **57**, 1938, pp. 713–723.

The following example illustrates how Boolean algebra is used in designing electrical circuits.

Let us suppose that certain principles call for the construction of the following circuit of Figure 7.3.

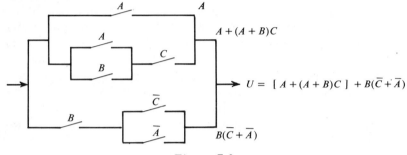

Figure 7.3

Now the output may be manipulated algebraically (according to the rules of Boolean algebra) until we show it equivalent to a simpler algebraic expression.

$$A + (A + B)C = A + (AC + BC) = (A + AC) + BC$$
$$= (A + A)(A + C) + BC$$
$$= A(A + C) + BC$$

Thus

$$U = A(A + C) + BC + B\overline{C} + B\overline{A}$$
$$= A(A + C) + B(C + \overline{C}) + B\overline{A} = A(A + C) + B + B\overline{A}$$
$$= A(A + C) + B(B + B\overline{A}) = A + B$$

This algebraic simplification means that the complicated circuit above can be replaced by the simpler one below.

$$U = A + B$$

This application is described very well in the quotation below, from F. Dinkines, *Elementary Theory of Sets* (New York: Appleton-Century-Crofts, 1964):

> To me, Boolean Algebra means electrical circuits, electrical networks. Professor Wiley teaches at the University of Oklahoma during the winter and in the summer he often goes to Westinghouse. Westinghouse is delighted to have him during the summer and the University of Oklahoma is delighted to have him in the winter. A couple of years ago, when he arrived at Westinghouse, they asked

him to come to building 7. The electrical engineers had a large blackboard which was filled with circuit diagrams — complicated circuit diagrams. They were pretty proud of it because they started out with a much bigger diagram and had condensed it down, and condensed it down, and condensed it down, taking out more and more relays and switches. Every time you take out a switch, not only does it save the cost of that switch, but it saves in repairs and maintenance. They triumphantly showed Professor Wiley the final diagrams. I think that they wanted to brag a bit. He sat down and covered a piece of paper with symbols involving letters and horseshoes and croquet wickets and pretty soon he said, "I think maybe you can simplify that even more." The Westinghouse engineers had been working for several weeks on the circuits and they had to be shown that further improvements were possible. Wiley pushed his pencil a little more and said, "You can take out this switch, substitute this one in it, and hook it in this way and it will work out just the same." The engineers scratched their pencils and sure enough, they could. They were interested and they wanted to know how he did it. His answer was, "Boolean Algebra."

Before long they had actually taken out 5 switches. Five switches may not sound like very much to you, but if you eliminate five switches worth $4.00 each — that is $20. If you make 10,000 of these items, $200,000 is a rather healthy savings — the sort of thing that really pleases industry. If a man makes a discovery like this and doesn't make any other discovery during the next ten years, he has still earned his salary and more. Industry has awakened to the advantages of mathematical research.

The Need for Modern Mathematics, Richard V. Andree

3. FINITE GEOMETRIES (Optional)

A geometry is a mathematical system abstracted from the shapes and figures of objects in the real world. A finite geometry is concerned with a finite number of points and lines, as contrasted with Euclid's geometry, which is concerned with an infinite number of points and lines. A study of the finite geometry presented below will help us understand Euclid's geometry and will also help us understand the relationship between a mathematical system and the special subject matter in the real world.

Special Subject Matter. A certain geographic map consisting of roads and towns is to be made. There are two relations between roads; either they are **parallel,**[3] have no common town on both, or they intersect at a certain town. Certain observations reveal the following facts.

Facts:

1. There is at least one town on the map.
2. Every road has exactly two towns on it.
3. Every town is on exactly two roads.
4. Every road has exactly three roads parallel to it.
5. For every two roads, there is a road parallel to one and intersecting the other.

The special subject matter is now **abstracted.**

An Abstract Finite Geometry

Undefined concepts: point, line plane; on (corresponding to "town, road, map; on")

Definitions

1. *Parallel lines are two lines that do not have a point in common.*
2. *Intersecting lines are lines that are not parallel.* (In other words, intersecting lines do have a point in common.)

Axioms

1. There is at least one point on the plane.
2. Every line has exactly two points on it.
3. Every point is on exactly two lines.
4. Every line has exactly three lines parallel to it.
5. For every two lines, there is a line parallel to one and intersecting the other.

Theorem 1: There are at least two lines that intersect.

Proof

1. If there is a point, then there are two lines on it.	Axiom 3
2. There is a point on the plane.	Axiom 1
3. Thus there are two lines, and they intersect.	

---

[3] The concept "parallel" as used in this context does *not* have the same visual model as that of elementary plane geometry.

Theorem 2: For each line, there are at least two lines that intersect it.

Proof

1. If there are two intersecting lines, then there is a line parallel to one and intersecting the other.   Axiom 5
2. There are two intersecting lines.   Theorem 1
3. Thus there is another line intersecting one of the original intersecting lines.

Theorem 3: For each line, there are exactly two lines that intersect it.

Proof

1. Each line has exactly two points on it.   Axiom 2
2. Each of these two points has exactly two lines on it.   Axiom 3
3. Thus there are at most two lines intersecting the given line, one through each point of the line.
4. Each line has at least two lines intersecting it.   Theorem 2
5. Thus each line has exactly two lines intersecting it.

Theorem 4: There are exactly six lines.

Proof

1. There is at least one line.   Theorem 1
2. There are exactly two lines intersecting this line.   Theorem 3
3. There are exactly three lines parallel to this line.   Axiom 4
4. Thus there is a total of six lines. $(1 + 2 + 3 = 6)$

Theorem 5: There are exactly six points.

Proof

1. There are six lines.   Theorem 4
2. Each line has exactly two points on it.   Axiom 2
3. Each point is on exactly two lines.   Axiom 3
4. Thus there are exactly six points. $\left(\dfrac{6 \times 2}{2} = 6\right)$

It is now possible to construct a **model** of this system:

Points: *A, B, C, D, E, F*

Lines: *AB, BC, CD, DE, EF, FA*

The mathematical system can now be interpreted.

Interpretations. Various interpretations of the above system are possible. Two are given below.

1. Interpret "point," "line," "plane," as "politician," "committee," "room." Then if the axioms are restated using these words and if the axioms are true for this application, then the theorems must be true. Thus there must be exactly six politicians and exactly six committees.

2. Interpret "point," "line," "plane" as "direct wire," "employee," "office." Then the system describes an interoffice telephone system.

EXERCISES

1. a. Look up the word "remark" in a dictionary and list its synonyms.
   b. Look up each of the synonyms of "remark" and list these synonyms.
   c. Explain why some terms in mathematics are "undefined."
2. Criticize each of the following "definitions" by determining whether any of the criteria for definitions has been violated.
   a. An elephant has a trunk and ivory tusks.
   b. An elephant is an animal with four legs.
   c. A diamond is a pure or nearly pure crystallized form of carbon, of great hardness and brilliance, and often used as a stone in jewelry.
3. Jack stated that Mr. Wise was an educated man. John said he was not because he had never been to college. Could this argument be resolved by a definition? How?
4. Read the Declaration of Independence and make a list of the axioms in this document; that is, the statements that are assumed to be true.
5. The *commutative* property states that it does not matter in which *order* an operation is performed. Determine whether or not the commutative property is satisfied by each of the operations below.
   a. Putting on your shoes and socks.
   b. Combining the letters "o" and "n" to make a word.
   c. Eating your salad course and your meat course.
   d. Putting salt and pepper on your food.
   e. Traveling to San Francisco and New York City.
6. The *associative* property states that the manner in which elements or objects are *grouped* does not affect the final result. Determine whether or not the associative property is satisfied by each of the following.
   a. Does (meat + salt) + pepper = meat + (salt + pepper)?

    b. Does (hamburger + onions) + ice cream = hamburger + (onions + ice cream)?

    c. Does (hot water + tea) + ice = hot water + (tea + ice)?

    d. Does $10 - (5 - 2) = (10 - 5) - 2$?

    e. Does $(50 \div 5) \div 5 = 50 \div (5 \div 5)$?

7. Determine which of the following operations have *inverses* and then state the inverse.

    a. Falling in love.

    b. Walking 2 miles north.

    c. 20° drop in temperature.

    d. Scrambling eggs.

    e. Parachute jumping.

    f. Sitting down.

    g. Growing older.

    h. Graduating from college.

    i. Stretching a rubber band.

    j. Depositing money in a bank.

8. Let $S = \{0, 1, 2, 3, 4, 5, \cdots\}$. For each of the following operations on S, determine whether the system has the *identity* property or not. Do this by finding the identity element and then noting whether it is in S or not.

    a. $a * b = (a + b) - 5$. [Add a to b and then subtract 5.]

    b. $a * b = (a + b) + 5$. [Add a to b and then add 5.]

    c. $a \# b$ means "select the larger number."

    d. $a \circ b$ means "select the smaller number."

    e. $a \uparrow b = (5 \times a) + b$. [Multiply a by 5 and then add b.]

9. Make a table of the multiplication facts of the clock arithmetic on a 12-hour clock. Perform each of the calculations below, if possible. If more than one answer is possible, list all of them. If no answer is possible, write "Impossible."

    a. $9 + 7$ c. $4 - 10$ e. $5 - 7$ g. 8×7 i. $5 \div 3$

    b. $8 + 6$ d. $2 - 5$ f. 4×9 h. $7 \div 11$ j. $9 \div 3$

10. Construct the addition and multiplication tables for modulo-5 arithmetic and then do the following:

    a. Calculate: $2 - 3 =$ $4 - 1 =$ $4 \div 3 =$ $4 \div 2 =$

                         $3 - 2 =$ $1 - 4 =$ $3 \div 4 =$ $2 \div 4 =$

    b. Determine whether the closure, identity, inverse, and commutative properties are satisfied for each of the operations of addition, multiplication, subtraction, and division by copying the table below and writing the word "Yes" or "No" in each of the blanks.

OPERATION	CLOSURE	COMMUTATIVITY	IDENTITY	INVERSE	ASSOCIATIVITY
Addition					
Multiplication					
Subtraction					
Division					

   c. Verify the associative and distributive properties for addition and multiplication using $a = 2, b = 3, c = 4$.

11. *Modulo-6 arithmetic:*

   a. Construct the addition and multiplication tables.

   b. Calculate, if possible: $3 - 5, 0 - 4, 5 - 3, 2 \div 5, 4 \div 2, 3 \div 2$.

   c. List all the elements that do *not* have multiplicative inverses.

   d. Verify the associative and distributive properties using $a = 2$, $b \doteq 5, c = 3$.

   e. State what group properties are satisfied for each of the four arithmetic operations and give a reason for each of your answers.

12. *Calendar arithmetic* is a name for *modulo-7 arithmetic*. A one-to-one correspondence is established between the days of the week and the numbers 0, 1, 2, 3, 4, 5, and 6 as indicated below. Any number larger than 6 is reduced to one of the modulo-7 numbers by dividing by 7 and retaining the remainder only. For example, $67 = 63 + 4 = (7 \times 9) + 4 = 4$ modulo-7.

Sunday — 0	EXAMPLE. What day of the week is 20 days after
Monday — 1	Friday?
Tuesday — 2	*Solution.* In modulo-7 Friday is 5 and 20 is 6
Wednesday — 3	since $20 = 14 + 6 = (7 \times 2) + 6$.
Thursday — 4	Thus $5 + 6 = 4$
Friday — 5	Thursday is 4 and therefore
Saturday — 6	Thursday is 20 days after a Friday.

   a. What day of the week is 47 days after a Sunday?

   b. What day of the week is 39 days after a Tuesday?

   c. Today is Thursday. There are 40 days until Christmas. What day of the week will Christmas fall on?

   d. What day of the week will Christmas fall on next year if next year is not a leap year? What day if next year is a leap year?

13. A mathematical system consists of the set $S = \{A, B, C, D\}$ and the operations $\oplus$ and $\odot$ defined by the tables below.

$\oplus$	A	B	C	D
A	B	C	D	A
B	C	D	A	B
C	D	A	B	C
D	A	B	C	D

$\odot$	A	B	C	D
A	A	B	C	D
B	B	D	B	D
C	C	B	A	D
D	D	D	D	D

   a. State why $S, \oplus$ and $S, \odot$ are closed.

   b. State why $S, \oplus$ and $S, \odot$ are commutative.

   c. Name the identities of $S, \oplus$ and $S, \odot$.

    d. State why S, $\oplus$ satisfies the inverse property.

    e. State why S, $\odot$ does not satisfy the inverse property by naming the elements that do not have inverses.

    f. Verify the associative and distributive properties for S, $\oplus$ and S, $\odot$ for any two different cases.

14. Determine which of the commutative group properties is *not* satisfied by each of the mathematical systems below.

a.

*	A	B
A	A	A
B	B	A

b.

#	0	1	2
0	0	0	0
1	0	2	0
2	0	0	1

c.

$\otimes$	0	1	-1
0	0	1	-1
1	1	2	0
-1	-1	0	-2

d.

$\downarrow$	A	B	C	D
A	A	B	C	D
B	B	A	B	C
C	C	B	A	B
D	D	C	B	A

e.

$	A	B	C	D
A	A	B	C	D
B	B	D	B	D
C	C	B	A	D
D	D	D	D	D

f.

#	1	2	3	4	5	6
1	1	2	3	4	5	6
2	2	1	4	5	6	3
3	3	4	1	6	2	5
4	4	5	6	1	3	2
5	5	6	2	3	1	4
6	6	3	5	2	4	1

15. Using the symbols of Boolean algebra, write an expression for the output of each of the following circuits.

a.
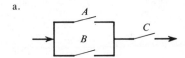

e.
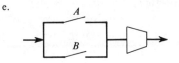

b.
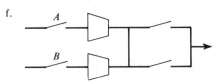

f.
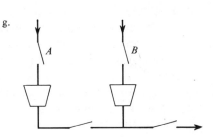

c.
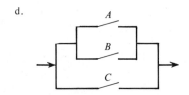

g.
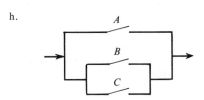

d.

h.

16. Determine if any of the circuits in Exercise 15 are equivalent.
17. Illustrate the following axioms by drawing the corresponding circuits.
    a. $A + B = B + A$.
    b. $AB = BA$.
    c. $(A + B) + C = A + (B + C)$.
    d. $(AB)C = A(BC)$.
    e. $A(B + C) = AB + AC$.
18. A certain group of politicians have assembled in a room and have decided to form committees according to the following rules, called axioms:

    Axiom 1: There is at least one committee.
    Axiom 2: Every man is on exactly two committees.
    Axiom 3: Every committee has exactly two men on it.
    Axiom 4: Every committee has exactly two committees parallel to it.

Definition: Parallel committees *are ones that do not have the same man on both committees.*

a. Restate the axioms and definition, replacing "politician," "committee," and "room" by "point," "line," and "plane," respectively.

b. Prove the following theorems.

   1. There is at least one point on the plane.

   2. Every line has exactly two lines intersecting it.

   3. There are exactly five lines.

   4. There are exactly five points.

c. Reinterpret the theorems by replacing "point," "line," and "plane" by "politician," "committee," and "room," respectively.

d. Interpret the axioms and theorems in terms of towns and roads on a map. Draw a model of the mathematical system.

19. Consider the mathematical system obtained from that in the text by replacing Axiom 5 by Axiom 5' stated below.

   Axiom 5': For every two intersecting lines, there is no line parallel to one and intersecting the other.

   a. Construct a model of this system.

   b. Prove that there are exactly six lines and exactly six points in this system.

CHAPTER VIII

Elementary Euclidean Geometry

Euclid alone has looked on Beauty bare.
Let all who prate of Beauty hold their peace,
And lay them prone upon the earth and cease
To ponder on themselves the while they stare
At nothing, intricately drawn nowhere
In shapes of shifting lineage; let geese
Gabble and hiss, but heroes seek release
From dusty bondage into luminous air.
O blinding hour, O holy, terrible day,
When first the shaft into his vision shone
Of light anatomized! Euclid alone
Has looked on Beauty bare. Fortunate they
Who, though once only and then but far away,
Have heard her massive sandal set on stone.

Collected Poems, Edna St. Vincent Millay

1. EUCLID'S TEN ASSUMPTIONS

Elements, written by Euclid around 300 B.C., has been known as one of the greatest, most elegant mathematical systems ever devised. Euclid organized almost all the mathematical knowledge known at his time into one logically developed whole. In his work he exhibited the essence of the Greek philosophy: logic and the search for universal truths, those truths perfected or abstracted from objects in the real world. These are the words of Plato, as written in his *Republic*: ". . . this knowledge at which geometry aims is of the eternal, and not of the perishing and transient . . . geometry will draw the soul toward truth, and create the spirit of philosophy."

Elements is divided into 13 sections called "Books." The subject matter of our high school geometry of today is taken from 6 of these 13 books, almost exactly as Euclid wrote it.

The contents of the 13 books are as follows:

Book 1.   Definitions, Postulates and Common Notions, Congruent Triangles, Theory of Parallels, Areas, Theorem of Pythagoras

[147]

Book 2.   Geometric Algebra
Book 3.   The Circle
Book 4.   Constructions of Regular Polygons
Book 5.   Theory of Proportion
Book 6.   Similar Figures
Books 7–9. Number Theory
Book 10.   Theory of Irrationals
Book 11.   Solid Geometry, Simple Volumes
Book 12.   Areas and Volumes, "Method of Exhaustion"
Book 13.   Construction of the Five Regular "Platonic" Solids

In Book 1, Euclid listed 10 assumptions which he divided into two sets called **postulates** and **common notions.** The common notions were assumptions relating to all branches of knowledge while the postulates were concerned specifically with geometric concepts. Today this distinction is no longer made and all assumptions are called either **axioms** or **postulates.**

Following the assumptions are 465 propositions (or theorems) together with their logical arguments. These propositions, together with the definitions and assumptions, comprise the contents of the 13 books of *Elements.*

The common notions and postulates of Euclid are listed below.

Common Notions

1. Things which are equal to the same thing are equal to one another.
2. If equals be added to equals, the wholes are equal.
3. If equals be subtracted from equals, the remainders are equal.
4. Things which coincide with one another are equal to one another.
5. The whole is greater than the part.

Postulates.   Let the following be postulated:

1. To draw a straight line from any point to any point.
2. To produce a finite straight line continuously in a straight line.
3. To describe a circle with any center and distance.
4. That all right angles are equal to one another.
5. That, if a straight line falling on two straight lines makes the interior angles on the same side less than two right angles, the two straight lines, if produced indefinitely, meet on that side on which the angles are less than two right angles.

Postulate 5, the **parallel postulate,** has become, perhaps, the most famous statement ever to be made in mathematical history. A more familiar form of this postulate is the one made famous by the Scottish mathematician, John Playfair (1748–1819), which states that through a point not on a line there is not more than one line that does not intersect the given line (that is, is parallel to the given line).

For over 2000 years scholars attempted either to prove this postulate or, failing this, to substitute another more "favorable" postulate. Toward the end of the eighteenth century new attempts were made using the methods of indirect proof. The hope was that the assumption of the negation of the parallel postulate would lead to a contradiction.

However, amazingly enough, this new set of postulates turned out to be the basis of a new kind of geometry, now called non-Euclidean geometry. (This geometry will be discussed more fully in Chapter 12.) Euclid was right to include Postulate 5 and mathematics was enriched by the many related developments, including investigations into the logical foundations of the subject of mathematics itself.

2. CONSTRUCTIONS

The first three postulates indicate that only straight lines and circles are to be drawn and thus the only instruments permitted are the unmarked straightedge and compass. It is surprising how many complex figures can be constructed in this manner. It is even more surprising how many simple figures *cannot* be so constructed. The geometry of curves other than the circle and straight line originated in attempts to solve the three famous construction problems:

1. The trisection of any angle (division of any angle into three congruent[1] angles).
2. The quadrature of the circle (construction of a square having an area equal to that of a given circle).
3. The duplication of the cube (construction of the side of a cube having twice the volume of a given cube).

It was not until the nineteenth century that these constructions (limited to the use of the straightedge and compass) were proved impossible. However, the 2000-year period of attempts yielded some amazing results. Not only were many geometric discoveries made (including those about the conic sections) but also there were profound discoveries in algebra, including the theory of equations and group theory.

---

[1]**Congruent** geometric figures may be thought of as figures that are exact duplicates of each other. If a measurement is introduced, the congruent figures will be equal in measure. Thus two congruent line segments have *equal* lengths.

Some examples of some elementary constructions of plane geometry are illustrated in Figure 8.1. In each case, Euclid's figure involving the complete circle is contrasted with the modern simplified construction that uses only arcs or parts of circles.

CONSTRUCTION PROBLEM	EUCLID'S CONSTRUCTION	MODERN CONSTRUCTION
Construct an equilateral triangle. Given $\overline{AB}$.	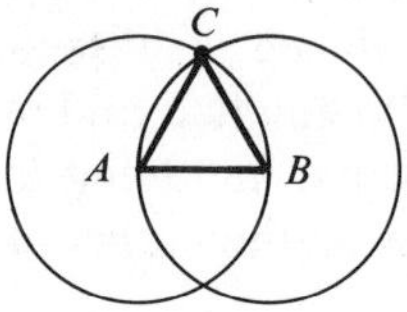 $\triangle ABC$ is equilateral	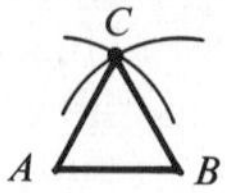 $\triangle ABC$ is equilateral
Bisect an angle (divide an angle into two congruent parts). Given $< ABC$.	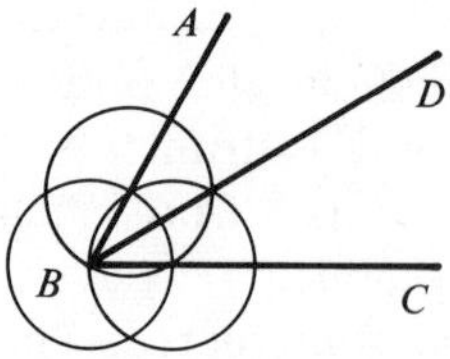 Ray $\overrightarrow{BD}$ bisects $< ABC$	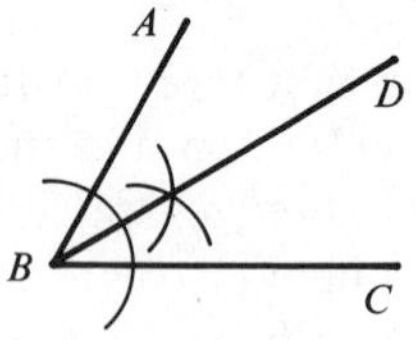 Ray $\overrightarrow{BD}$ bisects $< ABC$
Bisect a line segment. Given $\overline{AB}$.	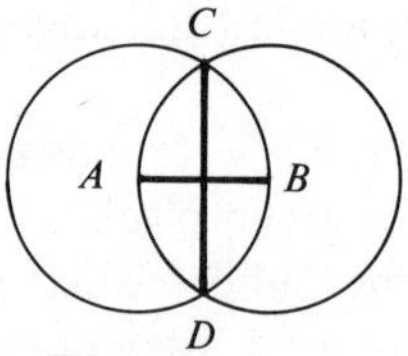 $\overline{CD}$ bisects $\overline{AB}$	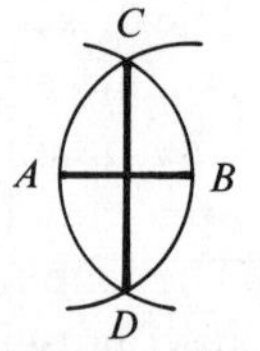 $\overline{CD}$ bisects $\overline{AB}$

Figure 8.1

In a geometry text, each of these constructions must be accompanied by a proof. In other words, the methods of logic must be used to show why these marks made here by using the straightedge and compass actually do produce a triangle with three congruent sides in the first case, or an angle divided into two congruent angles in the second, or a line segment divided into two congruent line segments in the third.

Here only the diagrams are presented for the purpose of helping the reader understand what is meant by a "construction" in geometry.

3. MODERN MODIFICATIONS

Although Euclid's *Elements* was the standard geometry text and the classical example of the mathematical method for over 2000 years, it did contain some logical defects. The most important of these was the use of tacit assumptions; that is, statements assumed mentally but not stated in words due to their obvious or elementary contents. For example, Euclid assumed in his argument for the construction of an equilateral triangle that the two circles intersected without stating the conditions for two circles to intersect (such as he did for two lines in Postulate 5). Other tacit assumptions involved the concepts of "betweenness," "super-position," and "continuity."

Euclid's list of definitions has also been criticized because there is no listing of the undefined concepts or primitive terms as required in the exposition of a modern mathematical system. For example, we find included in the definitions the following statements:

A **point** is that which has no part.

A **line** is length without breadth.

A **straight line** is a line that lies evenly with the points on itself.

A **surface** is that which has only length and breadth.

A **plane surface** is a surface which lies evenly with the straight lines on itself.

A modern development of elementary Euclidean geometry would begin with a list of *undefined* concepts that would include "point," "line," and "plane." This would then be followed by a list of definitions. However, a textbook usually includes some explanatory material to help the student understand what he is to be thinking about when the terms "point," "line," and "plane" are being used. More often than not, this explanation is essentially a rewording of the "definitions" of Euclid.

The first satisfactory set of axioms for Euclidean geometry and the one most in keeping with the spirit of Euclid was given by Professor David Hilbert (1862–1943) at the University of Göttingen during the winter semester of 1898–1899. In 1899 his lecture notes were published and his now famous *Grundlagen der Geometrie* ("Foundations of Geometry") came into existence.

Hilbert began with 6 undefined concepts: point, line, plane, on, between, congruent. He then listed 15 postulates for plane geometry (and 6 more for solid geometry) from which all the theorems were derived. The postulates were divided into 5 groups concerned respectively with the 5 concepts of on, between, congruence, parallel, and continuity.

The following material illustrates a modern treatment of elementary geometry as might be found in an introductory textbook. The modifications of Hilbert are incorporated into the geometry of Euclid and then other simplifications are made so that the subject may be more easily understood by those studying it for the first time. For example, some theorems whose proofs are very lengthy and involved are accepted as postulates without proof.

4. MODERN INTRODUCTION TO EUCLIDEAN GEOMETRY

Undefined concepts: point, line, plane; on, between, congruent

Point: A **point** is to be thought of as having position only. It has no size or shape but indicates a location. A point is represented by a dot and is named by stating a capital letter placed beside the dot, such as point A. A

Line: A **line** is to be thought of as a set of points having properties of length and position but not width and as extending indefinitely in two directions. A line is named by stating the names of any two points on the line. For example, in the figure below, point A and point B are on line AB, written also as $\overleftrightarrow{AB}$ to indicate that the line extends in both directions without limit. Thinking of the line as a set of points, the undefined concept of "on" can be expressed symbolically as follows:

$$A \in \overleftrightarrow{AB} \text{ and } B \in \overleftrightarrow{AB}$$
(point A is on line AB and point B is on line AB)

Plane: A **plane** is to be thought of as a flat surface infinite in length and width but having no thickness. A sheet of paper, the blackboard, the walls, ceiling, and floor of a room are all examples of objects in the real world from which has been abstracted the concept of "plane." A plane is also described as a set of points with at least three of the points not on the same line. Actually a plane has infinitely many points and infinitely many lines on it. It is usually named by stating a Greek letter, such as plane α.

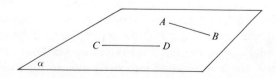

Definitions: Segments, Rays, Angles

Line segments: A **line segment,** written symbolically as $\overline{AB}$, is a set of two points, A and B (called **end points**), on a line and all the points on this line between A and B.

Every line segment on a line is a subset of this line.

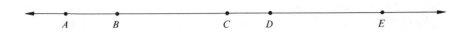

$\overline{AB} \subset \overleftrightarrow{AB}$ or line segment AB is a subset of line AB. Similarly, $\overline{BC} \subset \overleftrightarrow{AB}$ and $\overline{BE} \subset \overleftrightarrow{CD}$. Since the *union* of two sets of points is the totality of points in the sets, we can write symbolically $\overline{AB} \cup \overline{BC} = \overline{AC}$ and $\overline{BD} \cup \overline{BE} = \overline{BE}$.

Since the intersection of two or more sets consists of only those points which are common to all the sets, we can write the following: $\overline{AC} \cap \overline{BD} = \overline{BC}$ and $\overline{AB} \cap \overline{BC} = B$ and $\overline{AB} \cap \overline{CD} = \varnothing$.

Half-lines: Any point on a line separates the line into two **half-lines.**

The point P in the figure above separates the line into three sets:

1. The set of points on the left side of P, the half-line to the left.
2. The set of points on the right side of P, the half-line to the right.
3. The point P itself, which is *not* on either half-line.

Rays: A **ray** is the union of a half-line and the point that determines the half-line. This point is the end point of the ray.

If the end point of a ray is point P and if point Q is on the ray, then the ray is named $\overleftrightarrow{PQ}$.

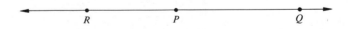

Note in the figure above, $\overrightarrow{PQ} \cap \overrightarrow{QP} = \overline{PQ}$ and $\overrightarrow{PQ} \cap \overrightarrow{PR} = P$ and $\overrightarrow{PQ} \cup \overrightarrow{PR} = \overleftrightarrow{PQ}$.

Angles: An **angle** is the union of two rays that are not on the same line and that have the same end point. The rays are called the **sides** of the angle, and their common end point is called the **vertex** of the angle.

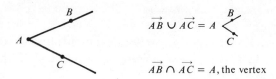

$$\overrightarrow{AB} \cup \overrightarrow{AC} = A$$

$$\overrightarrow{AB} \cap \overrightarrow{AC} = A, \text{ the vertex}$$

An angle is named by writing the symbol for an angle, $\angle$, followed by three capital letters, the middle one being the vertex and the other two being the names of points, one on each side of the angle; for example, $\angle BAC$. $\angle BAC$ can also be named $\angle CAB$ or by the vertex letter alone, $\angle A$, if there is no ambiguity as to which angle is meant.

Half-planes: Any line on a plane separates the plane into three sets, the line itself and two **half-planes.**

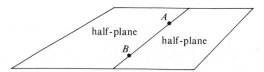

The line AB in the figure above separates the plane into three sets:

1. The set of points on the left side of $\overleftrightarrow{AB}$, the half-plane to the left.
2. The set of points on the right side of $\overleftrightarrow{AB}$, the half-plane to the right.
3. The line $\overleftrightarrow{AB}$ itself, which is *not* on either half-plane.

Interior and exterior of an angle: In Figure 8.2 the intersection of the right half-plane determined by line $\overrightarrow{AC}$ and the top half-plane determined by line $\overleftrightarrow{AB}$ is called the **interior** of $\angle CAB$.

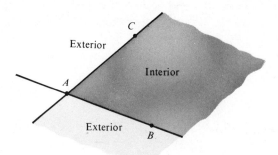

Figure 8.2

The complement of the angle and its interior is called the **exterior** of the angle.

Measurement of Angles. A common unit of measurement for angles is the degree, written symbolically as ° and defined as the measure of $\frac{1}{360}$ of a complete rotation. Thus a complete rotation measures 360°. One half a full rotation is 180°, one fourth is 90°, and one sixth is 60°.

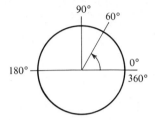

Each degree is divided into 60 minutes, and each minute into 60 seconds. Thus measurement by degrees is a base 60 system of measurement and it was originally used by the ancient Babylonians.

Definitions: Angles, Lines, Triangles

Adjacent angles: Adjacent angles are two angles that have the same vertex and a common side between them. For example, $\angle ABD$ and $\angle DBC$ below are adjacent angles.

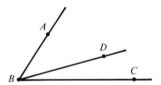

Right angle: A **right angle** is one of the two congruent adjacent angles formed by two straight lines. For example, in the figure at the right, $\angle ABD$ and $\angle CBD$ are formed by two lines, $\overleftrightarrow{ABC}$ and $\overrightarrow{BD}$, and $\angle ABD \cong \angle CBD$.[2] Thus. $\angle ABD$ is a right angle. $\angle CBD$ is also a right angle. A right angle has a measure of 90°.

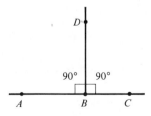

---

[2] The symbol $\cong$ means "is congruent to."

Acute angle: An **acute angle** is an angle smaller than a right angle. It has a measure less than 90°

Obtuse angle: An **obtuse angle** is an angle larger than a right angle but smaller than two right angles. Thus an obtuse angle has a measure between 90° and 180°.

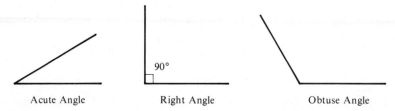

Acute Angle   Right Angle   Obtuse Angle

Perpendicular lines: Perpendicular lines are two lines that intersect to form a right angle. In each of the examples illustrated below, lines $\overleftrightarrow{AD}$ and $\overleftrightarrow{CD}$ are perpendicular; in symbols, $\overleftrightarrow{AD} \perp \overleftrightarrow{CD}$.

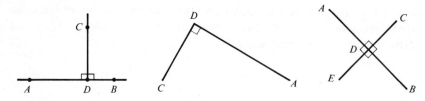

Parallel lines: Parallel lines are lines in the same plane whose intersection is the empty set; that is, they do not intersect. In the figures below, lines AB and CD are parallel. In symbols, we write $\overleftrightarrow{AB} \parallel \overleftrightarrow{CD}$.

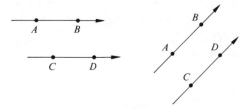

Triangle: A triangle is the union of the three line segments determined by three points not on the same line. For example, in the figure, triangle

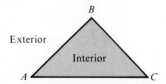

ABC, or △*ABC*, is the union of three segments, $\overline{AB}$, $\overline{BC}$, and $\overline{AC}$, determined by points *A*, *B*, and *C*. In symbols, △*ABC* = $\overline{AB}$ ∪ $\overline{BC}$ ∪ $\overline{AC}$.

The line segments $\overline{AB}$, $\overline{BC}$, and $\overline{AC}$ are called the sides of the triangle. The points *A*, *B*, and *C* are called the vertices of the triangle.

$$\overline{AB} \cap \overline{BC} = B$$
$$\overline{AC} \cap \overline{BC} = C$$
$$\overline{AB} \cap \overline{AC} = A$$

A triangle has an interior and an exterior, the interior being the intersection of the interiors of the three angles ∠*A*, ∠*B*, and ∠*C*, the angles of the triangle.

Interior △*ABC* = interior ∠*A* ∩ interior ∠*B* ∩ interior ∠*C*

Sides *AB* and *AC* are said to *include* ∠*A* while side *BC* is said to be *opposite* angle *A*.

A **scalene triangle** (Figure 8.3) is a triangle with no two of its sides congruent.
An **isosceles triangle** is a triangle with two congruent sides.
An **equilateral triangle** is a triangle with three congruent sides.
An **acute triangle** is a triangle with three acute angles.
An **obtuse triangle** is a triangle with one obtuse angle.
A **right triangle** is a triangle with one right angle.

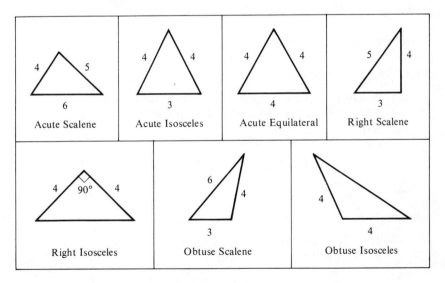

Figure 8.3

Congruent triangles: Two triangles are **congruent** if a one-to-one correspondence can be established between their sets of vertices so that the resulting corresponding sides and angles are congruent.

EXAMPLE. Consider $\triangle ABC$ and $\triangle DEF$ with the correspondence A, B, C
$$\updownarrow \quad \updownarrow \quad \updownarrow$$
$$D, E, F$$

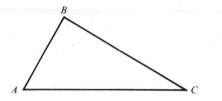 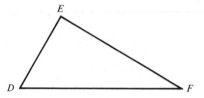

Now, suppose that

$$\angle A \cong \angle D \quad \text{and} \quad \overline{AB} \cong \overline{DE}$$
$$\angle B \cong \angle E \qquad\qquad \overline{BC} \cong \overline{EF}$$
$$\angle C \cong \angle F \qquad\qquad \overline{AC} \cong \overline{DF}$$

Then, by definition, $\triangle ABC$ is congruent to $\triangle DEF$. In symbols, we write $\triangle ABC \cong \triangle DEF$.

We think of congruent triangles as ones having the same size and shape. In other words, one is the exact duplicate of the other. A machine producing the same part over and over again is producing congruent parts. The tiles seen on floors and counters are examples of congruent figures.

Postulates

The "On" Postulates

1. There is exactly one line on two distinct points.
2. There are at least two points on any line and at least one point not on the line.

The "Between" Postulates

3. If A, B, and C are three points on a line and if B is between A and C, then B is between C and A.

4. If A and B are any two points on a line, then there is a point C on the line between A and B and a point D so that B is between A and D.

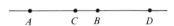

5. Of three points on a line there is exactly one between the other two.

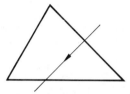

6 (Pasch's postulate). A line that intersects one side of a triangle but does not pass through any of the vertices of the triangle must also intersect another side of the triangle.

The "Parallel" Postulate

7 (Playfair's postulate). In a given plane and through a given point not on a given line, there is no more than one line that does not intersect the given line. This line is called the **parallel** to the given line.

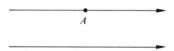

The "Congruent" Postulates

8. *Construction of a line segment congruent to a given line segment*. If a line segment is given, then on a given side of a point A on any line there is exactly one point B on this line so that line segment AB is congruent to the given line segment. Given $\overline{PQ}$. Then on the line on A, on the right side of A, there is exactly one point B so that $\overline{AB} \cong \overline{PQ}$.

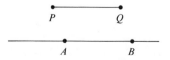

9. *Construction of an angle congruent to a given angle*. If an angle is given, then on a given side of a ray with end point A there is

exactly one ray also having end point *A* so that the angle formed by the union of these two rays is congruent to the given angle.

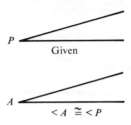

Given

∠*A* ≅ ∠*P*

10. *Reflexive property of the congruent relation.* Every line segment is congruent to itself. $\overline{AB} \cong \overline{AB}$. Every angle is congruent to itself. ∠*A* ≅ ∠*A*.
11. *Symmetric property of the congruent relation.* If $\overline{AB} \cong \overline{CD}$, then $\overline{CD} \cong \overline{AB}$. If ∠*A* ≅ ∠*B*, then ∠*B* ≅ ∠*A*.
12. *Transitive property of the congruent relation.* Line segments congruent to the same line segment are congruent to each other.

A   *B*   *C*   *D*   *E*   *F*

If $\overline{AB} \cong \overline{CD}$ and $\overline{CD} \cong \overline{EF}$, then $\overline{AB} \cong \overline{EF}$.

Angles congruent to the same angle are congruent to each other.

13. *Addition of line segments and angles*

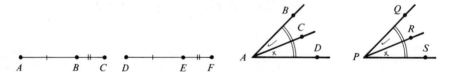

If $\overline{AB} \cong \overline{DE}$ and $\overline{BC} \cong \overline{EF}$, then $\overline{AC} \cong \overline{DF}$. If ∠*BAC* ≅ ∠*QPR* and ∠*CAD* ≅ ∠*RPS*, then ∠*BAD* ≅ ∠*QPS*.

14. *Subtraction of line segments and angles.* If $\overline{AC} \cong \overline{DF}$ and $\overline{AB} \cong \overline{DE}$, then $\overline{BC} \cong \overline{EF}$. If ∠*BAD* ≅ ∠*QPS* and ∠*BAC* ≅ ∠*QPR*, then ∠*CAD* ≅ ∠*RPS*.

15. *SAS.* If two sides and the included angle of one triangle are congruent respectively to two sides and the included angle of another triangle, then the two triangles are congruent.

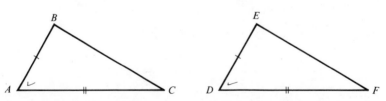

If $\overline{AB} \cong \overline{DE}$ and ∠*A* ≅ ∠*D* and $\overline{AC} \cong \overline{DF}$, then △*ABC* ≅ △*DEF*.

16. *ASA.* If two angles and the included side of one triangle are congruent respectively to two angles and the included side of another triangle, then the two triangles are congruent.

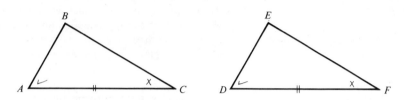

If $\angle A \cong \angle D$ and $\overline{AC} \cong \overline{DF}$ and $\angle C \cong \angle F$, then $\triangle ABC \cong \triangle DEF$.

17. *SSS.* If three sides of one triangle are congruent respectively to three sides of another triangle, then the triangles are congruent.

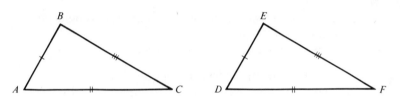

If $\overline{AB} \cong \overline{DE}$ and $\overline{AC} \cong \overline{DF}$ and $\overline{BC} \cong \overline{EF}$, then $\triangle ABC \cong \triangle DEF$.

Theorems and the Formal Proof. The principles of logic are applied to the postulates; and new statements, called **theorems,** are obtained. Thus the subject matter of geometry is developed. The theorems are listed in order and each theorem is accompanied by its proof.

Instruction in geometry has two main objectives: to teach the subject matter itself and to teach the basic principles of logic. The student is first introduced to a formal proof involving just the **direct proof pattern.** Such a proof is illustrated below.

Theorem: The angles at the base of an isosceles triangle are congruent to each other.

Given: $\overline{AB} = \overline{AC}$
Prove: $\angle B = \angle C$

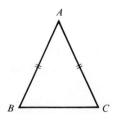

STATEMENTS	REASONS
1. $\overline{AB} \cong \overline{AC}$	1. Given (assumed true for the proof).
2. $\overline{AC} \cong \overline{AB}$	2. Symmetric property of the congruent relation.
3. $\overline{BC} \cong \overline{BC}$	3. Reflexive property of the congruent relation.
4. $\triangle ABC \cong \triangle ACB$ under the correspondence A, B, C $\updownarrow \updownarrow \updownarrow$ A, C, B	4. If three sides of one triangle are congruent respectively to three sides of another triangle, then the triangles are congruent (SSS postulate).
5. $\angle B \cong \angle C$	5. If two triangles are congruent, then their corresponding angles are congruent (definition).

According to Proclus (460 A.D.) a proof similar to the one above was given by Pappus around 300 A.D. This is also the proof that Hilbert gives.

There are several important observations that should be made in the formal proof above.

First, there are five parts to a formal proof:

1. The statement of the theorem in words.
2. The figure.
3. The statement in symbols from the figure of what is given (the "if" part of the theorem).
4. The statement in symbols from the figure of what is to be proved (the "then" part of the theorem).
5. The proof proper, divided into two columns headed "Statements" and "Reasons."

The reasons, statements in the reasons column, must be either a definition, a postulate, or a theorem that has already been proved.

The reason stated in the reasons column must be selected according to the following pattern, which is a variation on the direct proof pattern we met earlier in our study of logic.

DIRECT PROOF PATTERN	PATTERN USED IN A FORMAL PROOF
1. If P, then Q.	1. P 1.
2. P	2. Q 2. If P, then Q.
3. Therefore Q.	

Another proof of the theorem concerning the base angles of an isosceles triangle uses the method of auxiliary lines. One or more lines are added to the figure to assist in establishing the proof. For the proof below, we shall postulate the existence of the midpoint of a line segment. Postulate: A line segment has exactly one midpoint, that is, a point between its end points that divides the line segment into two congruent segments.

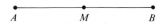

If *M* is the midpoint of $\overline{AB}$, then $\overline{AM} \cong \overline{MB}$.

Theorem: The base angles of an isosceles triangle are equal.

Given: $\overline{AB} \cong \overline{AC}$
Prove: $\angle B \cong \angle C$

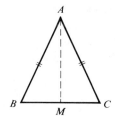

STATEMENTS	REASONS
1. Let *M* be the midpoint of $\overline{BC}$, making $\overline{BM} \cong \overline{MC}$.	1. A line segment has exactly one midpoint that divides it into two congruent line segments.
2. Draw $\overline{AM}$.	2. There is exactly one line on two points.
3. $\overline{AB} \cong \overline{AC}$.	3. Given.
4. $\overline{AM} \cong \overline{AM}$.	4. Any line segment is congruent to itself (reflexive property of congruence relation).
5. Thus $\triangle ABM \cong \triangle ACM$.	5. SSS postulate.
6. Thus $\angle B \cong \angle C$.	6. Corresponding parts of congruent triangles are congruent (definition of $\cong \triangle S$).

Pons Asinorum. The theorem about the base angles of an isosceles triangle has an interesting history. Euclid's proof of this theorem, Proposition 5 of Book I, involves auxiliary lines and two pairs of congruent overlapping triangles.

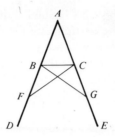

In the figure above, triangles FAC and GAB are first proved congruent by the SAS method and then triangles FBC and GCB are proved congruent. The congruent corresponding angles FCB and GBC are subtracted from the congruent corresponding angles FCA and GBA of the first pair of congruent triangles. As a result $\angle ABC \cong \angle ACB$.

The difficulties involved in following this proof caused this theorem to be a stumbling block to many a student. During the Middle Ages it marked the end of many courses of instruction. The figure suggested a bridge so steep that fools could not pass over it. Thus it became known as the **bridge of fools,** or **pons asinorum,** as it was called in Latin.

Mathematical Elegance.   Three different proofs of the same theorem have been stated in the preceding section. Of these three, the first is considered the most "elegant." Not only is the proof simpler and free of auxiliary lines but also it exhibits the essence of the concept of congruence.

5. THEORY OF PARALLELS AND INDIRECT PROOF

5:1 Indirect Proof

As a course in geometry progresses, the student is usually introduced to the indirect method of proof when he begins his study of parallel lines.

The indirect method of proof is based on the tautology below. (Recall that a tautology is a statement that is always true, because of its logical structure.)

$$[\overline{Q} \to (R \wedge \overline{R})] \to Q$$

Informally stated, this tautology is equivalent to the following: *If an assumption leads to a contradiction, then the assumption is false and its negation is true.*

The pattern of the indirect method of proof as it appears in a formal proof follows.

Theorem: If P, then Q.

STATEMENTS	REASONS
1. P	1. Given.
2. Assume $\overline{Q}$.	2. Q or $\overline{Q}$ (the law of the excluded middle). (The method of the indirect proof.)
.	.
.	.
.	.
x. R	x. ⎫
y. $\overline{R}$	y. ⎬ (These reasons depend on the particular proof.)
z. R and $\overline{R}$ is a contradiction.	z. R and $\overline{R}$ (the law of contradiction). ⎫ This step is usually ⎭ omitted.
w. Therefore Q.	w. If an assumption leads to a contradiction, then the negation of the assumption is true.

The indirect method of reasoning is used in many everyday situations. The garage mechanic, for example, in trying to determine why your car won't run, may narrow the difficulty down to three different causes: faulty points and spark plugs, a faulty fuel pump, or a faulty carburetor. He replaces the points and plugs. The car doesn't run. He installs a new fuel pump. Still the car doesn't run. Now he knows for certain that the carburetor is faulty and must be replaced.

The lawyer often uses the indirect method. In proving a person innocent, for example, he might begin by stating that if his client were guilty, then he had to be at the scene of the crime. Then the lawyer establishes by witnesses or other methods that his client was somewhere else and *not* at the scene of the crime. Thus, the lawyer reasons, his client is *not* guilty.

When a doctor diagnoses a case, he often uses the indirect method. He observes that his patient has certain symptoms. He may know, for example, that these symptoms appear only in diseases A, B, and C. By various tests he establishes that the patient does not have disease A or B. Therefore, he concludes that his patient has disease C.

5:2 Theory of Parallels

Let us recall the definition of parallel lines and the parallel postulate.

Definition: *Two lines are* **parallel** *if and only if their intersection is empty.* (In other words, the two lines do not intersect.)

Parallel postulate: In a given plane and through a given point there is not more than one line parallel to a given line.

The following theorem illustrates the indirect method of proof.

Theorem: If a line is parallel to one of two parallel lines, then it is parallel to the other.

Given: $\overleftrightarrow{AB} \parallel \overleftrightarrow{CD}$

$\overleftrightarrow{AB} \parallel \overleftrightarrow{EF}$

Prove: $\overleftrightarrow{CD} \parallel \overleftrightarrow{EF}$

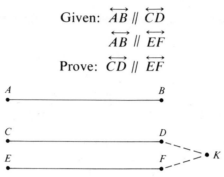

STATEMENTS	REASONS
1. $\overleftrightarrow{AB} \parallel \overleftrightarrow{CD}$, $\overleftrightarrow{AB} \parallel \overleftrightarrow{EF}$.	1. Given.
2. Assume $\overleftrightarrow{CD}$ not $\parallel \overleftrightarrow{EF}$; that is, $\overleftrightarrow{CD}$ intersects $\overleftrightarrow{EF}$ at K.	2. Either Q or $\overline{Q}$ (method of indirect proof).
3. Through point K there are two lines $\parallel \overleftrightarrow{AB}$.	3. Reasons 1 and 2.
4. But through point K there are *not* two lines $\parallel \overleftrightarrow{AB}$.	4. Parallel postulate. Through a point there is not more than one line parallel to a given line.
5. Therefore $\overleftrightarrow{CD} \parallel \overleftrightarrow{EF}$.	5. If an assumption leads to a contradiction, then the negation of the assumption is true.

6. AREAS (Optional)

We have seen that the ancient Egyptians and Babylonians had formulas for determining certains areas and volumes, and not only did these formulas provide good measurements but many were actually correct. The verification by logical proof that these methods were valid was accomplished by the Greeks. The next section illustrates this deductive treatment of areas. It also illustrates the idea of sequential development of theorems. One theorem is derived from another in order. In this section the proofs of the theorems are given informally. The student should test his understanding by supplying the formal proof for himself.

The Quadrilateral Family. A **quadrilateral** is a set of points in a plane that is the union of four line segments so that (1) each end point is the end point of exactly two segments, (2) no two segments intersect except at an end point, and (3) no two segments with the same end point are on the same line (Figure 8.4).

> A **trapezoid** is a quadrilateral having exactly one pair of sides parallel.
> A **parallelogram** is a quadrilateral whose opposite sides are parallel.
> A **rhombus** is an equilateral parallelogram.
> A **rectangle** is a parallelogram all of whose angles are right angles.
> A **square** is an equilateral rectangle.

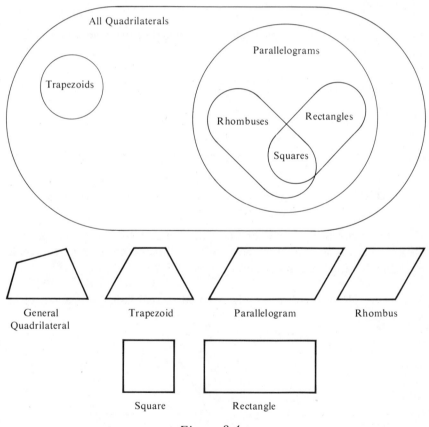

Figure 8.4

Unit of Measurement. The area inside a geometric figure is a number indicating how many unit squares are required to cover the region inside the figure. For example, one common unit of area is the square inch, a square each of whose sides is 1 inch long.

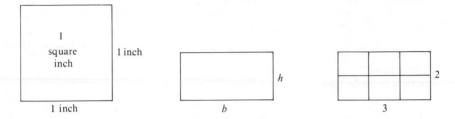

Postulate: The area of a rectangle is equal to the product of the length of its base and the length of its altitude. $A = bh$.

For example, in the figure, the area of the rectangle, A, is $3 \times 2 = 6$ square units.

Theorem: The area of a parallelogram is equal to the product of its base and its altitude. $A = bh$.

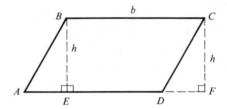

Given: $\square ABCD$ with base $AD = b$ and altitude $BE = h$
Prove: Area of $\square ABCD = bh$

This theorem is proved by showing that $\triangle ABE \cong \triangle DCF$ and thus area $\square ABCD$ = area rectangle $BCFE$. Since the area of rectangle $BCFE = bh$, the area of $\square ABCD = bh$.

Theorem: The area of a triangle is equal to one half the product of its base and its altitude. $A = bh/2$.

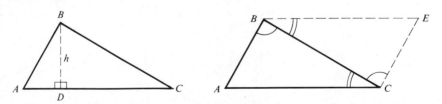

Given: $\triangle ABC$ with base $AC = b$ and altitude $BD = h$
Prove: Area of $\triangle ABC = \dfrac{bh}{2}$

This theorem is proved by showing that the triangle is one half of a parallelogram having the same base and altitude. The figure at the right suggests the proof, which involves showing that $\triangle ABC \cong \triangle ECB$, by the ASA method. Angle EBC is constructed congruent to its alternate interior angle BCA and angle BCE congruent to angle ABC. Then quadrilateral $ABEC$ can be proved a parallelogram.

Theorem: The area of a trapezoid is equal to one half the product of its altitude and the sum of its bases. $A = [h(a + b)]/2$.

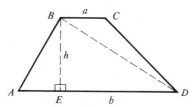

Given: Trapezoid $ABCD$ with base $AD = b$,
base $BC = a$, and altitude $BE = h$
Prove: Area of trapezoid $ABCD = \dfrac{h(a + b)}{2}$

This theorem is proved by showing that the area of the trapezoid $ABCD$ is equal to the sum of the areas of the two triangles, $\triangle ABD$ and $\triangle BCD$.

The unit on areas provides a good illustration of the concept of sequential order in proving theorems. The postulate concerning the area of a rectangle is used to derive the formula for the area of a parallelogram. Then the area of a parallelogram is used to obtain the area of a triangle. The area of a triangle, in turn, is used to establish the formula for the area of a trapezoid.

Illustration of sequential order:

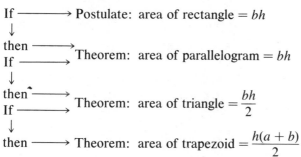

7. THEOREM OF PYTHAGORAS

The theorem of Pythagoras, which we have seen can be traced to the Babylonians, states that in a right triangle the square upon the hypotenuse, the side opposite the right angle, is equal to the sum of the squares upon the sides that include the right angle.

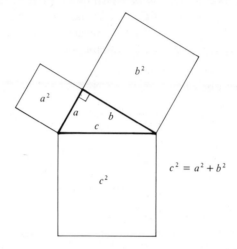

Many writers, including Proclus and Plutarch, credit Pythagoras with the first proof of this proposition. Although there is no evidence to support this claim, there is equally no evidence to deny it. Accepting the tradition that Pythagoras did offer the first proof, we still do not know exactly what proof he may have given.

Some authorities believe that Pythagoras gave a dissection proof suggested by the figure below.

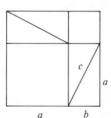 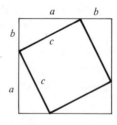

Today there exist several hundred proofs of this theorem. Elisha S. Loomis, in a volume called *The Pythagorean Proposition*, gives 367 different proofs, all classified by types.

8. SIMILAR TRIANGLES

Geometric figures that have the same size and shape are said to be *congruent*. Geometric figures that have the same shape but not necessarily the same size are said to be *similar*. In the real world a photographic enlargement of another photograph is an example of two similar figures. Maps, blueprints, and scale models furnish other examples of the concept of similarity.

Definition: *Two triangles are* **similar** *if a one-to-one correspondence can be established between their sets of vertices so that the resulting corresponding angles are congruent and the corresponding sides are proportional.*

For example, consider $\triangle ABC$ and $\triangle DEF$ with the correspondence

$$A, \quad B, \quad C$$
$$\updownarrow \quad \updownarrow \quad \updownarrow$$
$$D, \quad E, \quad F$$

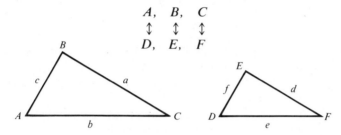

so that

$$\angle A \cong \angle D \quad \text{and} \quad \frac{a}{d} = \frac{b}{e} = \frac{c}{f} = r$$
$$\angle B \cong \angle E$$
$$\angle C \cong \angle F$$

Then, by definition, $\triangle ABC$ is similar to $\triangle DEF$. In symbols, we write $\triangle ABC \sim \triangle DEF$.

The common ratio, r, tells how many times a side of one triangle is larger (or smaller) than the corresponding side of the other triangle. The scale on a map or a blueprint (for example, 1 inch = 6 feet) is a practical example of this ratio of similitude.

An important theorem that provides us with a useful test for determining whether two triangles are similar or not is the following.

Theorem: If two angles of one triangle are congruent respectively to two angles of another triangle, then the triangles are similar.

Thus whenever we know that two triangles have two pairs of angles congruent, we may conclude by using this theorem that the corresponding sides of the two triangles are in proportion.

Applications. Similar triangles are useful in determining the measurements of unknown parts of triangles.

EXAMPLE. $\triangle ABC \sim \triangle DEF$ with $A \longleftrightarrow D$, $B \longleftrightarrow E$, $C \longleftrightarrow F$ and with the measurements of the sides as indicated on the figures below. Find the measurements of the remaining two sides of $\triangle DEF$.

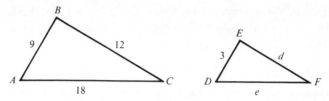

Solution. $\dfrac{12}{d} = \dfrac{18}{e} = \dfrac{9}{3}$. Since $\dfrac{9}{3} = 3$, the ratio of similarity is 3 to 1. Thus

$$3 \times d = 12 \qquad \text{or} \qquad d = 4$$

$$3 \times e = 18 \qquad \text{or} \qquad e = 6$$

Similar triangles are particularly important in determining the measurements of inaccessible distances or measurements which cannot be made directly. This concept is basic in the applications of elementary trigonometry to surveying and navigation.

Manufacturers, engineers, and architects use similar figures either as designs, blueprints, or small-scale models to help plan and direct their operations.

How Thales Measured the Heights of the Pyramids.   Historical accounts from Hieronymus, a pupil of Aristotle, and from Pliny indicate that Thales measured the heights of pyramids by measuring their shadows at the time when a body and its shadow were equal in length.

An account by Plutarch credits Thales with using the more general method of similar triangles, by setting up a stick at the end of the shadow (Figure 8.5).

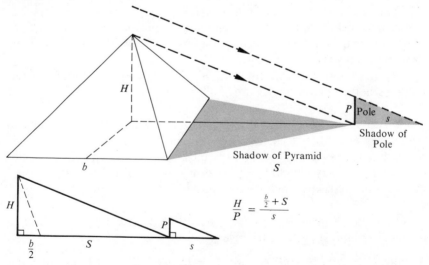

$$\frac{H}{P} = \frac{\frac{b}{2} + S}{s}$$

Figure 8.5

9. ERATOSTHENES AND EARTH MEASUREMENT (Optional)

Around 240 B.C. Eratosthenes, a Greek mathematician who was a friend of Archimedes, measured the circumference of the earth (the length of the equator) with an error of only 1 percent.

At this time it was common knowledge that the noon sun on the day of the summer solstice (around June 21) was directly overhead at Syene (now called Aswan); that is, a vertical pole cast no shadow and the bottom of a deep well was completely lit up. At the same time in Alexandria, which was 5000 stadia north of Syene, a vertical pole did cast a shadow. Eratosthenes found that the angular measure of this shadow, known as the sun's zenith distance, was 7.2° or $\frac{1}{50}$ of a complete rotation (Figure 8.6).

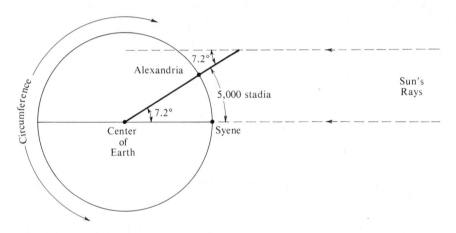

Figure 8.6

As observed on the earth, the sun's rays are almost parallel. Assuming that they are parallel, the alternate interior angles in the figure above are equal. Thus the distance from Syene to Alexandria must be $\frac{1}{50}$ of the circumference of the earth. Thus the circumference of the earth = 50 × 5000 stadia = 250,000 stadia.

According to later writers, this figure is given as 252,000 stadia, so it seems possible that Eratosthenes corrected 250,000 to 252,000, perhaps to get a number divisible by 60 or possibly to avoid using fractions.

From statements made by Pliny, it can be derived that 252,000 stadia = 24,662 miles. Thus the error of the measurement of Eratosthenes was less than 1 percent, a truly remarkable approximation.

10. ARCHIMEDES (Optional)

Most of the works of Archimedes are concerned with pure mathematics. Some of his problems are in the realm of differential and integral calculus, so great was his vision and power as a mathematician.

In *The Measurement of the Circle*, Archimedes justifies the formulas for the area and circumference of a circle ($A = \pi r^2$ and $C = \pi d$). Then Archimedes computes the lengths of an inscribed and a circumscribed regular polygon of 96 sides. From this he derives the following approximation to π:

$$3\frac{10}{71} < \pi < 3\frac{1}{7}$$

In his work *On the Sphere and Cylinder*, Archimedes proves a theorem which was his favorite. He shows that the volume of a sphere is two-thirds that of its circumscribed cylinder.

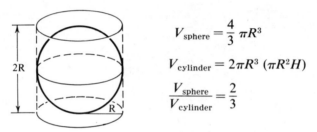

$$V_{\text{sphere}} = \frac{4}{3}\pi R^3$$

$$V_{\text{cylinder}} = 2\pi R^3 \ (\pi R^2 H)$$

$$\frac{V_{\text{sphere}}}{V_{\text{cylinder}}} = \frac{2}{3}$$

Archimedes was so proud of this result that he wanted it engraved on his tombstone. Cicero writes that he found this tombstone of Archimedes when he was quaestor in Sicily.

A variation of this favorite theorem of Archimedes states that the volumes of the (double) cone, the sphere, and the cylinder illustrated below are in the ratio 1:2:3.

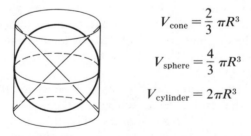

$$V_{\text{cone}} = \frac{2}{3}\pi R^3$$

$$V_{\text{sphere}} = \frac{4}{3}\pi R^3$$

$$V_{\text{cylinder}} = 2\pi R^3$$

Thus cone:sphere:cylinder = 1:2:3.

EXERCISES

1. Examine the figures below and then state a condition for any two circles to intersect.

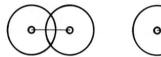 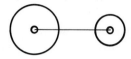

2. For each of the following undefined concepts of geometry, select from the set that accompanies it the element that most nearly describes it in the real world.
   a. Point — {sharp end of a pencil, eraser end of a pencil, intersection of two streets}
   b. Line — {a pencil, a wire, a strand of very thin nylon thread}
   c. Plane — {a piece of cardboard, a piece of onion skin paper, a piece of plywood}

3. Using the figure, and using symbols only, complete each of the following.

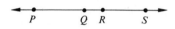

   a. $\overline{PR} \subset$
   b. $\overline{PQ} \cup \overline{QR} =$
   c. $\overline{PQ} \cup \overline{PR} =$
   d. $\overline{PQ} \cap \overline{QR} =$
   e. $\overline{PQ} \cap \overline{PR} =$
   f. $\overline{PQ} \cap \overline{RS} =$
   g. $\overline{PR} \cap \overline{QS} =$
   h. $\overleftrightarrow{PQ} \cup \overrightarrow{RQ} =$
   i. $\overrightarrow{PQ} \cap \overrightarrow{QP} =$
   j. $\overrightarrow{PR} \cap \overrightarrow{RP} =$
   k. $\overrightarrow{QP} \cap \overrightarrow{QR} =$
   l. $\overrightarrow{QP} \cup \overrightarrow{QR} =$
   m. $\overrightarrow{PQ} \cap \overrightarrow{PR} =$
   n. $\overrightarrow{QP} \cap \overrightarrow{RQ} =$
   o. $\overrightarrow{QP} \cup \overrightarrow{RQ} =$

4. Using the figure, and using symbols only, complete each of the following.

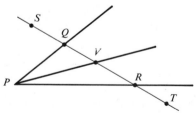

   a. $\overrightarrow{PQ} \cup \overrightarrow{PR} =$
   b. $\overrightarrow{PQ} \cap \overrightarrow{PR} =$
   c. $\angle QPV \cup \angle VPR =$
   d. $\angle QPV \cup \angle VPQ =$
   e. $\angle QPV \cap \angle RPV =$
   f. $\angle QPV \cap \angle QPR =$
   g. $\angle QVP \cap \angle QPV =$
   h. $\overleftrightarrow{ST} \cap$ interior $\angle QPR =$
   i. $\overleftrightarrow{ST} \cap$ exterior $\angle QPR =$
   j. $\overleftrightarrow{ST} \cap \angle QPR =$
   k. $\overline{PQ} \cup \overline{QR} \cup \overline{RP} =$
   l. Interior $\angle QPR \cap$ interior $\angle PRQ \cap$ interior $\angle RQP =$

5. Since the statement $(Q \rightarrow P)$ is *not* logically equivalent to the state-ment $(P \rightarrow Q)$ of which it is the converse, a separate proof must be given for each theorem which is the converse of another. Supply the missing reasons in the formal proof below. Note that this theorem is the converse to one given in the text.

Theorem: If two angles of a triangle are congruent, then the sides op-posite these angles are congruent.

Given: $\angle A \cong \angle C$
Prove: $\overline{AB} \cong \overline{BC}$

STATEMENTS		REASONS
1. $\angle A \cong \angle C$	1.	
2. $\angle C \cong \angle A$	2.	
3. $\overline{AC} \cong \overline{AC}$	3.	
4. $\triangle BAC \cong \triangle BCA$	4.	
5. $\overline{AB} \cong \overline{BC}$	5.	

6. Proclus states that Thales used the ASA method to determine the distances of ships at sea. How Thales did this is not known for cer-tain but it may have been as follows.

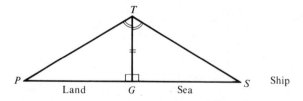

If the ship S at sea is sighted from the top of the cliff T, then by using an instrument, probably like the astrolabe, the angle GTS can be measured. Then point P on the ground is sighted so that $\angle GTP \cong \angle GTS$. Then the distance on the ground $\overline{PG}$ is measured. Write a formal proof to show that $\overline{PG} \cong \overline{GS}$, the inaccessible distance along the sea.

7. A man asked his wife to cut eight triangles of cloth to cover his umbrella. He told her that the ribs were each 26 inches long, and that when the umbrella was open, they met at angles of 45°. His wife told

him she could not cut the triangles until she also knows how far apart they are at the outer ends. The man tells her she does not need this extra information. Who is right? Why?

8. A carpenter sometimes determines whether a floor is horizontal by using the instrument shown. The sides $\overline{AB}$ and $\overline{AC}$ are equal in length and there is a mark at the middle point D of $\overline{BC}$. Show that $\overline{BC}$ is horizontal (perpendicular to the plumb line) if the plumb bob hangs at D.

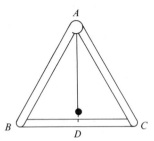

9. Complete the proof below. Note that the indirect method of proof is used.

Theorem: If a line intersects one of two parallel lines, then it intersects the other also.

Given: $\overleftrightarrow{AB} \parallel \overleftrightarrow{CD}$
$\overleftrightarrow{PQ}$ intersects $\overleftrightarrow{AB}$ at Q
Prove: $\overleftrightarrow{PQ}$ intersects $\overleftrightarrow{CD}$

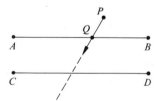

STATEMENTS	REASONS
1. $\overleftrightarrow{AB} \parallel \overleftrightarrow{CD}$, $\overleftrightarrow{PQ}$ intersects $\overleftrightarrow{AB}$ at Q.	1.
2. Assume _____	2.
3. Then, through point Q, both $\overleftrightarrow{AB}$ and $\overleftrightarrow{PQ}$ are parallel to $\overleftrightarrow{CD}$.	3. Reasons 1 and 2
4. But $\overleftrightarrow{AB}$ and $\overleftrightarrow{PQ}$ cannot both be parallel to $\overleftrightarrow{CD}$.	4.
5. Therefore, _____	5.

10. Using the figure with *AEFC* a rectangle, indicate informally how it may be shown that the area of $\triangle ABC = \dfrac{bh}{2}$ by showing area of $\triangle ABC$ equal to one half area of rectangle *AEFC*.

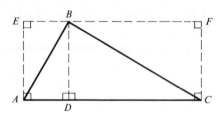

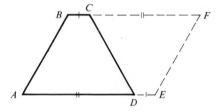

11. Using the figure with *ABFE* a parallelogram, indicate informally how area of trapezoid *ABCD* equals $\dfrac{h}{2}(a + b)$.

12. Around 1100 A.D. a Hindu mathematician Bhaskara presented the diagram on the left below as a "proof" of the theorem of Pythagoras. If the measurements of the sides of the figures are as indicated in the figure at the right below, indicate the method of this proof.

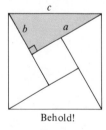

Behold!

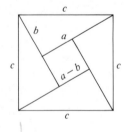

13. President Garfield's proof of the theorem of Pythagoras (published in 1876) is the only contribution to mathematics ever made by a president of the United States. Garfield, then a Republican congressman from Ohio, wrote that he hit on the proof during some mathematical amusements with other congressmen, and "we think it something on which the members of both houses can unite without distinction of

party." Garfield's figure is shown. Indicate his proof by considering the area of trapezoid *ABED*.

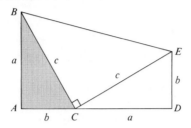

14. A vertical yardstick casts a shadow 20 inches long at the same time that a building casts a shadow 25 feet long. How high is the building?

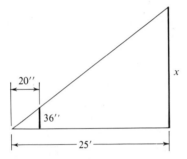

15. If the state of Wyoming is represented on a map by a rectangle 7 inches long by $5\frac{1}{2}$ inches wide, what is the area of the state of Wyoming if the scale of the map reads "1 inch = 50 miles"?

16. To determine the distance *AB* across a lake, a man measured the distances $CD = 200$ feet, $DE = 120$ feet, and $BE = 180$ feet. Find *AB*.

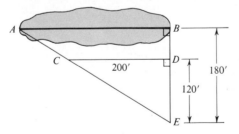

17. The height of a tree can be found by placing a mirror on the horizontal ground and walking away until the top of the tree can be seen in the mirror. If the eye of a person is 5 feet from the ground when he is

6 feet from the mirror and the mirror is 20 feet from the tree, how high is the tree? (In the figure, $\angle 1 = \angle 2$; that is, the angle of incidence is equal to the angle of reflection. This is a property of light.)

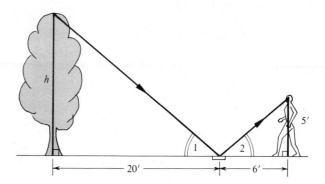

CHAPTER IX

Greek Arithmetic (Optional)

Number rules the universe.

Pythagoras

The study of the properties of numbers, or **number theory,** as this subject is now known, originated in the school of Pythagoras around 540 B.C. These ancient Greeks called this study **arithmetic,** which they distinguished from **logistic,** the name they gave to the art of computation; that is, addition, subtraction, multiplication, division, and problem solving. It is interesting to note that today in continental Europe "arithmetic" still retains the original Greek meaning. In England and America, however, the word "arithmetic" is used for the Greek "logistic."

The Greeks thought of a number as a quantity made up of units. Unity, or 1, was not considered a number until modern times but was regarded as the measure of number.

The distinction between *odd* and *even* numbers was known to the Pythagoreans. An **even number** was described as one that could be divided into two equal parts while an **odd number** could not be so divided. (The set of even numbers $= \{2, 4, 6, 8, \cdots\}$ and the set of odd numbers $= \{3, 5, 7, 9, \cdots\}$.)

1. POLYGONAL NUMBERS

Polygonal numbers, also called **figurate numbers,** are numbers that can be arranged to form a geometric shape.

Triangular numbers are those numbers that can be pictured as triangles, such as the ones below. The numbers 3, 6, and 10 are called the first three triangular numbers.

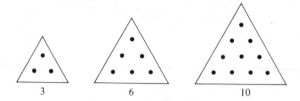

Square numbers are those that can be pictured as squares, such as those below. The numbers 4, 9, and 16 are the first three square numbers.

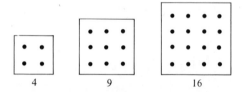

Pentagonal numbers are those that can be represented as pentagons, five-sided figures. One such arrangement is a square with a triangle on top. The numbers 5, 12, and 22 are called the first three pentagonal numbers.

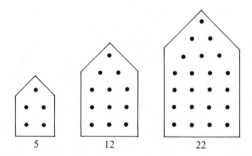

In a similar manner, hexagonal (six-sided) and other polygonal (many-sided) numbers may be described.

2. EUCLIDEAN ALGORITHM

2:1 Greatest Common Divisor

The **greatest common divisor,** or **G.C.D.,** of two natural numbers is the largest natural number that divides each of the two numbers. (The set of natural numbers = the set of counting numbers = {1, 2, 3, 4, 5, · · · }.)

For example, the G.C.D. of 12 and 20 is 4 because 4 divides both 12 and 20 and no number larger than 4 will divide both 12 and 20.

The **direct method** for finding the G.C.D. is to list the divisors of each number and select the largest number appearing on both lists.

EXAMPLE. Find the G.C.D. of 12 and 20.

Solution. The divisors of 12 are 1, 2, 3, *4*, 6, 12. The divisors of 20 are 1, 2, *4*, 5, 10, 20. Thus the G.C.D. of 12 and 20 is 4, the largest number on both lists.

2:2 Euclidean Algorithm

The **Euclidean algorithm** is a process developed by Euclid for finding the G.C.D. It is described at the beginning of Book VII of *Elements*. This method is in general more rapid than the direct method, particularly when the numbers are very large. The method is as follows.

1. Divide the larger number by the smaller, the divisor.
2. Divide the divisor by the remainder obtained in step 1.
3. Repeat the process in step 2 until the division is exact, that is, until the remainder is zero.

The last divisor used is the G.C.D.

EXAMPLE. By using the Euclidean algorithm, find the G.C.D. of 210 and 270.

Solution

$$
\begin{array}{r}
1 \\
1.\ 210\ \overline{)270} \\
210 \\
\hline
60
\end{array}
$$

$$
\begin{array}{r}
3 \\
2.\quad 60\ \overline{)210} \\
180 \\
\hline
30
\end{array}
$$

$$
\begin{array}{r}
2 \\
3.\quad 30\ \overline{)60} \\
60 \\
\hline
0
\end{array}
$$

Thus 30 is the G.C.D. of 210 and 270.

In computational arithmetic, one useful application of the G.C.D. is in simplifying fractions.

EXAMPLE 1. Simplify $\dfrac{12}{20}$.

Solution. Since the G.C.D. of 12 and 20 is 4,

$$\frac{12}{20} = \frac{4 \times 3}{4 \times 5} = \frac{3}{5}$$

EXAMPLE 2. Simplify $\dfrac{210}{270}$.

Solution. Since the G.C.D. of 210 and 270 is 30,

$$\frac{210}{270} = \frac{30 \times 7}{30 \times 9} = \frac{7}{9}$$

3. PERFECT AND FRIENDLY NUMBERS

3:1 Perfect Numbers

The Greeks were concerned with certain numbers called perfect numbers and with certain pairs of numbers called *friendly* numbers. It is believed that these descriptions started with the Pythagoreans.

A **perfect number,** as defined by Euclid in Book VII, is a natural number that is the sum of all its proper divisors, where 1 is counted as a proper divisor but the number itself is not.

The smallest perfect number is 6 because $6 = 1 + 2 + 3$. The first four perfect numbers are 6, 28, 496, and 8128.

It is not known today whether there are any *odd* perfect numbers or not. This problem is a famous unsolved problem in number theory. However, it has been established with the help of the electronic computer that there is no odd perfect number smaller than 10 billion.

3:2 Friendly Numbers

Two numbers are called **friendly,** or **amicable,** if each is the sum of the proper divisors of the other. (A proper divisor includes the number 1 but not the number itself.)

For example, the numbers 220 and 284 are friendly. The proper divisors of 220 are 1, 2, 4, 5, 10, 11, 20, 22, 44, 55, 110, and

$$1 + 2 + 4 + 5 + 10 + 11 + 20 + 22 + 44 + 55 + 110 = 284$$

The proper divisors of 284 are 1, 2, 4, 71, 142, and

$$1 + 2 + 4 + 71 + 142 = 220$$

For many years, these numbers were thought to have a mystical or religious relationship to human friendship. Strangely enough, a second pair was not found until 1636 when the French mathematician, Pierre Fermat, discovered that 17,296 and 18,416 were friendly numbers. He also found a rule for finding friendly numbers.

In 1638 the French mathematician, René Descartes, found a third pair.

In 1747 the Swiss mathematician, Leonard Euler, gave a list of 30 pairs and later extended this list to 60 pairs.

Another strange development was the discovery in 1866 by a 16-year-old Italian schoolboy, Nicolo Paganini, of a pair that had been over-looked by everyone else, the pair 1184 and 1210.

Today over 400 pairs of friendly numbers are known.

4. PRIME NUMBERS

The distinction between odd and even numbers was known to the Pythagoreans. Many superstitions have been associated with this division of numbers into odd and even classes. The Pythagoreans believed that the odd numbers were masculine and thus divine and heavenly while the even numbers were feminine and thus human and earthly. This belief persisted into the days of Shakespeare, who wrote in the *Merry Wives of Windsor* that "there is divinity in odd numbers, either in nativity, chance, or death."

Most odd numbers have been considered lucky with the exception of 13, and the fear of 13 was known to exist long before the time of the Last Supper.

Numbers were also classified by being called prime or composite.

A **prime number** is a natural number larger than 1 that is divisible by no other number except itself and 1.

A **composite number** is a natural number that is *not* prime.

Thus the first few primes are 2, 3, 5, 7, 11, 13, 17, 19, 23.

The number 6, for example, is *not* prime, but composite, because $6 = 2 \times 3$.

In Book VII of *Elements,* Euclid has definitions for the concepts "unit," "number," "even," "odd," "prime," "composite," and "perfect" as well as many theorems concerned with these concepts.

The prime numbers are thought of as the basic building units from which all the numbers are made. Thus a knowledge of the properties of prime numbers would provide a key to understanding the structural properties of all numbers.

4:1 Euclid's Theorem

Proposition 20 of Book IX of *Elements* states "There are infinitely many prime numbers." This theorem, together with the proof that Euclid gave, is considered as an example of **elegance** in mathematics. Not only are both the idea and proof easy to understand but, in addition, the theorem and its proof are just as important and meaningful as they were 2000 years ago.

Euclid's proof involves the method called *reductio ad absurdum*, that is, the indirect method of proof. The assumption is made that there is a largest prime and then it is shown that this assumption leads to a contradiction. Therefore, the assumption must be false and its negation must be true. Thus there is no largest prime.

The proof proceeds as follows.

Assume there is a largest prime, P.

Then form the number N by adding 1 to the product of the natural numbers from 1 to P.

$$N = (1 \times 2 \times 3 \times \cdots \times P) + 1$$

Since N is larger than P, it must be composite, since we assumed P is the largest prime.

Then some number smaller than N divides N. If this number is not prime itself, then a prime divisor of it must also divide N. Let Q be the smallest prime divisor of N.

Now Q is a prime and P is the largest prime, so Q must be one of the numbers $1, 2, 3, \cdots, P$.

But each of these numbers does *not* divide N because each leaves a remainder of 1.

Thus we have a contradiction and thus there is no largest prime.

4:2 Sieve of Eratosthenes

Around 230 B.C., the Greek mathematician Eratosthenes developed a method for listing all the primes less than some given number.

For example, let us find all the primes less than 100.

Step 1. Write the numbers from 1 to 100 in a rectangular array as shown in Figure 9.1.

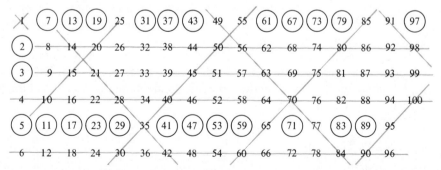

Figure 9.1

Step 2. Cross out all multiples of 2 by drawing horizontal lines across every other row. Circle 2.

Step 3. Cross out all multiples of 3 remaining by drawing a horizontal line across the third row. Circle 3.

Step 4. Circle 5. Cross out the multiples of 5 by drawing diagonal lines sloping upward to the right as indicated.

Step 5. Circle 7. Cross out the multiples of 7 by drawing diagonal lines sloping downward to the right as indicated.

Step 6. Cross out the number 1 and circle the remaining numbers that have not been crossed out.

Excluding the number 1, which mathematicians do not like to consider a prime, we find that there are 25 numbers that have "fallen through the sieve." These are the circled numbers in the array and are called the first 25 prime numbers.

To find more primes, the array is extended to some desired number. Then lines are drawn in a similar manner for each prime less than the square root of the last number in the array.

4:3 Twin Primes and Unproved Conjectures

Twin primes are a pair of prime numbers whose difference is 2. For example, each of the pairs below is called a pair of twin primes.

3 and 5

5 and 7

11 and 13

17 and 19

An unproved conjecture states that there are infinitely many twin primes. Although this statement resembles Euclid's theorem in its content and in its simplicity, no one has ever been able to find a proof of it.

Another unproved statement is the famous Goldbach conjecture made in 1742 in a letter to Euler. Goldbach suggested that every even natural number, except 2, could be expressed as the sum of two primes. For example, $6 = 3 + 3$, $8 = 5 + 3$, and so on. However, this statement also remains unproved.

One of the most challenging problems in number theory is to find a formula that would produce prime numbers only, that is, a prime-number generating function. The primes seem to be scattered among the natural numbers in some kind of pattern. The pattern is not a random one and yet no one has been able to give a precise description of it.

A step in this direction is provided by the expression $N^2 + N + 41$ (discovered by Euler). This expression produces prime numbers for each value of N from N to 40. When $N = 41$, however, we obtain $41^2 + 41 + 41 = 41 \times 43$, which is not prime.

5. GEOMETRIC ALGEBRA

Although the Greeks did not have the advantages of the symbolism and notations of our present-day algebra, still they could solve many algebraic problems by geometric methods.

Number properties were exhibited as geometric theorems. The solution of an equation was accomplished by the geometric construction of a line segment, the number that measured the length being the solution of the algebraic problem.

This geometric algebra is presented in Book II of Euclid's *Elements*. It is the subject matter that is the most closely related to our algebra of today.

Some of the theorems concerned with number properties are illustrated below. The proofs are mostly dissection proofs and are only suggested here.

The distributive property, $A(B + C) = AB + AC$:

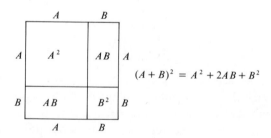

The perfect square:

$$(A + B)^2 = A^2 + 2AB + B^2$$

The difference of two squares:

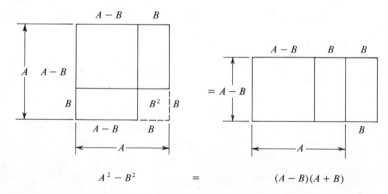

$$A^2 - B^2 \qquad = \qquad (A - B)(A + B)$$

EXAMPLE. A solution of a quadratic equation by a geometric dissection method. Solve $N^2 + 6N = 16$ (see Figure 9.2).

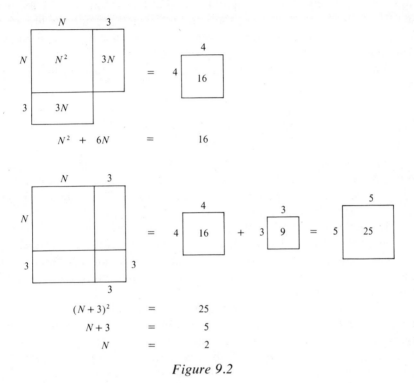

Figure 9.2

The Greeks had much more sophisticated methods than this for solving equations. The example above serves only to give us an idea of what their methods were like.

6. DIOPHANTUS

The greatest Greek achievements in the areas of number theory and algebra were made by *Diophantus* of Alexandria around 250 A.D. in his work *Arithmetica*.

About all that is known about the life of Diophantus is found in his epitaph as quoted in the *Greek Anthology* compiled by Metrodorus about 500 A.D. Book XIV, Problem 126.[1]

"This tomb holds Diophantus. Ah, how great a marvel! the tomb tells scientifically the measure of his life. God granted him to be a boy for

---

[1] Midonick, *The Treasury of Mathematics*: Metrodorus, "The Greek Anthology," p. 502.

the sixth part of his life, and adding a twelfth part to this, he clothed his cheeks with down; He lit him the light of wedlock after a seventh part, and five years after his marriage He granted him a son. Alas! late-born wretched child; after attaining the measure of half his father's life, chill Fate took him. After consoling his grief by this science of numbers for four years he ended his life."

Translated into the modern language of algebra, this problem would be written:

$$\frac{N}{6} + \frac{N}{12} + \frac{N}{7} + 5 + \frac{N}{2} + 4 = N$$

The solution of this equation is $N = 84$. Thus we see that Diophantus lived to the age of 84. He was a boy for 14 years, a youth for 7, a bachelor for 12 more years, and was married when he was 33. When he was 38 his son was born and his son lived to be 42 years old.

In *Arithmetica* we find the first systematic use of algebraic symbols. Diophantus had special signs for the unknown, powers and reciprocals of the unknown, and the symbol, $\uparrow$, for the subtraction operation. This improvement in notation had the advantage that it made some complicated problems much easier to solve.

Although Diophantus dealt with a variety of problems and equations, many reminding us of the algebraic-type problems of the ancient Egyptians and Babylonians, he is most noted for what are today called "indeterminate" equations. His contribution in this area was so great that today this branch of the theory of numbers is named after him and is called **Diophantine analysis.**

Diophantine analysis is concerned with finding natural numbers as solutions of an equation that in general has many possible solutions.

An indeterminate problem with which we are familiar is the problem of finding Pythagorean triplets; that is, solve $X^2 + Y^2 = Z^2$, where the solutions must be natural numbers, members of the set $\{1, 2, 3, 4, \cdots\}$.

We have already seen that a solution to this problem was known to the ancient Babylonians:

$$X = u^2 - v^2, \qquad Y = 2uv, \qquad Z = u^2 + v^2$$

where u and v can be *any* natural numbers. Thus, when $u = 2$ and $v = 1$, we have $X = 4 - 1 = 3$, $Y = 4$, $Z = 4 + 1 = 5$, and $3^2 + 4^2 = 5^2$.

Pythagoras gave the following solution:

$$X = N, \text{ an odd number}, \qquad Y = \tfrac{1}{2}(N^2 - 1), \qquad Z = \tfrac{1}{2}(N^2 + 1)$$

Indeterminate equations are not easy to solve in general, particularly those like the example above, which are called **quadratic,** because they involve the square of the unknown number.

EXERCISES

1. Illustrate the following numbers as geometric shapes.
   a. The first five triangular numbers.
   b. The first five square numbers.
   c. The first five pentagonal numbers.
   d. The first three hexagonal numbers.
2. Illustrate geometrically that the square number 16 is the sum of the triangular numbers 6 and 10. Similarly, illustrate geometrically that $25 = 10 + 15$. Present a convincing argument for the theorem of Theon: Every square number is the sum of two triangular numbers.
3. An oblong number is one that can be arranged to form a rectangle whose base is 1 unit longer than its height.
   a. Illustrate the first three oblong numbers, beginning with $6 = 3 \times 2$.
   b. Show that every oblong number is the sum of two equal triangular numbers.
4. Using the Euclidean algorithm, find the G.C.D. of
   a. 12 and 18   f. 165 and 182
   b. 30 and 45   g. 455 and 845
   c. 60 and 84   h. 1225 and 2451
   d. 51 and 71   i. 1725 and 2576
   e. 43 and 92   j. 2931 and 5244
5. Using the results of Exercise 4, simplify each of the following fractions.
   a. $\dfrac{12}{18}$ b. $\dfrac{30}{45}$ c. $\dfrac{60}{84}$ d. $\dfrac{51}{71}$ e. $\dfrac{43}{92}$ f. $\dfrac{165}{182}$

   g. $\dfrac{455}{845}$ h. $\dfrac{1225}{2451}$ i. $\dfrac{1725}{2576}$ j. $\dfrac{2931}{5244}$
6. Show that 496 is a perfect number.
7. Show that 1184 and 1210 are friendly numbers.
8. Find the perfect number furnished by Euler's formula, $2^{n-1}(2^n - 1)$, using $n = 5$. Show that this number *is* perfect.
9. Show that Fermat's pair, 17,296 and 18,416, are friendly numbers. (*Hint:* $17{,}296 = 2^4 \times 23 \times 47$ and $18{,}416 = 2^4 \times 1151$.)
10. Determine whether each of the numbers below is prime or composite.
    a. 83   d. 301   g. 153
    b. 97   e. 377   h. 429
    c. 127   f. 151   i. 461
11. Using the sieve of Eratosthenes, find the primes less than 200. How many primes less than 200 are there?
12. List the twin primes less than 100.
13. Illustrate geometrically $A(B + C + D) = AB + AC + AD$.
14. Illustrate geometrically $A(B - C) = AB - AC$.
15. Illustrate geometrically $2(A^2 + B^2) = (A + B)^2 + (A - B)^2$.

16. Solve in a geometric manner: $N^2 + 8N = 9$.
17. Solve in a geometric manner: $N^2 + 10N = 144$.
18. Find the first five triplets, solutions of $X^2 + Y^2 = Z^2$, by using the solution of Pythagoras; $X = N$, $Y = \frac{1}{2}(N^2 - 1)$, $Z = \frac{1}{2}(N^2 + 1)$, with $N = 3, 5, 7, 9$, and 11, respectively. Verify that each of these five triplets is a solution.
19. Find at least three different pairs of natural numbers that satisfy each of the following *linear indeterminate* equations. Try to find an expression that would yield all the natural number solutions of each of the following.
    a. $2X - Y = 5$.   b. $2X - 3Y = 5$.
20. Among the many indeterminate equations of Diophantus are found

$$X^2 - 26Y^2 = 1 \quad \text{and} \quad X^2 - 30Y^2 = 1$$

which are now called **Pell equations.** These are difficult to solve. Find some natural number solutions of the simpler equation $X^2 - 3Y^2 = 1$. Try the trial and error process.

PART IV

THE HINDU-ARABIC-EUROPEAN PERIOD

At the beginning of the Christian era Greece and all the Orient had become colonies ruled by Roman officials. Although the Romans collected heavy taxes, they did not interfere with the basic economic structure, which was chiefly agricultural. The western part of the Roman Empire had developed an extensive agriculture which required many slaves, while the eastern part had an intensive agriculture which used slaves for domestic services and public works only.

The spread of a slave economy proved to be fatal to both science and society. Technical discoveries are not needed when slaves can cheaply perform most tasks. The ruling classes valued the arts and sciences less and less. Education received little encouragement from either prestige or financial reward. As the slave market declined, the Roman economy dropped to a point beyond recovery. By 400 A.D. mathematics had been reduced to a status of mediocrity. Creativity had disappeared. Only commentaries and compilations were being written.

The plundering of Rome by the Goths marked the end of the western part of the Roman Empire. With the destruction of the University at Alexandria, the doors to learning were closed to the Europeans. They would not reopen until 1000 years later, when Europe emerged from the Dark Ages.

The eastern part of the Roman Empire did not suffer such a dire effect on its economy as did the western part. Their civilization had always been more advanced than that of the West and their caste system may have effected a more stable social structure.

It is in this part of the world that mathematics continued its existence. It is to the people in India and Arabia that we are indebted for preserving the world's intellectual possessions — our cultural heritage brought to so great a height by the Greeks.

India

The earliest record of civilization in India is found at Mohenjo Daro on the Indus river. The ruins of an ancient city indicate that around 3000 B.C. the people living here were every bit as advanced as those in Egypt and Babylonia. What eventually became of them is not known.

Around 2000 B.C. the *Aryans* (a Sanskrit word meaning "noblemen" or "landowners") crossed the Himalaya mountains and established themselves first in India and later in Europe. These people formed what is called the Indo-European branch of man.

The Aryan influence extended to all of India. These are the people who perfected the written and spoken Sanskrit language and who introduced the caste system.

During the period from 700 B.C. to 300 B.C. the Persians often had holdings in the northern part of India. The sacred rituals called the *Sulvasutras* (meaning "the rules of the cord") were probably written during this time. These rules are of mathematical interest because they explain the construction of sacrificial altars in terms of the geometric properties of squares, rectangles, circles, and special Pythagorean numbers.

In 326 B.C. Alexander the Great began his invasions of India. As a result of his conquests, Persia and India came under Greek rule for the next 200 years or so, and the Hellenistic culture, a blending of the Persian with the classical Greek, entered the area.

After the decline of the Roman Empire, India experienced several invasions until finally the Gupta dynasty was established under native Indian rule. This period, beginning around 500 A.D., became known as the Golden Age of India. India became a center of learning with important universities located at Ujjain in Central India and at Mysore in Southern India.

The historical documents indicate that Hindu mathematics was now free of religion, although it remained a servant to astronomy, chiefly studied by the priests. Their language was poetic, mystic, and often vague. Their attention was focused on the properties of numbers, the arithmetic and algebraic side of mathematics. This was a direct contrast to Greek mathematics, which had reached an independent existence and could be studied by anyone who was interested. The Greeks strove for clarity in their language and insisted on rigorous proofs, their mind primarily concerned with geometric concepts.

In 1881 a birch bark manuscript was found at Bakhshali, a village in northwest India. Mainly because of the peculiarities of its language and verse forms, the contents have been dated about 400 A.D. If this dating is correct, this arithmetical work would be particularly significant because it would exhibit the first documentary appearance of zero.

Around 500 A.D. there appeared the work of the noted Hindu astronomer, Aryabhata, who wrote that he was born in 476 A.D. and that he was 23 years old when he wrote this work in Kusumapura, the "city of flowers," near the Ganges. His verses on mathematics give rules for the extraction of square and cube roots and the solutions of various quadratic equations.

In 628 Brahmagupta, the greatest of the Hindu mathematicians, wrote his *Brahma-sphuta-siddhanta* ("The Revised System of Brahma"), a 21-chapter work on astronomy with two chapters devoted to mathematics. Brahmagupta the chief astronomer at Ujjain, was so revered that his work was studied and copied word for word for centuries later.

In 1150 Bhaskara, also an astronomer at Ujjain, wrote a work on astronomy that showed little advance over that of Brahmagupta. His two mathematical chapters are called *Lilavati* ("the beautiful," or arithmetic) and *Vija-ganita* ("root extraction," or algebra).

From this time on Hindu mathematics retrogressed until 1900.

Arabia

In 395 the Byzantine Empire was founded with its capital at Constantinople. While fighting invaders for the next 1000 years, it also maintained communications between East and West and preserved the Greek culture.

As early as 266, Mesopotamia, formerly Babylonia, had acquired Persian rulers, the Sassanians. After 622, the flight of Mohammed from Mecca, the Arabs, united by religious fervor, conquered vast territories of land, extending from India on the East as far West as North Africa and Spain.

Although the official language changed from Greek or Latin to Arabic, still the native cultures of these regions continued to exist and the Greek cultural influence persisted.

Following the Arabic conquest of Sassanian Persia in 641, the city of Bagdad became the leading cultural center and Mesopotamia, centrally located between Constantinople, Alexandria, India, and China, again enjoyed its role as the great commercial and cultural exchange.

The caliphs of Bagdad became patrons of learning and encouraged its scholars. Around 766 Brahmagupta's works were brought to Bagdad and translated into Arabic. This is probably the way that the Hindu numerals reached the Arabs and then later the people of Europe.

Next the Greek classics, including Euclid's *Elements* and Ptolemy's *Almagest,* were translated into Arabic. Greek manuscripts were held in such high esteem that they were obtained from a Byzantine emperor as a condition in a peace treaty.

The most famous scholar of this period lived around 825. He was Mohammed ibn Musa al-Khowarizmi (Mohammed, the son of Moses of Khwarezm, now Khiva), who wrote a book on arithmetic and a work on algebra. The arithmetic book, known as *Algorithmi de numero Indorum* by its Latin translation in the twelfth century, was one of the main sources by which western Europe was introduced to the Hindu-Arabic numerals and the computations using them (that is, our arithmetic of today).

Al-Khowarizmi's treatise on algebra was called *Hisab al-jabr wal-muqabala,* which literally means "the science of reduction and cancellation." Our word "algebra" is derived from the word "al-jabr" (reduction), and our word "algorithm," meaning a rule for a computation, is derived from the Latin form of the author's name, "al-Khowarizmi."

Perhaps the most original contribution of the Moslems was made by the astronomer and philosopher, Omar Khayyam, who gave a geometric solution of the cubic equation around 1100. Khayyam was also known for his very accurate calendar reform and as the poet who wrote the *Rubaiyat.*

Europe

After the fall of the western part of the Roman Empire in 476, the slave-based agricultural economy was gradually replaced by a new feudal system with the Greek-Roman world governed by the popes in Rome and the emperor in Constantinople.

For the next few centuries, commercial and intellectual exchange between the European world of the West and the Arabic world of the East was almost nonexistent. After a period of decadence with Western Europe reduced to semibarbarism, the landed aristocracy became more and more powerful and the society became feudal and church-oriented.

Charlemagne was crowned Emperor of the Holy Roman Empire in 800, and during the next few centuries the needs of the primitive agricultural society evoked little interest in mathematics. Nothing more advanced than the computation of Easter by the monks was of concern.

As the villages of Europe grew into towns, these towns became self-governing units similar to the Greek city-states. However, since there was no way to procure slaves, the medieval European could not develop the Greek life of leisure based on slavery. Instead the Europeans had to use their resourcefulness and inventive powers and improve their standard of living by improving their technology.

Following the Norman Conquest under William the Conqueror in 1066, the loss of Toledo in Spain by the Moors to the Christians in 1085, and the proclamations of the Crusades (1095–ca. 1270), we find a reestablishment of commercial and intellectual relations between East and West.

Christian scholars flocked to Spain to obtain the knowledge of the Arabs. During the twelfth century the Greek and Arabic works, including Euclid's *Elements* and al-Khowarizmi's algebra, were translated from Arabic into Latin.

The Norman kingdom in Sicily established this island as a link between the East and West. Diplomatic and commercial exchange between Constantinople and Bagdad, with concurrent usage of the Greek, Arabic, and Latin languages, further promoted the translation of scientific and mathematical manuscripts.

At the beginning of the thirteenth century, the European universities started to evolve from the Church schools. The Universities of Paris, Padua, Naples, Oxford, and Cambridge were the first.

The cities in Italy on the Mediterranean were again the centers of trade. Again the merchants developed a keen interest in the knowledge to which they were exposed, just like the Ionian merchants of the Greek world 2000 years ago. Such a merchant was Leonardo Fibonacci (Leonardo, son of Bonaccio), also known as Leonardo Pisano (Leonardo of Pisa), (born 1170 and died 1250), the most noted mathematician of this time, known as the Renaissance or Re-birth of Civilization.

On his return from the Orient, Leonardo wrote his *Liber Abaci* (1202), which is a treatment of arithmetic and elementary algebra. This book is especially significant because it was an important means by which the Hindu-Arabic numerals were transmitted into Europe.

The fourteenth and fifteenth centuries were years of little intellectual progress. In 1348–1350 the Black Death (bubonic plague) brought death to a third of the population of Europe. From 1337 to 1453 the two most powerful monarchies in Europe, England and France, fought the Hundred Years' War, a war that greatly weakened both countries but from which they finally recovered by the end of the fifteenth century.

By the end of the fifteenth century feudalism had collapsed and the authority of the Church was greatly weakened. Strong central governments became established in Europe and the Renaissance had developed in man a new outlook on life.

Original Greek manuscripts were brought into Italy by refugees from the collapse of the Byzantine Empire as the Turks took Constantinople in 1453.

The invention of the printing press in 1438, which revolutionized the transmission of knowledge, and the new geographical discoveries of Diaz, Vasco da Gama, and Columbus toward the end of the fifteenth century heralded the beginning of man's new world.

Some progress in mathematics was achieved in the fifteenth century. This was made in the areas of arithmetic, algebra, and trigonometry and was stimulated chiefly by the practical requirements of the merchants.

The sixteenth century was an age of great discoveries, not only geographically but also scientifically. New mathematics was created, inspired by the demands of engineering, surveying, navigation, astronomy, and business. The subject of algebra was the mathematical center of attention while the new astronomical theories of Copernicus, Tycho Brahe, and Kepler brought about a new conception of the universe.

The productive use and subsequent perfection of machines was also an important factor in the now rapid development of mathematics. The importance of the machine led to scientific studies of motion and change. Galileo Galilei (1564–1642), one of the world's great scientists, developed the spirit of modern science by establishing a proper relationship between experiment and theory. He developed theories of motion involving the concepts of distance, velocity, and acceleration.

The Seventeenth Century

The pioneering spirit of the seventeenth century witnessed by the European colonization of territories all over the world was paralleled by the creativity of its mathematicians. New results were produced in a wide variety of subjects: algebra, number theory, analytic geometry, projective geometry, and the new theory of probability. In the foreground were the French mathematicians: Descartes, Fermat, Pascal, and Desargues. By "standing on the shoulders of these giants," mathematicians near the end of the seventeenth century envisioned one of the greatest triumphs of all. This was the calculus, discovered independently by Sir Isaac Newton (1643–1727) in England and by Gottfried Wilhelm Leibniz (1646–1716) in Germany.

René Descartes (1596–1650)

René Descartes was a frail child born to a French aristocratic family, from whom he inherited sufficient money to afford him a life of study and travel. He completed his schooling at the Jesuit College of La Fleche at the age of 16. A year later he went to Paris. Soon tiring of the social life, he returned to his studies and received a law degree in 1616. Desiring to know more of the world, he entered military service, first with the army of Prince Maurice of Orange and later with Maximilian I, Duke of Bavaria. Finally, in 1628, Descartes settled in Holland, where the climate for religious and civil freedom was unequaled anywhere in Europe.

Most of the published works of Descartes were written during his 21-year stay in Holland. After four years writing *Le Monde,* a physical account of the universe, he abandoned this work upon hearing of the condemnation of Galileo by the Church. Instead he devoted his efforts to a philosophical treatise on method in science, *Discours de la méthode pour bien conduire sa raison et chercher la vérité dans les sciences* (A Discourse on the Method of Rightly Conducting the Reason and Seeking Truth in the Sciences), published in 1637. Among the three appendices to this work was one entitled *La Géométrie.*

In *La Géométrie,* Descartes introduced a greatly improved symbolism for algebra, he made important contributions in the study of equations, and, what is most significant, he related the subjects of algebra and geometry by assigning two numbers, coordinates, to establish the position of a point on a plane. This invention of a coordinate system whereby equations can be pictured geometrically and geometric figures can be represented by number relations initiated a revolutionary change in the methods of mathematics and science. For this contribution, Descartes is honored by being called the founder of analytic geometry.

In 1649 Descartes accepted the offer of Queen Christina of Sweden to aid in the intellectual development of her country and to instruct her as well. For a man accustomed to rising at 11 A.M., the new routine of daily instruction at 5 A.M. and the severe winter climate proved to be too much. Four months after his arrival, he contracted pneumonia, and he died February 11, 1650.

Pierre de Fermat (1601–1665)

A humble and modest man, Pierre de Fermat was a lawyer by profession and a mathematician during his leisure time. Although he published little, he is regarded as one of the greatest French mathematicians of the seventeenth century. Most of his significant contributions are found in the marginal notes he wrote on books in his library and in the letters he wrote to other mathematicians.

Fermat is called the founder of the modern theory of numbers. With Pascal, he developed the foundations of the theory of probability, and by 1629 he had developed many of the basic ideas of analytic geometry.

Blaise Pascal (1623–1662)

Blaise Pascal, the son of the mathematician for whom the curve known as the *limaçon of Pascal* is named, exhibited his mathematical genius at an early age. He wrote a manuscript on conics at 16, and at 19 invented a computing machine, the forerunner of our modern calculators. His arrangement of the coefficients of the powers of a binomial is well known as *Pascal's triangle*. In addition to his work with Fermat on the theory of probability, he is noted for his geometrical discoveries.

Suffering from physical pain most of his life, he abandoned mathematics at the age of 25 to devote his life to religion and philosophy. On occasion he returned to mathematics, once in response to what he considered a divine omen when his toothache suddenly stopped as some geometrical ideas occurred to him. He died in Paris at the age of 39.

Gérard Desargues (1593–1662)

A self-educated engineer and architect, Gérard Desargues was the most original mathematician of the seventeenth century in the area of pure geometry. He is chiefly noted for his work on conics, which formed the basis for the modern theory of projective geometry.

Projective geometry and the concept of perspective had a great impact on the artists of the Renaissance by providing techniques for making a painting three-dimensional. By 1700, the laws of perspective had become so well mastered that artists deliberately carried this ability to extremes by painting amusing and distorted scenes.

Isaac Newton (1642–1727)

Sir Isaac Newton, one of the three greatest mathematicians of all times, was born on Christmas day in Woolsthorpe, England, in 1642, the year that Galileo died. His father, a farmer, died before he was born. According to Newton's own statement, he was not very attentive during the years of his early schooling and ranked among the lowest in his class. His mother withdrew him from school at the age of 14 to help her on the farm. Newton, however, preferred to spend his time reading books on mathematics and making mechanical models, such as a wooden water clock and a toy mouse-driven mill that ground wheat to flour.

Upon the advice of his uncle, Newton was entered at Trinity College, Cambridge, in 1661. Here the great mathematician Sir Issac

Barrow soon recognized the genius of his student, who, at the age of 23, had created his methods of fluxions, the techniques of differential calculus. The next two years Newton spent at his home, the university being closed due to the bubonic plague. During this time he continued work on his calculus, developed the basic principles of his theory of gravitation, and also began his optical researches.

In 1669 Newton began his 18 years as the Lucasian professor of mathematics at Cambridge, a position that Barrow resigned in his favor.

Newton's mathematical and scientific discoveries were well known for many years before they were published. His works on differential and integral calculus were written during the years 1666–1676, but one written in 1669 was published in 1711, and his *Method of Fluxions,* written in 1671, was not published until 1736, nine years after his death. His great work, the *Principia,* was published in 1687 only by the insistence of his friend, Edmund Halley, the English astronomer.

Newton's reluctance to publish seemed to be based on his great distaste for controversy. This was most unfortunate, because it had its consequences in the priority dispute with Leibniz concerning the discovery of the calculus. The priority dispute, in turn, was a major factor in retarding mathematical progress in England for almost 100 years.

In 1692 Newton suffered a nervous breakdown from which he took almost two years to recover. Afterward, he accepted an appointment as Warden of the Mint, and, three years later, in 1699, he became Master of the Mint. He remained in this position for over 30 years, devoting most of his leisure time to theological writings and problems in alchemy and chemistry, subjects that had always interested him. On occasion, he would return to mathematics.

After a prolonged illness, he died in 1727 at the age of 84 and was buried in Westminster Abbey. Voltaire attended the funeral, and afterward told with pride of the land he once had lived in where a professor of mathematics had been buried like a king only because he was great in his vocation.

Gottfried Wilhelm Leibniz (1646–1716)

Gottfried Wilhelm Leibniz, who also developed the calculus, independently of Newton, was born in Leipzig, Germany. Before he was 20, he had mastered most of the important works on mathematics. He began a diplomatic career in Nuremburg, and during his travels he became acquainted with many mathematicians in France, England, and Holland. From 1676 until his death, he enjoyed a life of luxury while in the service of the Duke of Brunswick at Hanover. His position afforded him a great deal of leisure time which he devoted to mathematics.

Leibniz envisioned a universal mathematics, a symbolic logic from which all of mathematics could be derived. He made many contributions to the subject of logic but his ideas were not immediately developed, and it is only recently that his goal has begun to be realized.

His differential and integral calculus were invented between 1673 and 1676, although he did not publish his results until 1684, having waited in vain for Newton to publish first. It was unfortunate that the last years of the lives of both men were saddened by the bitter priority dispute concerned with the invention of the calculus.

The followers of both men, motivated by national rivalry and political interests, fought the battle. Newton, although not politically active, was a member of the House of Lords and a Tory. Leibniz was highly active politically, being employed by the House of Hanover, who hoped to make political gains in England through the Whig party. The facts are that the basic discoveries in calculus, including the fundamental theorem of the calculus, can be found in the works of Isaac Barrow, with which both mathematicians were acquainted. Newton's discoveries were made before Leibniz began his investigations. Although Leibniz was familiar with the works of Newton, he did invent a far superior notation and he approached the subject from a completely different point of view. The only fair decision is to award each man the honor of independently developing the calculus.

Our modern notation is that created by Leibniz, the $\int$ symbol for integration and the dy/dx symbolism for the derivative in contrast to the dot, as in $\dot{x}$, used by Newton. It was over a hundred years before England abandoned the awkward notation of Newton, and finally the Analytical Society was formed at Cambridge to establish "the principles of pure d-ism (the notation of Leibniz) as opposed to the dot-age of the university (the notation of Newton)."

The Eighteenth Century

During the eighteenth century, mathematicians concentrated on the development and applications of the newly discovered calculus. A wealth of information was accumulated in this area as calculus proved to be an amazing and powerful tool with a wide range of practical interpretations.

Most mathematicians and scientists of this period were either supported by royalty or they were subsidized by membership in a learned Academy such as those at Paris, Berlin, and St. Petersburg. Their time was devoted to research, with university teaching only a minor part of their activity. The leading European rulers enjoyed having learned men at their courts. Not only were they aware of the importance of mathematics in increasing military efficiency and in improving manufacturing but also the presence of these learned men provided the rulers with a feeling of intellectual superiority.

The outstanding mathematicians of this century were the remarkable Bernoulli family of Switzerland, the great Leonhard Euler of Switzerland, and the "three L's" of France: Joseph Louis Lagrange, Pierre-Simon Laplace, and Adrien-Marie Legendre.

The Bernoulli Family

Among the first to realize the great power of the calculus were the two brothers, Jacob Bernoulli (1654–1705) and Johann Bernoulli (1667–1748). This remarkable Swiss family produced a total of nine eminent mathematicians. Jacob, the elder brother, abandoned theology, against his father's wishes, and later in 1687 became professor of mathematics at the University of Basel in Switzerland. He chose as his motto "Invito patre sidera verso" ("I study the stars against my father's will"), accompanied by a picture of Phaethon driving the chariot of the sun. Jacob analyzed many curves and, in imitation of Archimedes, directed that one of these curves, the logarithmic spiral, should be engraved on his tombstone with the words, "Eadem mutata resurgo" ("I shall arise the same, though changed").

The brothers, Johann and Jacob, although there was bitter resentment and ill-feeling between them, exchanged ideas with each other and also with Leibniz. Their combined results constitute much of the content of our elementary calculus texts. Johann, more prolific than his brother, was one of the most influential advocates of the calculus. The term "integral" is due to him and he was the first to use the imaginary unit $\sqrt{-1}$ in a practical way.

Johann's son Daniel (1700–1782) was the most outstanding of the descendants of the two brothers. Most of his works were devoted to science but he also made contributions in pure mathematics. Strangely enough, Johann also tried to force his son Daniel into a different vocation, that of a merchant, just as Johann's father had done to him.

The other sons of Johann were Nicolaus (1695–1726) and Johann II (1710–1790), both of whom originally studied law and later became professors of mathematics.

Other significant mathematicians of the Bernoulli family included Nicolaus Bernoulli (1687–1759), a nephew of Jacob and Johann; and Johann III (1744–1807), Daniel II (1751–1834), and Jacob II (1759–1789), sons of Johann II.

Leonhard Euler (1707–1783)

Leonhard Euler, born in Basel, Switzerland, brought this city to even greater distinction than did the Bernoullis. Euler, who studied under

Johann Bernoulli, was a most prolific writer, publishing during his lifetime over 600 original treatises and producing results in every field of mathematics that existed at his time. He is known as the founder of pure mathematical analysis.[1] His *Introductio* (1748) is considered to be the first text on analytic geometry, and his other great textbooks, *Institutiones calculi differentialis* (1755) and *Institutiones calculi integralis* (1768–1774), are essentially our elementary differential and integral calculus of today.

Euler's contemporary, the French scientist Arago, said "Euler calculated without effort, as men breathe or as eagles sustain themselves in the wind."

In 1725 Euler went to the Academy at St. Petersburg with Nicolaus Bernoulli, son of Johann, and remained there until 1741. Then he spent 25 years at the Berlin Academy with Frederick the Great as his patron. Finally, he returned to St. Petersburg in 1766 upon the invitation of Catherine the Great.

The English logician Augustus DeMorgan (1806–1871) related a much repeated story that is probably not true. Diderot, invited to the Russian Court by the Empress, conversed very freely on the subject of atheism. The Empress persuaded Euler to assist her in checking his antireligious views. Diderot was told that an eminent mathematician was capable of proving algebraically that God existed and Diderot consented to hear the proof. Euler advanced toward Diderot and in a serious, convincing tone, said: "Sir, $(a + b^n)/n = x$, thus God exists; reply!" Diderot, ignorant of algebra, was embarrassed and disconcerted as the laughter filled the room. He asked to return to France at once and permission was granted.

This anecdote, although widely quoted, is probably false. Diderot had written on evolutes and probability and *did* know mathematics. Moreover, the personalities of Diderot and Euler were such as to deny this behavior.

Most likely this story evolved from the controversies concerning Newton's theory of gravitation and the theory of Descartes. The Cartesian theory required the earth to be elongated at the poles while Newton's theory predicted it to be flattened. To test the theories, an expedition was sent to Peru in 1735 and one to Lapland in 1736–1737 under the direction of the scientist Pierre De Maupertuis. The results were a triumph for Newton and Maupertuis, who became president of the Berlin Academy under the patronage of Frederick the Great. However, in 1750 Maupertuis entered a controversy related to his investigations concerning a general unifying principle for the laws of the universe. Unfortunately, he included in his discussions a proof of the existence of God. He was so

---

[1] Analysis is the name given to that area of mathematics in which the methods of calculus are used.

ridiculed by Voltaire that even the support of the king and the defense of Euler could not raise his spirits, and he died soon afterward.

In addition to analysis, Euler wrote works on number theory, algebra, astronomy, mechanics, and music. When he lost his right eye in 1735 due to excessive work, he commented philosophically, "From now on, I shall have fewer distractions." He lost his other eye in 1766 but continued working without complaint until his death. Following a discussion on mathematics, he had dinner, a cup of tea, a pipe, and then in an instant he stopped calculating and living.

Joseph Louis Lagrange (1736–1813)

Lagrange and Euler were the two greatest mathematicians of the eighteenth century. Born in Turin, Italy, Lagrange was of French descent and a Parisian by choice. In 1766 he began his 20 years as mathematical director of the Berlin Academy, a post vacated by Euler. He accepted the invitation of Frederick the Great, who wrote Lagrange that "the greatest king in Europe" wanted "the greatest mathematician of Europe" at his court.

Upon the death of Frederick in 1787, the intellectual climate of Prussia became disagreeable to Lagrange and he accepted the invitation of Louis XVI to reside in Paris. Lagrange was made head of a commission to convert France to the metric system. Although Lagrange had been granted immunity from a decree to banish foreigners, he was so embittered by the death on the guillotine of Lavoisier and other scientists that he decided to leave France. However, the establishment of two new schools, the École Normal and the École Polytechnique, enticed him to remain.

The democratic ideas associated with the French Revolution entered the academic world. Lagrange was equal to the challenge to develop these new institutions of learning, which were later to become famous due to the high standards that he established.

The greatest contributions of Lagrange were concerned with the development of calculus, differential equations, and the calculus of variations.

Pierre-Simon Laplace (1749–1827)

Laplace was born in poverty but his mathematical ability earned him his education and good teaching positions. During the hectic days of the French Revolution, he sided with whatever political party was in power, to further his personal interests. Napoleon made him a count and minister of the interior in 1799. Later in 1817 he was made a marquis by Louis XVIII.

Laplace is most famous for his works on astronomy, celestial mechanics, probability, calculus, differential equations, and geodesy. The story is told that Napoleon chided Laplace because he did not mention God in his work on celestial mechanics. Laplace replied, "Sir, I did not need that hypothesis."

The American astronomer Nathaniel Bowditch (1773–1838) remarked, "I never come across one of Laplace's 'thus it plainly appears' without feeling sure that I have hours of hard work before me to fill up the chasm and find out and show how it plainly appears."

Adrien-Marie Legendre (1752–1833)

In elementary mathematics, Legendre is best known for his work on geometry, *Éléments de géométrie,* one of the best textbooks ever written and the prototype of that subsequently used in the secondary schools of England and America, replacing Euclid's *Elements.* Legendre rearranged and simplified the contents of Euclidean geometry without disturbing the logical foundations of the subject.

In higher mathematics, Legendre is known for his contributions to the theory of numbers, calculus, higher geometry, astronomy, and physics.

The Nineteenth and Twentieth Centuries

Stimulated by the French Revolution near the end of the eighteenth century, the new democratic way of life had its impact on both the social and the scientific worlds. As the Industrial Revolution spread from England to the continent of Europe, schools and universities were revised and modernized in response to the increased interest in scientific and technical education. The royal courts and academies declined as the centers of learning. Scientific Latin was gradually replaced by the national languages, and the universities and technical schools included in their responsibilities both research and instruction.

The greatest mathematical progress was made in France and later in Germany, where the political and economic changes were the most dramatic. Although England was at the heart of the Industrial Revolution, for around 100 years her mathematical contributions were minimal, probably due to a slavish devotion to the awkward notation introduced by Newton and a refusal to accept the works of Leibniz.

There was a pessimistic feeling at this time among some of the leading mathematicians that everything significant in mathematics had been discovered. Astronomy and mechanics had long been the motivating forces beginning with the ancient Babylonians and now apparently ending with the works of Euler and Laplace.

How wrong this attitude was soon became evident. As the old ways of thought were severely criticized and carefully scrutinized, a vast new world of mathematics was revealed.

Blazening the paths of modern mathematics with his startling discoveries stood the towering genius of Carl Friedrich Gauss (1777–1855), "Prince of Mathematicians." Born in Brunswick, Germany, the son of a day laborer, Gauss rose from this humble birth to a position of the highest eminence, being ranked with Archimedes and Newton as one of the three greatest mathematicians of all times.

The genius of Gauss was evident before he was three years old, when he discovered an error in his father's weekly payroll calculations. All his life he was noted for his ability to perform involved mental calculations. The Duke of Brunswick subsidized his education, and, from 1807 until his death, he worked quietly as professor of mathematics and director of the observatory at the University of Göttingen.

The publications of Gauss do not reveal the extent of his greatness. Many of his original contributions lay unpublished in his notes and diaries. His great work *Disquisitiones arithmeticae* is considered as fundamental in modern number theory. He is also noted for his work in astronomy, geodesy (determination of the curvature, shape, and dimensions of the earth), differential geometry, non-Euclidean geometry, differential equations, the hypergeometric series by which logarithmic, trigonometric, and other functions can be calculated and tabulated, the method of least squares, the beginnings of potential theory, complex numbers and the beginning of analytic functions of a complex variable, and electromagnetism. Among other inventions, Gauss in 1833 invented the electric telegraph. He had the foresight to predict that *analysis situs* (topology) would become an important area of study in the future.

It has been estimated that the mathematics created during the nineteenth century is from three to four times as much as all the mathematics up to the end of the eighteenth century. And the twentieth century so far has been even more prolific than the nineteenth.

With the appearance of contradictions and absurdities in the amazingly successful new subject of calculus, mathematicians of the nineteenth century began to devote their attention to establishing a rigorous logical foundation for analysis. The most significant contributions in this area were made by the French mathematician Augustin-Louis Cauchy (1789–1857) with his theory of limits in 1821 and the German mathematician Karl Weierstrass (1815–1864) with his work on the *arith-*

metization of analysis, which demonstrates that all of analysis can be derived logically from the properties of the set of real numbers.

Events of major importance occurred in geometry and algebra as well as in analysis. Gauss was the first to investigate the logical foundations of the geometry of Euclid. This led to the creation of non-Euclidean geometries with the works in 1829–1830 of the Russian Nicolai Ivanovitch Lobachevsky (1793–1856) and that in 1832 of the Hungarian Janos Bolyai (1802–1860), who constructed *hyperbolic* geometries assuming that there was *more* than one line through a point parallel to a given line. The German mathematician Bernhard Riemann (1826–1866) generalized these theories in 1854 and developed another type of non-Euclidean geometry, called *elliptic,* by assuming there was *no* line through a point parallel to a given line.

Algebra, at the beginning of the nineteenth century, was considered to be a generalization of arithmetic. The structure of this algebra was discovered as the commutative, associative, distributive, and other properties were revealed. Just as Euclidean geometry had been considered to be *the* geometry for many years, so was the algebra of arithmetic considered *the* algebra. However, in likeness to the development of non-Euclidean geometries, the doors to modern abstract algebra were thrust open with the discovery of a noncommutative algebra in 1843 by the Irish mathematician William Rowan Hamilton (1805–1865). His algebra of quaternions can be applied in the physical world to the rotations of an object in three-dimensional space. Later, in 1857, the English mathematician Arthur Cayley (1821–1895) developed the algebra of matrices, another noncommutative algebra. Following this came the nonassociative Jordan and Lie algebras, named after the Norwegian mathematician Sophus Lie (1842–1899) and the French mathematician Camille Jordan (1838–1922). Today in the twentieth century, abstract algebra is a major area of research, exhibiting the processes of generalization and abstraction which characterize modern mathematics.

Toward the end of the nineteenth century so much new mathematics was being created that the mathematicians became "specialists," such as algebraists, geometers, analysts, and logicians, in contrast to the "universal" mathematicians of previous days. It was also during this time that mathematicians became classified as "pure" and "applied."

Pure mathematics refers to the totality of *abstract* mathematical systems in the mathematical world while **applied mathematics** refers to the totality of *concrete* interpretations of these systems in the real world. There is no sharp line of demarcation between these two areas; usually one stimulates and motivates the other.

In fact, the essence of mathematical creativity lies in a constant exchange of ideas between pure and applied mathematics: the processes of generalization, abstraction, and logical deduction working with those of specialization, interpretation, and imagination. Moreover, the terms "abstract" and "concrete" must be considered as dynamic and not stable in meaning. A well-known mathematical system may be considered as "concrete" and then "abstracted," thus creating a new system.

Deriving conclusions from assumptions using the methods of logic is the essential feature of a mathematical system. Now logic, itself, is being examined as a mathematical system. The investigations into the foundations of calculus and geometry established the real number system as the basis for almost all of existing mathematics. In the late-nineteenth century it was shown that the real number system can be derived from the set of natural numbers, through the works of the Germans Richard Dedekind (1831–1916) and Georg Cantor (1845–1918) and the Italian Giuseppi Peano (1858–1932).

During the years 1910–1913 Whitehead and Russell devoted their energies to the derivation of the natural number system from the principles of set theory and logic. It seemed as if the goal of Leibniz had been realized until Goedel's proof in 1932 established that it is impossible to derive all the theorems about the natural numbers from a finite set of assumptions that are free of contradiction.

The discovery of paradoxes in set theory has caused a crisis in the foundations of mathematics, because most of mathematics has been shown to depend on set theory. Today mathematicians are attempting to resolve this crisis.

Twentieth-century research continues in the subject of logic and in many other areas as well. The real world continues to provide motivation for creativity. Nuclear power, electronic computers, business, economics, politics, psychology, and biology are some of the sources that present problems. Hopefully, after generalization and abstraction, these problems may be solved in the mathematical world.

Topology, probability, control theory, the theory of games and economic behavior, and numerical analysis are some of the active areas of mathematical research responding to the needs of today and tomorrow. Man continues to probe for a better understanding of himself and his universe.

REFERENCES FOR HINDU-ARABIC—EUROPEAN PERIOD

Cajori, *A History of Mathematics,* pp. 83–129.

Eves, *An Introduction to the History of Mathematics,* pp. 181–238 and 241–379.

Midonick, *The Treasury of Mathematics*:
  "Arybhata," pp. 37–44.
  "The Bakhshali Manuscript," pp. 91–105.
  "Isaac Barrow," pp. 106–115.
  "Bhascara," pp. 116–140.
  "Brahmagupta," pp. 166–180.
  "Georg Cantor," pp. 181–195.
  "Arthur Cayley," pp. 196–211.
  "René Descartes," pp. 289–308.
  "Gottlob Frege," pp. 361–379.
  "Carl Freidrich Gauss," 380–405.
  "Al-Khowarizmi," pp. 418–434.
  "Gottfried Wilhelm Leibniz," pp. 435–456.
  "Sir Isaac Newton," pp. 540–564.
  "Omar Khayyam," pp. 583–598.
  "Robert Recorde," pp. 689–704.
  "Simon Stevin," pp. 733–750.
Newman, *The World of Mathematics*, Vol. 1:
  "Robert Recorde," pp. 210–217.
  "René Descartes," pp. 235–253.
  "Isaac Newton," pp. 254–285.
  "Carl Freidrich Gauss," pp. 380–405.

Smith, *History of Mathematics*, Vol. I, pp. 148–546; Vol. II, pp. 1–269, 378–417.

Struik, *A Concise History of Mathematics*, pp. 83–285.

CHAPTER X

The Development of Arithmetic

This boke is called the boke of algorym or Augrym
after lewder use. And this boke tretys the Craft
of Nombrying, the quych craft is also called
Algorym. Ther was a kyng of Inde the quich heyth
Algor, & he made this craft. And aft his name he
called hit algory.

Craft of Nombrying (ca. 1300), now in the
British Museum (one of the earliest mathematical
manuscripts in English)

Some call it Arsemetrick, and some Augrime . . . Both
names are corruptly written: Arsemetrick for
Arithmetick, as the Greeks call it, and Augrime
for Algorisme, as the Arabians found it: which
both betoken the Science of Numbring: for
Arithmos in Greek is called Number: and of it
commeth Arithmetick, the Art of Numbering. So
that Arithmetick is a Science or Art teaching the
manner and use of Numbring: This Art may be
wrought diversly, with Pen or with Counters.

Declaration of the Profit of Arithmeticke, Robert
Recorde (1540)

Mathematics is the Queen of the Sciences and
Arithmetic the Queen of Mathematics.

Carl Friedrich Gauss

It was not until 1600 that our modern Hindu-Arabic decimal system of
numeration became generally accepted as the standard system for computations, replacing the use of Roman numerals.

Although the Hindu numerals appeared earlier, their first systematic
use was in the twelfth century with the Latin translation of al-Khowarizmi's arithmetic. During the next 400 years the Abacists (proponents of
the Roman numerals) battled the Algorists (proponents of the Hindu-
Arabic numerals). This was not simply a struggle over expressing numbers in a simple grouping system as opposed to a positional system but

[211]

it was also a matter of two very different types of computational techniques, or arithmetics.

Around 1100 the general public used Roman numerals and an abacus. Businessmen sat before a line abacus or counting table or "counter" (from which we obtain our present word *counter* as used in stores). Lines were ruled on the table to indicate the powers of 10 and loose counters were placed on these lines or between them and then moved as the calculations were performed. Below 867¢, or $8.67, is represented by these counters.

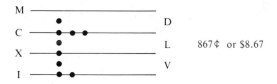

In contrast to the method of the abacist, the Hindus wrote with a pen dipped in white paint upon a small blackboard or with a stick upon a white tablet sprinkled with red flour or with a stick upon sand. Instead of moving counters, they calculated by writing and erasing, using certain rules called **algorithms.** (Algorithmi was a Latin form of al-Khowarizmi.)

At first the public strongly opposed the use of Hindu-Arabic numerals. The symbols were objected to as making commercial accounts difficult to read and easy to forge. In 1299 a law was passed in Florence, Italy, forbidding the use of Arabic numerals, as they were then called.

With the revival of scientific interest during the next 200 years, with the introduction of writing paper during the fourteenth century, and with the standardization of the Hindu numerals after the invention of the printing press in 1438, as writing paper became more and more common, the Algorists finally won the battle from the Abacists around 1500.

By 1600 about 300 arithmetic textbooks had been printed. By 1700 the abacus was rarely seen in western Europe.

This new arithmetic was not just a triumph of pen and paper over the abacus and counters but a triumph of the more adaptable methods (algorithms) of a well-developed ciphered positional numerical system with zero over a simple grouping system. Not only were the methods of numeration (writing numbers) different but the calculation processes were also different.

1. COMPUTATIONS BY ABACUS

The abacus methods, or methods of calculating using a simple grouping numeral system, have already been explained in Chapter 5. Here the computations are briefly illustrated using Roman numerals with the reminder that the only memory work involved are the exchanges; V for IIIII, X for VV, L for XXXXX, and so on.

Addition and Subtraction

EXAMPLE 1. Add:

$$\begin{array}{r} DCXXXVII \\ \underline{CLXVIIII} \\ DCCLXXXXVVIIIIII \rightarrow DCCLLVI \rightarrow DCCCVI \end{array}$$

EXAMPLE 2. Subtract:

DCXXXVII		CCCCC LL XX VV IIIII II	
CLXVIIII	→	C L X V IIII	
CLXVIIII		CCCC L X V	I II or CCCCLXVIII

Duplation and Mediation. Duplation was the Egyptian multiplication process, which can best be thought of as doubling and adding.

EXAMPLE. Multiply LIII by XVIII using duplation:

$$\begin{array}{cl} I & LIII \\ \diagdown II & CVI \diagup \\ IIII & CCXII \\ VIII & CCCCXXIIII \\ \diagdown XVI & DCCCXXXXVIII \diagup \\ \hline XVIII & DCCCCLIIII \end{array}$$

Early arithmetic texts also discuss the operation of mediation, which involves a halving process.

EXAMPLE. Multiply LIII by XVIII by duplation and mediation:

Halve on this side
Discard remainders
Check odd numbers

$$\begin{array}{cl} XVIII & LIII \\ \diagdown VIIII & CVI \diagup \text{Double on this side} \\ IIII & CCXII \\ II & CCCCXXIIII \\ \diagdown I & DCCCXXXXVIII \diagup \\ \hline & DCCCCLIIII \end{array}$$

2. COMPUTATIONS BY ALGORITHMS

2:1 Addition (The Union of Disjoint Sets)

Definition: *The **sum** of two numbers that are the numbers of disjoint sets is the number of the union of the sets.*

If $A \cap B = \varnothing$, then $n(A) + n(B) = n(A \cup B)$. Recall that disjoint sets are those whose intersection is empty.

Suppose we let set A be a set of 4 objects and set B be a set of 3 other objects.

$$A = \left(\square\ \bigcirc\ \triangle\ \hexagon \right) \quad \text{and} \quad B = \left(\star\ \clubsuit\ \rightleftharpoons \right)$$

Then the number of set A is $n(A) = 4$, and the number of set B is $n(B) = 3$. The union of sets A and B is

$$A \cup B = \left(\begin{array}{c} \square\ \bigcirc\ \triangle\ \hexagon \\ \star\ \clubsuit\ \rightleftharpoons \end{array} \right)$$

and $n(A \cup B) = 7$.

Thus our definition states that $4 + 3 = n(A \cup B) = 7$.

Terms.   The numbers that are added are called **addends,** and the result is the **sum.**

With this definition of addition we can establish some important properties of the addition operation, with respect to the set of natural numbers and zero, the number of the empty set. Let $U = \{0, 1, 2, 3, 4, \cdots\}$.

Closure.   If $a \in U$ and $b \in U$, then $a + b \in U$. The sum of any two numbers in U is again a number in U.

Commutativity.   If $a \in U$ and $b \in U$, then $a + b = b + a$.

EXAMPLE. $4 + 3 = 3 + 4$. Since $A \cup B = B \cup A$, it is clear that $n(A \cup B) = n(B \cup A)$.

Thus the *order* of adding two numbers does not change the sum.

Associativity.   If $a \in U$, $b \in U$, and $c \in U$, then $(a+b)+c = a+(b+c)$.

EXAMPLE

$$(3 + 4) + 2 = 7 + 2 = 9$$
$$3 + (4 + 2) = 3 + 6 = 9$$

Thus $(3 + 4) + 2 = 3 + (4 + 2)$. In other words, the result of adding is unchanged whether 4 is associated with 3 or with 2.

Since we know that $(A \cup B) \cup C = A \cup (B \cup C)$, or the manner of grouping sets when uniting them does not affect the result, thus

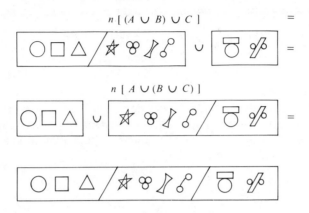

The following sections describe different algorithms for addition which eventually evolved into our present method.

Bhaskara's Method. In a commentary on Bhaskara's *Lilavati* is found the method used below for the sum of 278 and 356.[1]

Sum of the units	$8 + 6 = 14$
Sum of the tens	$7 + 5 = 12 \cdot$
Sum of the hundreds	$3 + 2 = \underline{5 \cdot \cdot}$
Sum of the sums	634

The Hindu-Scratch Method. The Hindus probably began their addition at the right with the units' column and wrote the sum at the bottom as we do. However, with Arabic and European influences a method developed where the calculation proceeded from left to right and the sum was written at the top as illustrated below.

$$
\begin{array}{c}
63 \\
5\!\!\!\diagup 2 4 \\
2\!\!\!\diagup 7\!\!\!\diagup 8 \\
3\!\!\!\diagup 5\!\!\!\diagup 6
\end{array}
$$

$$
\text{Add} \quad
\begin{array}{c}
 \\
5 \\
278 \\
356
\end{array}
\rightarrow
\begin{array}{c}
6 \\
52 \\
278 \\
356
\end{array}
\rightarrow
\begin{array}{c}
63 \\
524 \\
278 \\
356
\end{array}
$$

---

[1] The Hindus used the dot, $\cdot$, as the symbol for zero.

Before the use of pen and paper, when this sum was done on the "dust" boards, the digits were erased as they were used instead of being scratched out. Successive phases of the above problem would then be

$$
\begin{array}{c} 278 \\ 356 \end{array} \rightarrow
\begin{array}{c} 578 \\ 56 \end{array} \rightarrow
\begin{array}{c} 628 \\ 6 \end{array} \rightarrow
\begin{array}{c} 634 \\ \end{array}
$$

This left to right process required more writing than our familar right to left one and gradually it was replaced by our present method, where the sum is written at the bottom after the addition is performed from right to left, with the "carry" numbers either written at the top or "kept in mind" without being written.

$$
\begin{array}{ccc}
11 & & \\
278 & \text{or} & 278 \\
\underline{356} & & \underline{356} \\
634 & & 634
\end{array}
$$

Importance of Positional Notation.   It will be noted from the above that many algorithms or processes of addition are possible. It should be especially noticed that all the above procedures depend on the fact that we are using a *positional* numeral system.

The principle of place value is used when the numbers to be added are arranged in columns with the units under the units, the tens under the tens, the hundreds under the hundreds, and so on. The "carry" or "keep in mind" process is also an application of the principle of place value.

With the exception of the use of the facts memorized from the addition table, the algorithms above can be used with *any* positional system and *any* base.

Checking.   The commutative and associative properties provide useful checks of addition problems.

For example, if we begin by adding downward from top to bottom

$$
\begin{array}{l}
①② \\
278 \\
356 \\
\underline{409} \\
1043
\end{array}
\qquad
\begin{array}{l}
(8+6)+9 = 23 \\
(7+5)+0 = 12 \quad \text{and} \quad 12+2 = 14 \\
(2+3)+4 = 9 \quad \text{and} \quad 9+1 = 10
\end{array}
$$

we can check with our associative law by adding upward from bottom to top.

$$
\begin{array}{l}
278 \\
356 \\
409 \\
\textcircled{12} \\
\hline
1043
\end{array}
\quad
\begin{array}{ll}
8 + (6 + 9) = 23 \\
7 + (5 + 0) = 12 \quad \text{and} \quad 12 + 2 = 14 \\
2 + (3 + 4) = 9 \quad \text{and} \quad 9 + 1 = 10
\end{array}
$$

Our commutative law gives us the right to rearrange the order of the addends and we could also check our results by changing the order as follows.

$$
\begin{array}{cc}
278 & 356 \\
356 & 278 \\
\underline{409} & \underline{409} \\
 & 1043
\end{array}
$$

Since $278 + 356 = 356 + 278$, we have

$$(278 + 356) + 409 = (356 + 278) + 409$$

2:2 Subtraction (The Inverse of Addition)

Definition: *The* **difference** *between two numbers a and b, a − b, is defined to be that unique number, d, if it exists, so that a = b + d. Thus* $a - b = d$ *if and only if* $a = b + d$*. For example,* $7 - 3 = 4$ *because* $7 = 3 + 4$.

Terms. Many words have been used to describe the numbers involved in the subtraction operation. The result, d, is called both the **difference** and the **remainder** in school. In everyday situations we also find the words "rest" ("Deduct what I owe and pay me the rest"), "excess," and "balance."

The technical terms "minuend" and "subtrahend" have been more commonly referred to as the "higher" and the "lower" numbers, respectively, and also as the "upper" and the "under" numbers.

Methods. There are several methods in existence today for the subtraction operation. None seems to be particularly superior to any other and thus the process of subtraction is not standardized. Two of the most popular methods are the decomposition, or borrow, method and the equal additions, or carry, method.

Decomposition or borrow (from the *upper* number)

Subtract   73   73
            48   48   ↓

Step 1. Decompose the seven 10s into six 10s and ten   6   13
1s. Combine the ten 1s with the three 1s to make   4   8
thirteen 1s.   ↓
Step 2. Use the facts from the addition table.   6   13
    $8 + 5 = 13$ and $4 + 2 = 6$ 4   8
    Thus $13 - 8 = 5$ and $6 - 4 = 2$.   2   5
In shortened form, this would be written

6
$\not{7}3$
48
25

Equal additions or carry (to the *lower* number)

Step 1. Add ten 1s to the three 1s to make thirteen 1s. ⎫ The equal
Step 2. Add one 10 to the four 10s to make five 10s. ⎬ additions.
Step 3. Use the facts from the addition table, $8 + 5 = 13$ and $5 + 2 = 7$.
    Thus $13 - 8 = 5$ and $7 - 5 = 2$.

73   7   13   7   13
48   →   5   8   →   5   8
                       2   5

This last method is based on the fact that addition and subtraction
are inverse operations. Thus if we add 10 and then subtract 10 from a
number, we end up with the number with which we started.

$$(N + 10) - 10 = N   \text{ or }   (5 + 10) - 10 = 15 - 10 = 5$$

Adding 10 to the lower number or subtrahend is the same as subtracting 10 from the upper number or minuend. Thus when we add 10 to
the minuend and add 10 to the subtrahend, the equal additions, we do
not change the result.

Checking. Subtraction problems are best checked by using the inverse
property or the addition operation. The difference is added to the subtrahend and if the result is the minuend, then the subtraction problem
was done correctly.

EXAMPLE. Subtract

$$73$$
$$\underline{48}$$
$$25$$

Check by adding

$$48$$
$$\underline{25}$$
$$73$$

2:3 Multiplication (The Cartesian Product of Two Sets)

Multiplication, literally "a folding together of many," was first introduced as the repeated addition of equal counting numbers. For example, 3×4 was defined as $4 + 4 + 4$, or the sum of 3 fours.

When thought of in this way, the commutative property of multiplication, $3 \times 4 = 4 \times 3$, does not seem especially obvious.

Since $3 \times 4 = 4 + 4 + 4$ and $4 \times 3 = 3 + 3 + 3 + 3$, why should $4 + 4 + 4 = 3 + 3 + 3 + 3$? (If this does seem obvious, then so should $4 \times 4 \times 4 = 3 \times 3 \times 3 \times 3$. But $4 \times 4 \times 4 = 64$ and $3 \times 3 \times 3 \times 3 = 81$, and 64 does *not* equal 81.)

In fact, when the sums are arranged vertically instead of horizontally,

$$
\begin{array}{cc}
4 & 3 \\
4 & 3 \\
4 & 3 \\
  & 3
\end{array}
$$

the relationship seems even less apparent. However, both of the above sums *do* produce the same result, 12.

$$12 = 4 + 4 + 4 = 3 + 3 + 3 + 3 = 12$$

or

$$3 \times 4 = 4 \times 3$$

If we exhibit the number 12 as a rectangular array of 3 rows and 4 columns, we can gain insight into the nature of the multiplication operation and at the same time we can develop a set definition of multiplication from which we can easily establish the commutative and associative properties.

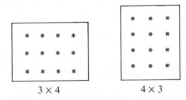

$$3 \times 4 \qquad\qquad 4 \times 3$$

We see from these arrays that the total number of ✱s in the 3 × 4 array is the same as that in the 4 × 3 array. The Greeks developed the idea of a geometric representation of number and we see how useful and revealing it is.

Now let us name each position in an array in the following manner.

ax	*ay*	*az*	*aw*	
bx	*by*	*bz*	*bw*	$A \times B$
cx	*cy*	*cz*	*cw*	

If we consider two sets, $A = \{a, b, c\}$ and $B = \{x, y, z, w\}$, and the set of all ordered pairs, $A \times B$ (read "A cross B"), obtained by taking first an element of A and then an element of B, then it is clear that the number of elements in $A \times B$, called the **Cartesian product** of A and B, is what we want the product of $n(A)$ and $n(B)$ to be.

Definition: *The **product** of two numbers that are the numbers of two sets is the number of the Cartesian product of these two sets:*

$$n(A) \times n(B) = n(A \times B)$$

Terms. The numbers that are being multiplied are called **factors,** although some books also refer to these numbers as the multiplicand and the multiplier. The result of multiplication is called the **product.**

With this definition of multiplication we can establish some properties of the multiplication operation with respect to the set of natural numbers, $N = \{1, 2, 3, 4, \cdots\}$.

Closure. If $a \in N$ and $b \in N$, then the product $ab \in N$. The product of any two natural numbers is again a natural number.

Commutativity. If $a \in N$ and $b \in N$, then $ab = ba$. For example, $3 \times 4 = 4 \times 3$.

The diagram below suggests that $n(A \times B) = n(B \times A)$. Thus $n(A) \times n(B) = n(B) \times n(A)$ or $ab = ba$.

ax	*ay*	*az*	*aw*		*xa*	*xb*	*xc*
bx	*by*	*bz*	*bw*		*ya*	*yb*	*yc*
cx	*cy*	*cz*	*cw*		*za*	*ab*	*zc*
					wa	*wb*	*wc*

$$A \times B \qquad\qquad B \times A$$

Associativity. If $a \in N$, $b \in N$, and $c \in N$, then $(ab)c = a(bc)$. This follows immediately from $(A \times B) \times C = A \times (B \times C)$, since the set of triples (a, b, c) would be the same no matter what grouping was used in forming them. Figure 10.1 illustrates the associative property of multiplication.

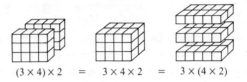

$$(3 \times 4) \times 2 \quad = \quad 3 \times 4 \times 2 \quad = \quad 3 \times (4 \times 2)$$

Figure 10.1

Distributive property. Multiplication is distributive over addition. If $a \in N$, $b \in N$, and $c \in N$, then $a(b + c) = ab + ac$. For example, $3(2 + 5) = 3 \cdot 2 + 3 \cdot 5$ since $21 = 3 \cdot 7 = 6 + 15 = 21$. To prove this property we need to show that

$$n(A \times (B \cup C)) = n(A \times B) + n(A \times C)$$

or

$$A \times (B \cup C) = (A \times B) \cup (A \times C).$$

The general proof is suggested by the diagram below, which illustrates the special case above.

	2		5				
	ax	ay	$a1$	$a2$	$a3$	$a4$	$a5$
3	bx	by	$b1$	$b2$	$b3$	$b4$	$b5$
	cx	cy	$c1$	$c2$	$c3$	$c4$	$c5$

$$A \times B \qquad\qquad A \times C$$

$$A \times (B \cup C) = (A \times B) \cup (A \times C)$$

In the figure above, $A = \{a, b, c\}$, $B = \{x, y\}$, and $C = \{1, 2, 3, 4, 5\}$, so that $n(A) = 3$, $n(B) = 2$, and $n(C) = 5$. Then

$$A \times B = \begin{Bmatrix} ax,\ ay \\ bx,\ by \\ cx,\ xy \end{Bmatrix} \quad \text{and} \quad A \times C = \begin{Bmatrix} a1, a2, a3, a4, a5 \\ b1, b2, b3, b4, b5 \\ c1, c2, c3, c4, c5 \end{Bmatrix}$$

$$B \cup C = \{x, y,\ 1, 2, 3, 4, 5\}$$

Thus

$$A \times (B \cup C) = \begin{Bmatrix} ax,\ ay,\ a1, a2, a3, a4, a5 \\ bx,\ by,\ b1, b2, b3, b4, b5 \\ cx,\ xy,\ c1, c2, c3, c4, c5 \end{Bmatrix} = (A \times B) \cup (A \times C)$$

At the time of the printing of the first mathematical books in Europe,[2] Luca Pacioli in his *Summa de Arithmetica* of 1494 lists eight different methods of multiplication. We shall consider some of these early methods, in order to afford us an understanding of how the principles of positional notation are involved and how our present method was finally established.

The Hindu-Scratch Method. In the scratch method the order of the work is from left to right with the final answer appearing at the top of the work. Whereas the Hindu erased his figures as he used them, the European scratched them out. The example below shows the successive stages in the multiplication of 54 by 37.

Step 1. 30 × 50 = 1500. Record 15.

Step 2. 30 × 4 = 120 and 1500 + 120 = 1620. Record 62.

Step 3. Shift 54 for the multiplication by 7. 7 × 50 = 350 and 1620 + 350 = 1970. Record 97.

Step 4. 7 × 4 = 28 and 1970 + 28 = 1998. Record 98. Result is 1998.

The Gelosia (or Grating or Lattice) Method. This method is very old and was a favorite for generations. It most likely developed in India because it appears in a commentary on Bhaskara's *Lilavati*. It also appears in other Hindu works, from which it passed to China, Arabia, and later to Italy.

Pacioli states: "The sixth method of multiplying is called *gelosia* or *graticola* . . . because the arrangement of the work resembles a lattice or gelosia. By gelosia we understand the grating which it is the custom to place at the windows of houses where ladies or nuns reside, so they cannot easily be seen. Many such abound in the noble city of Venice."

The "grating" is a rectangle ruled into cells by vertical, horizontal, and diagonal lines. The number to be multiplied is written across the top and the multiplier down the right side. The products of the digits are writ-

---

[2] The first was a commercial arithmetic, *Treviso*, 1478.

ten in their appropriate cells and then these partial products are added diagonally from right to left. The example below illustrates the multiplication of 54 by 37.

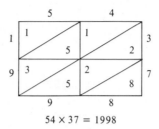

$$54 \times 37 = 1998$$

This method is easy and rapid after the grating is drawn. The time consumed in drawing the grating is a disadvantage that probably prevented this method from becoming our present one.

The Scacchero (Chessboard) Method. This is the forerunner of our present method of multiplying. The Venetians called this method "per scachieri" because it looked like a chessboard to them, while the Florentines called it "per bericuocolo" because to them it resembled the cakes of this name that were sold in the fairs of Tuscany. In Verona it was called "per organetta" because the lines looked like those of a pipe organ and others called it "a scaletta" because of the "little stairs" in the figure.

The example below illustrates the multiplication of 54 by 37.

```
        5  4
        3  7
     ┌──┬──┬──┐
     │ 3│ 7│ 8│
  ┌──┼──┼──┼──┘
  │ 1│ 6│ 2│
  └──┴──┴──┘
  1  9  9  8
```

Historical Examples. The product of 9876 and 6789 from Pacioli's book.

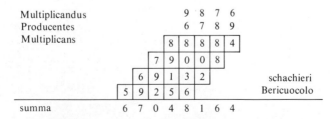

Figure 10.2

The Treviso arithmetic (1478) does not mark off the squares, but uses the name scacchero and sometimes places the multiplier at the right, as illustrated below.

```
          9 3 4
        ─────────
        3 7 3 6 ╱ 4
          9 3 4 ╱ 1        934 × 314 = 293,276
      2 8 0 2 ╱ 3
      ─────────────
      2 9 3 2 7 6
```

Figure 10.3

Checking. The best check of multiplication is obtained by using the commutative property, $ab = ba$.

EXAMPLE. Multiply 54 by 37 and check.

Solution. Since $54 \times 37 = 37 \times 54$ by the commutative property, the multiplication and check would be done as follows.

Multiplication	*Check*
54	37
37	54
378	148
162	185
1998	1998

Importance of Positional Notation. It should be observed that in all the different methods of multiplication, the principles of the positional system of numeration require a careful arrangement of the partial products which are added to obtain the final product. When the places are preserved by "shifting," as in our modern method, it is not necessary to write the zeros involved at the end of numerals.

If the above problem were written with every partial product written in full, the multiplication would appear as follows.

	54
	37
	28
Partial	350
products	120
	1500
Sum of partial products	1998

See Table 10.1.

TABLE 10.1 JUSTIFICATION OF THE MULTIPLICATION ALGORITHM FOR THE PRODUCT 54×7

1. $54 \times 7 = (5 \cdot 10 + 4) \times 7$		1. Positional principle
2. $\quad\quad = (5 \cdot 10 \times 7) + (4 \cdot 7)$		2. Distributive property
3. $\quad\quad = (5 \times 10 \cdot 7) + (4 \cdot 7)$		3. Associative property for multiplication
4. $\quad\quad = (5 \times 7 \cdot 10) + (4 \cdot 7)$		4. Commutative property for multiplication
5. $\quad\quad = (5 \cdot 7 \times 10) + (4 \cdot 7)$		5. Associative property for multiplication
6. $\quad\quad = (35 \times 10) + 28$		6. Multiplication facts
7. $\quad\quad = 350 + 28$		7. Positional principle
8. $\quad\quad = (3 \cdot 100 + 5 \cdot 10) + (2 \cdot 10 + 8)$		8. Positional principle
9. $\quad\quad = 3 \cdot 100 + (5 \cdot 10 + 2 \cdot 10) + 8$		9. Associative property of addition
10. $\quad\quad = 3 \cdot 100 + (5 + 2) \cdot 10 + 8$		10. Distributive property
11. $\quad\quad = 3 \cdot 100 + 7 \cdot 10 + 8$		11. Addition fact
12. $\quad\quad = 378$		12. Positional principle

2:4 Division (The Inverse of Multiplication)

Definition: *The* **quotient** *of two numbers a and b, a/b, is defined to be that unique number q, if it exists, so that* $a = b \times q$.

Thus $\dfrac{a}{b} = q$ if and only if $a = bq$.

For example, $\dfrac{12}{4} = 3$ because $12 = 3 \times 4$.

The division of a by b is also written symbolically as $a \div b$.

Terms. The number to be divided is called the **dividend,** the dividing number is called the **divisor,** and the result is called the **quotient.**

Thus in the division problem $\dfrac{12}{4} = 3$, 12 is the dividend, 4 is the divisor, and 3 is the quotient.

When the result of dividing one natural number by another is *not* a natural number, then the **difference** obtained by subtracting the product of the partial integral quotient and the divisor from the dividend is called the **remainder.**

For example, in the division problem $\dfrac{23}{4} = 5 + \dfrac{3}{4}$, or, as it is also written,

$$\begin{array}{r} 5 \\ 4\overline{)23} \\ 20 \\ \hline 3 \end{array}$$

the number 3 is the remainder, and the number $5\frac{3}{4}$ is the quotient.

The Repeated Subtraction Method.   This method reflects the fact that the division operation is the inverse of multiplication. Since multiplication can be thought of as the *sum* of equal addends, division can be considered as the *subtraction* of equal amounts.

This method is the one that is used with most machines, from the abacus to the electronic calculator.

EXAMPLE. Divide 468 by 78.

Solution. Subtract 78 repeatedly from 468 until no remainder or a remainder less than 78 is obtained. Record the number of subtractions.

$$
\begin{array}{rl}
468 & \\
\underline{78} & \quad 1 \\
390 & \\
\underline{78} & \quad 2 \\
312 & \\
\underline{78} & \quad 3 \\
234 & \\
\underline{78} & \quad 4 \\
156 & \\
\underline{78} & \quad 5 \\
78 & \\
\underline{78} & \quad 6 \\
\end{array}
$$

Since six subtractions were made, $\dfrac{468}{78} = 6$.

This method is very rapid on a machine with the number of subtractions being automatically recorded. However, it is rather laborious using paper and pen or pencil.

The Galley (or Batello or Scratch) Method.   This method was the favorite before 1600. It is probably of Hindu origin and was used by the Arabs from the time of al-Khowarizmi. It was called the "galley" method because the completed work suggested the form of a ship or boat. Tartaglia writes that the teachers of Venice required their students to embellish their finished problem with flags, masts, and other such figures.

The successive steps in the galley division of 2106 by 78 are illustrated below.

| Step 1 | 2 | 3 | 4 | 5 |

Step 1. Subtract $700 \times 2 = 1400$, leaving 706.
Step 2. Subtract $80 \times 2 = 160$, leaving 546.
Step 3. The divisor 78 is "shifted" to the right.
Step 4. Subtract $70 \times 7 = 490$, leaving 56.
Step 5. Subtract $7 \times 8 = 56$, leaving no remainder.

The work that appears in step 5 is all that appears on the paper.

The arrangement of the work in this method may appear strange, but the general plan is very much like our present method. The important differences are that the divisor is written on the bottom here and the subtractions are formed on the top instead of the bottom.

The "A Danda" Method. Our present algorithm for division evolved from a method called *a danda* (literally, "by giving"). The name is derived from the process of *giving* to the remainder a digit from the dividend after a partial product has been subtracted.

The origin of the method is not known for certain, but it seems to have had a gradual development.

An advance over the scratch method, believed to be an Arab device, was given in the fourteenth century by Maximus Planudes. It is illustrated below for the division of 2106 by 78.

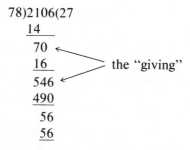

This differs from our present method only in that the quotient is written at the right of the dividend instead of on top.

Calandri's arithmetic of 1491 was the first printed book to exhibit the *a danda* method. It is illustrated below for the division of 2106 by 78. Here the divisor is written at the right and the quotient on top of the dividend.

Divide 2106 by 78

0027

2106 |78

156

546

546

0

This method began to appear more and more often in the arithmetic texts, first as just an interesting device. At the beginning of the seventeenth century it began to replace the galley method and by the end of the seventeenth century the *a danda* method had become the accepted division algorithm.

Checking.   Division problems are best checked by using the property that division and multiplication are inverse operations. The quotient is multiplied by the divisor and if the product obtained is the dividend, then the division was performed correctly.

EXAMPLE.   Divide 2106 by 78 and check.

Solution.   *Division*   *Check*

$$
\begin{array}{r}
27 \\
78\,)\overline{2106} \\
156 \\
\hline
546 \\
546 \\
\hline
\end{array}
\qquad
\begin{array}{r}
78 \\
27 \\
\hline
546 \\
156 \\
\hline
2106 \ \text{(check)}
\end{array}
$$

3. PROBLEM SOLVING BY INVERSION

A favorite Hindu method of solving problems was the method of inversion. This is illustrated below in the solution of a problem stated by the elder Aryabhata around 500.

"Beaming maiden with beaming eyes, tell me, as thou understandst the right method of inversion, which is the number which multiplied by 3, then increased by $\frac{3}{4}$ of the product, then divided by 7, diminished by $\frac{1}{3}$ of the quotient, multiplied by itself, diminished by 52, by the extraction of the square root, addition of 8, and division by 10 gives the number 2?"

The method of inversion requires that we start with the final number 2 and work backward, performing in order the inverse operation to each one stated in the problem.

For our convenience, these operations and their inverses are shown in Table 10.2 in a format to facilitate solution of the problem.

This procedure is the same as the one we use today for solving problems of this kind. The only difference is that the problem today is translated into an equation using algebraic symbols. The work is written in the form of equations but the operations are performed in the same inverse order.

TABLE 10.2

PROBLEM	SOLUTION	
Operation	*Inverse operation*	*Number*
Multiply by 3	Divide by 3	28 *Answer*
Multiply by $\frac{7}{4}$	Divide by $\frac{7}{4}$	84
$(\frac{3}{4} + 1 = \frac{7}{4})$	(multiply by $\frac{4}{7}$)	
Divide by 7	Multiply by 7	147
Multiply by $\frac{2}{3}$	Divide by $\frac{2}{3}$	21
$(1 - \frac{1}{3} = \frac{2}{3})$	(multiply by $\frac{3}{2}$)	
Multiply by itself (square)	Extract square root	14
Subtract 52	Add 52	196
Extract square root	Square	144
Add 8	Subtract 8	12
Divide by 10	Multiply by 10	20
The result is 2.		2 *Start here*

The modern solution of this problem would be written as follows:

$$\frac{\sqrt{\left(\frac{2}{3}\left[\frac{7}{4}\left(\frac{3N}{7}\right)\right]\right)^2 - 52} + 8}{10} = 2$$

$$\sqrt{\left(\frac{2}{3}\left[\frac{7}{4}\left(\frac{3N}{7}\right)\right]\right)^2 - 52} + 8 = 20$$

$$\sqrt{\left(\frac{2}{3}\left[\frac{7}{4}\left(\frac{3N}{7}\right)\right]\right)^2 - 52} = 12$$

$$\left(\frac{2}{3}\left[\frac{7}{4}\left(\frac{3N}{7}\right)\right]\right)^2 - 52 = 144$$

$$\left(\frac{2}{3}\left[\frac{7}{4}\left(\frac{3N}{7}\right)\right]\right)^2 = 196$$

$$\frac{2}{3}\left[\frac{7}{4}\left(\frac{3N}{7}\right)\right] = 14$$

$$\frac{7}{4}\left(\frac{3N}{7}\right) = 21$$

$$\frac{7}{4} \cdot 3N = 147$$

$$3N = 84$$

$$N = 28 \quad answer$$

This problem-solving technique (by inversion) is especially significant because it is a forerunner of our present techniques used in problem solving, particularly the use of the concept of inverse operations, which logically justify each step of the solution. All that is needed to change the solution into the modern version is to replace the words by our algebraic symbols.

EXERCISES

A. COMPUTATION BY ABACUS METHODS

1. Add DCCLXXXXIII   2. Subtract DCCCCXXXXV
    DLXXVII   CCLXXVIII

3. Multiply (duplation)
    LXXVIII by LVII

B. COMPUTATION BY ALGORITHMS

1. Add by using Bhaskara's method.
    a. 415   b. 789   c. 642   d. 1234   e. 7531
       938   678   358   5678   2468
       762   543   234   9109   9630

2. Add by using the Hindu scratch method, and check by using the commutative property of addition.
    a. 789   b. 496   c. 579   d. 7053   e. 4682
       943   255   421   8206   9999

3. Add by using the present addition algorithm, and check by using the associative property of addition.
    a. 35   b. 972   c. 49   d. 13   e. 732
       78   456   56   21   808
       64   301   63   34   414

4. Subtract by using the decomposition method, and check by using the inverse operation, addition.
    a. 652   b. 831   c. 1000   d. 5005   e. 4321
       444   797   456   4976   3690

5. Subtract by using the equal additions method, and check by using the inverse operation of addition.
    a. 714   b. 1000   c. 1999   d. 2021   e. 8374
       286   593   998   1876   7895

6. Multiply by using the Hindu scratch method, and check by using the commutative property of multiplication.
    a. 57   b. 245   c. 678   d. 792   e. 486
       23   48   111   86   957

7. Multiply by using the grating (or lattice) method, and check by using the commutative property of multiplication.
    a. 75 by 46   b. 238 by 94   c. 475 by 37
    d. 569 by 308   e. 792 by 546

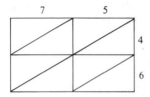 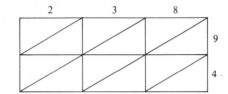

8. Multiply by using the scacchero method, and check by using the commutative property.
    a. 68 by 27   b. 536 by 204   c. 492 by 37
    d. 6305 by 790   e. 5416 by 2034
9. Divide by using the galley method, and check by using the inverse operation, multiplication.
    a. 975 by 75   b. 3542 by 154   c. 111,384 by 273
    d. 297,000 by 750   e. 56,182 by 49
10. Divide by using the *a danda* method, and check by using the inverse operation, multiplication.
    a. 6364 by 86   b. 9876 by 45   c. 97,300 by 350
    d. 12,131 by 45   e. 79,684 by 296

C. SOLUTION BY INVERSION

Solve each of the following problems by inversion by completing the formats below. (First, write down the inverse operations. Then find the numbers beginning at the bottom and working toward the top.)

1. Find the number *Inverse*
    which when

    multiplied by 7

    decreased by 5

    square root
      extracted

    increased by 6

    divided by 2

    squared

    results in 25   25

2. Find the number *Inverse*
    which when

    2 is subtracted

    the result squared

    increased by 5

    divided by 7

    multiplied by 18

    square root
      extracted

    results in 6   6

Solve the following problems by inversion.

3. Find the number which when squared, increased by 7, divided by 4, increased by 41, square root extracted, results in 7.
4. Find the number which when increased by 4, multiplied by 3, diminished by 8, squared, divided by 9, results in 4.
5. Find the number which when divided by 3, decreased by 4, multiplied by 12, increased by 6, cube root extracted, increased by 3, produces 5.

CHAPTER XI

Algebra

Ah, but my Computations, People say,
Have squared the Year to human Compass, eh?
'Twas only striking from the Calendar
Unborn Tomorrow, and dead Yesterday.

Rubaiyat, Omar Khayyam

By the help of God and with His precious assistance, I
say that Algebra is a scientific art . . . The perfection of this art consists in knowledge of the
scientific method by which one determines
numerical and geometric unknowns.

Algebra, Omar Khayyam

For want of a zero the world waited for thousands of years for an adequate numeral system. For want of an adequate numeral system it strug-
gled with an inferior arithmetic. As late as the time of Columbus, the
majority of the populace were adding and subtracting on their fingers;
only the privileged few had an abacus and were able to multiply and
divide. Now almost every young schoolboy can do these calculations with
ease.

The development of algebra, in turn, awaited the development of
arithmetic and a better understanding of the numbers that were involved.
For want of a symbolic notation, the subject matter of algebra remained
an unordered set of rules for solving problems, rules that seldom seemed
related.

What Euclid did for geometry in 300 B.C. (ordering its subject matter
according to the principles of logic) was not done for algebra until over
2000 years later. The traditional algebra and geometry textbooks have
reflected these different developments. It has only been in the last few
years that elementary texts have begun to reveal the logical structure of
algebra and arithmetic, a still unfinished project of the twentieth century.

1. DEVELOPMENT OF THE NUMBER SYSTEM

The complete number system of algebra is illustrated in Figure 11.1 by indicating its set and subset structure. Each of the different kinds of numbers will be introduced in the sections following.

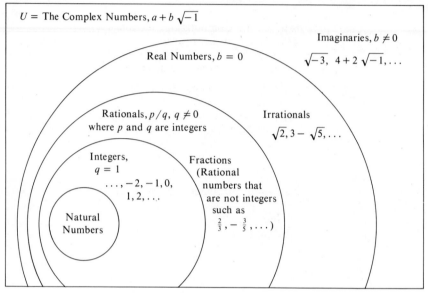

Naturals ⊂ Integers ⊂ Rationals ⊂ Reals ⊂ Complex Numbers

Figure 11.1

1:1 Positive Integers and Early Fractions

The natural numbers or counting numbers are also called the **positive integers.** These numbers were known when history began, and have been expressed in a variety of numeral systems, beginning with the simple grouping decimal system of the Egyptians and the positional sexagesimal system of the early Babylonians.

For most purposes of early man, the positive integers were all that were needed. Measuring units could be divided into subunits and the natural number could still be used to describe the measurement. For example, if 16 feet were divided into three equal parts, 16 could first be expressed as 15 feet and 12 inches. Then one third of this would be 5 feet 4 inches. Thus it was not necessary to use the fraction ⅓, because the submultiple 4 inches served just as well.

Later, as civilization became more complex, fractions were intro-duced. The Egyptian scribe Ahmes gave a very good treatment of unit fractions in the Rhind papyrus around 1650 B.C. The Babylonian tables of reciprocals dating around 1600 B.C. indicate a knowledge of positional sexagesimal fractions similar to our modern decimals.

1:2 Irrational Numbers

Irrational numbers are numbers, such as $\sqrt{2}$, that cannot be expressed as the quotient of two integers. The first recognition of their existence has been traced to the Babylonians. An early tablet gives a very good approximation to the length of the diagonal of a square, $d = \sqrt{2}s$, where s is the length of a side.

The discovery of the fact that these irrational numbers could not be expressed as the ratio of two integers caused a crisis in the Pythagorean brotherhood around 500 B.C. because it caused a logical flaw in their theory of proportion. By the time of Euclid (300 B.C.) this crisis had been resolved.

1:3 Common Fractions

The word "fraction" comes from the Latin *frangere,* meaning "to break." In fact, a fraction was often called a "broken number."

Notation. The early Egyptians used the symbol ⌒, which was placed above a numeral to indicate a unit fraction with the said numeral for its denominator. Thus $\frac{1}{3}$ was written ⌒̣ and $\frac{1}{12}$ was written ⌒̣ .
The Greeks tried to avoid fractions by using submultiples but as the fractions became needed, they developed a useful symbolism. The unit fraction was preferred and γ'' was written for $\frac{1}{3}$, and ϵ'' for $\frac{1}{5}$. (Recall in their alphabetically ciphered system, $\alpha = 1$, $\beta = 2$, $\gamma = 3$, and so on.)
Our present method for writing fractions is probably of Hindu origin. The Hindu fractions resembled ours except the bar was omitted.
Brahmagupta (628) and Bhaskara (1150) both wrote $\frac{2}{3}$ for our $\frac{2}{3}$. We also find a notation such as

$$4$$
$$2$$
$$3$$

for our $4\frac{2}{3}$.

The bar was introduced by the Arabs but it was not used by all writers. Early printing difficulties account for some variations in form and we find the common use of $^2/_3$ for $\frac{2}{3}$ a result of this problem.

The Latin expression *fractiones vulgares,* later called "vulgar fractions" in England and "common fractions" in America, was used originally to distinguish these fractions used in business from the sexagesimal positional fractions that were used in astronomy.

Interpretations. Man's difficulty in understanding fractions has not been limited to any historical period. The ancient Egyptians, resorting to unit fractions, were unable to grasp the concept of a pair of natural numbers being a single number, such as our fraction $\frac{5}{6}$, which is a single number made from the integers 5 and 6.

The Greeks before the time of Archimedes disliked the idea of breaking **unity** into parts and thus they worked with **ratios** of integers. Thus, if Alpha had 50 coins and Beta had 60 coins, the ratio of their amounts would be 5 to 6.

The Romans avoided fractions completely by the use of subunits; feet were subdivided into inches, pounds into ounces, and so on. A twelfth part of the Roman unit was called *uncia,* from which comes our modern "ounce" and "inch." For them a measurement of $\frac{5}{6}$ of a unit was considered as 10 uncias:

$$\frac{5}{6} = \frac{5 \times 2}{6 \times 2} = \frac{10}{12}$$

The practical necessity of obtaining greater accuracy in measurement was an important motivation for extending the number system to include the fractions. A theoretical factor was the desire to obtain **closure** with respect to the division operation.

The union of the set of fractions (positive) with the set of natural numbers is closed with respect to division; that is, every division problem has a solution. Not only is $\frac{12}{3}$ equal to the number 4 but the division $\frac{3}{12}$ also has a solution: the fraction $\frac{1}{4}$.

Some of the best geometric models for illustrating fractions are obtained by representing the "basic unit" by a line segment, or a rectangle, or a circle, or some finite set of objects. The unit is divided into congruent parts and the parts of the basic unit provide a model for a fraction.

Some examples are illustrated in Figure 11.2, with the shaded portions representing the fractions.

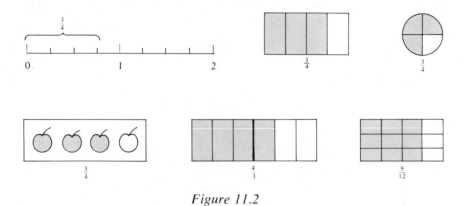

Figure 11.2

Equivalent Fractions. Observation of the preceding models of fractions indicates that it is possible to name a fraction using two integers in more than one way. In particular, we can see that $\frac{3}{4}$ and $\frac{9}{12}$ are names for the same number. In symbols, $\frac{3}{4} = \frac{9}{12}$.

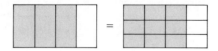

It can be noted that further subdivision of a basic unit causes a subdivision of the original parts of the unit used to represent the fraction.

Expressing this in general terms by considering the fraction a/b, where b is the number of parts into which the basic unit has been divided and a is the number of those parts represented, then further subdivision of each of the b parts into k congruent parts yields $b \times k$ congruent parts and the a original parts are now represented by $a \times k$ smaller parts.

Thus

$$\frac{a \times k}{b \times k}$$

is the same number as

$$\frac{a}{b} \qquad \text{or} \qquad \frac{a \times k}{b \times k} = \frac{a}{b}$$

The process of expressing a fraction with a denominator larger than the original one is called expressing the fraction in "higher terms."

The **simplification** of a fraction, or *reduction of a fraction to lowest terms,* means to express the fraction using the smallest number possible for the denominator. This process is just the reverse of the previous one.

EXAMPLE 1. Express $\frac{3}{5}$ with denominator 20.

Solution

$$\frac{3}{5} = \frac{3 \times 4}{5 \times 4} = \frac{12}{20}$$

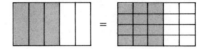

EXAMPLE 2. Simplify (reduce to lowest terms) $\frac{12}{18}$.

Solution

$$\frac{12}{18} = \frac{2 \times 6}{3 \times 6} = \frac{2}{3}$$

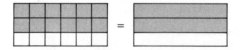

Addition and Subtraction of Fractions.   To add two fractions, subdivide the basic unit so that each fraction is represented by the same kind of subunit. Then add the number of these subunits represented by each fraction.

In other words, find a common denominator for the two fractions. Then add the resulting numerators and retain the common denominator.

In symbolic form,

$$\frac{a}{d} + \frac{b}{d} = \frac{a + b}{d}$$

Similarly, for subtraction,

$$\frac{a}{d} - \frac{b}{d} = \frac{a - b}{d}$$

EXAMPLE 1. Add $\frac{1}{3}$ to $\frac{1}{2}$.

Solution. $3 \times 2 = 6$ and $\frac{1}{3} = \frac{2}{6}$ and $\frac{1}{2} = \frac{3}{6}$:

$$\frac{1}{3} + \frac{1}{2} = \frac{2}{6} + \frac{3}{6} = \frac{5}{6}$$

EXAMPLE 2. Subtract $\frac{7}{10} - \frac{1}{4}$.

Solution. Since $10 = 2 \times 5$ and $4 = 2 \times 2$, $2 \times 2 \times 5 = 20$ is the smallest number that both 10 and 4 divide, and thus 20 is the least common denominator:

$$\frac{7}{10} - \frac{1}{4} = \frac{14}{20} - \frac{5}{20} = \frac{14 - 5}{20} = \frac{9}{20}$$

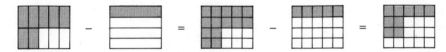

An early method of performing the addition of fractions is illustrated below in an example similar to one in the arithmetic text of Pacioli. Add $\frac{5}{6}$ to $\frac{3}{8}$:

$$
\begin{array}{ccc}
40 & 18 & 10 \\
\frac{5}{6} & \times \frac{3}{8} & \begin{array}{l} \cancel{58} \\ \cancel{48} \end{array} \quad \boxed{1\frac{5}{24}}
\end{array}
$$

Multiplication and Division of Fractions. The basis for our definition of the multiplication of fractions is related to our intuitive idea of the word "of" used in expressions such as $\frac{1}{3}$ of $\frac{1}{2}$ a pint. Our geometric models are based on the idea that one of the two congruent parts of a basic unit is further subdivided into three congruent parts. Since the total division of the basic unit is now into 3×2, or 6, congruent parts, one of these parts is represented as $\frac{1}{6}$, or $\frac{1}{3} \times \frac{1}{2} = \frac{1}{6}$.

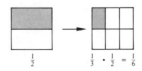

In general, the product

$$\frac{a}{b} \times \frac{c}{d}$$

is defined as follows.

Definition

$$\frac{a}{b} \times \frac{c}{d} = \frac{ac}{bd}$$

EXAMPLE. Multiply $\frac{2}{3}$ by $\frac{5}{8}$.

Solution

$$\frac{2}{3} \times \frac{5}{8} = \frac{2 \times 5}{3 \times 8} = \frac{10}{24} = \frac{5 \times 2}{12 \times 2} = \frac{5}{12}$$

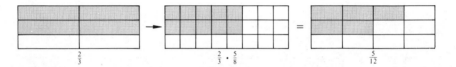

Division is defined as the inverse of multiplication.

Definition

$$\frac{a}{b} \div \frac{c}{d} = \frac{r}{s} \text{ if and only if } \frac{a}{b} = \frac{c}{d} \times \frac{r}{s}$$

Since

$$\frac{a}{b} = \frac{c}{d} \cdot \frac{d}{c} \cdot \frac{a}{b} = \frac{cd \times a}{cd \times b}$$

it follows that

$$\frac{r}{s} = \frac{a}{b} \times \frac{d}{c}$$

In other words, division by a fraction is the same as multiplication by the reciprocal[1] of the divisor:

$$\frac{a}{b} \div \frac{c}{d} = \frac{a}{b} \times \frac{d}{c}$$

---

[1] The reciprocal of a given number is that number which when multiplied by the given number produces 1. Thus the reciprocal of $\frac{2}{3}$ is $\frac{3}{2}$, because $\frac{2}{3} \times \frac{3}{2} = 1$.

EXAMPLE. Divide $\frac{3}{4}$ by $\frac{1}{2}$.

Solution

$$\frac{3}{4} \div \frac{1}{2} = \frac{3}{4} \times \frac{2}{1} = \frac{6}{4} = \frac{3 \times 2}{2 \times 2} = \frac{3}{2}$$

The early printed arithmetic texts listed two common methods for the division of fractions. In the first, the fractions were changed so they had a common denominator. Then the quotient of the resulting numerators was the solution of the division problem:

$$\frac{2}{3} \div \frac{3}{4} = \frac{8}{12} \div \frac{9}{12} = \frac{8}{9}$$

A second method was called the **cross-multiplication method,** as follows:

$$\frac{2}{3} \div \frac{3}{4} = \frac{2}{3} \times \frac{3}{4} = \frac{8}{9}$$

1:4 Decimal Fractions

Common fractions are those that permit any natural number as a denominator. A decimal fraction is one that permits only powers of 10, the number base, as denominator. Thus decimal fractions are positional fractions.

Definition: *A* **decimal fraction** *is a fraction whose denominator is a power of* 10. (Recall that the powers of 10 are 1, 10, 100, 1000, 10,000, and so on.)

The numbers $\frac{5}{10}$, $\frac{25}{100}$, and $\frac{75}{1000}$ are examples of decimal fractions, although these numbers are usually written 0.5, 0.25, and 0.075.

The positional structure of decimal fractions is indicated as follows:

Value of position	100	10	1	.	$\frac{1}{10}$	$\frac{1}{100}$	$\frac{1}{1000}$
Name of position	hundreds	tens	units		tenths	hundredths	thousandths
Number represented	2	0	8	.	9	3	7

The number 208.937 is illustrated above and is read "two hundred eight *and* nine hundred thirty-seven thousandths."

A positional system with base 60 was known to the ancient Babylonians, and their sexagesimal fractions, especially for astronomical calculations, continued in use into the Middle Ages. The need for positional decimal fractions gradually increased as practical uses of the common fractions required larger and larger numerators and denominators.

The decimal notation has several advantages. The computations are greatly simplified since the algorithms are very much like those for the natural numbers. Also the relative size of two numbers is easier to determine when the numbers are expressed in decimal form. For example, it is easier to see that 0.5625 is smaller than 0.6250 than it is to see that $\frac{9}{16}$ is smaller than $\frac{5}{8}$.

The first steps toward decimals in print arose in connection with tables of square roots and compound interest problems.

Christoff Rudolff (1530) was the first to really understand decimal fractions and calculate with them, although he did not explain them.

Simon Stevin in 1585 in his work *De Thiende* (Flemish), translated into French as *La Disme* in 1586, was the first to explain the theory of decimal fractions but his notation was poor.

Some of the different notations that have been used are summarized in Table 11.1.

TABLE 11.1

NAME OF USER	DATE	FORM FOR $24\frac{375}{1000}$
Rudolff	1530	24|375
Stevin	1585	24⓪3①7②5③
Vieta	1600	24|₃₇₅
Kepler	1616	24 (375
Napier	1617	24, 3'7"5'''
Briggs	1624	24^{375}
Oughtred	1631	24 |375
Bulan	1653	24:375
Ozanam	1691	24. 3 7 5 ⁽¹⁾ ⁽²⁾ ⁽³⁾

The modern forms became stabilized around 1800 and those in use today are

24.375   America
24·375   England
24,375   Continental Europe

Around 1700 an historian remarked that there were as many opinions on the subject of decimal fractions as there were people.

Addition and Subtraction of Decimals.   The numbers are arranged in columns according to their positions. The numbers are added or subtracted as if they were natural numbers. Then the decimal point is inserted in position below the other decimal points.

EXAMPLE

$$\text{Add} \quad \begin{array}{r} 35.24 \\ 107.50 \\ \underline{2.003} \\ 144.743 \end{array}$$

Justification

$$35.24 + 107.50 + 2.003 =$$

$$\frac{35240}{1000} + \frac{107500}{1000} + \frac{2003}{1000} = \frac{144,743}{1,000} = 144.743$$

Multiplication of Decimals. The numbers are multiplied as though they were natural numbers. Then the sum of the number of the decimal places of the factors is the number of decimal places in the product.

EXAMPLE

$$\begin{array}{rl} \text{Multiply} \quad 3.75 & \text{2 places} \\ \underline{1.2} & \text{1 place} \\ 750 & \\ \underline{375} & \\ 4.500 & \text{3 places} \end{array}$$

Justification

$$\frac{375}{100} \times \frac{12}{10} = \frac{4500}{1000} = 4.500$$

Division of Decimals. The divisor and dividend are first multiplied by the same power of 10 in order that the divisor becomes a natural number. The division is then performed as it is for natural numbers, with the decimal point placed in the quotient directly above its new position in the dividend.

EXAMPLE. Divide 15.275 by 3.25:

$$\begin{array}{r} 4.7 \\ 3.25 \overline{)\, 15.27.5} \\ \underline{13\ 00} \\ 2\ 27\ 5 \\ \underline{2\ 27\ 5} \end{array}$$

Justification

$$\frac{15.275 \times 100}{3.25 \times 100} = \frac{1527.5}{325} = \frac{15,275}{325} \times \frac{1}{10} = 47 \times \frac{1}{10} = \frac{47}{10} = 4.7$$

When the remainder is not zero, the division may be continued by adding more zeros to the dividend.

1:5 Negative Numbers and the Rationals

The counting numbers and the fractions came into existence in very ancient times; the Egyptians and Babylonians both had devised these sets of numbers to answer their practical needs.

Until the sixteenth century, however, the negative numbers were not even recognized as numbers, although there could be found scattered cases of ideas leading to this concept.

As science and commerce developed, a practical need arose for indicating the *direction* of counting or measuring from some fixed reference point. Examples involving this concept of **opposites** are illustrated by the pairs below, where one is tagged with the symbol + to indicate a measurement in one direction and the other member of the pair is tagged with the symbol − to indicate a measurement in the direction opposite to the first (Table 11.2).

TABLE 11.2

+ 30	− 30
A gain of $30	A loss of $30
30 feet above sea level	30 feet below sea level
30°F above zero	30°F below zero
30 miles north	30 miles south

The best geometric model to illustrate the concept of negative numbers is the number line, on which it is possible to represent all the rational numbers—the positive and negative integers, zero, and the positive and negative fractions.

Rational Numbers on the Number Line

In the number line model above, each rational number is matched with exactly one point on the geometric line. Zero is matched with the **origin,** the reference point that is selected first. Each number and its negative, such as 2 and −2, are placed symmetrically on opposite sides of the origin.

At a very early date the Chinese used black number rods for negative numbers and red number rods for positive numbers.

In his *Arithmetica,* Diophantus (ca. 275) called the equation $4x + 20 = 4$ absurd, because the Greeks did not have a number that they could multiply by 4 and then add 20 to the product to obtain a result of 4. Now we would say that the number x is equal to -4, knowing that $4 \times (-4) = -16$ and $-16 + 20 = 4$.

In India, negative and positive quantities are mentioned in the works of Brahmagupta (ca. 628), where he also stated the rules for addition, subtraction, multiplication, and division.

The Arab al-Khowarizmi (ca. 825) also stated the rules using the Hindu notation, which was the placing of a small circle or dot over or beside the number. For example, $\overset{.}{5}$ was written for our -5. Also the Hindus denoted a negative number by enclosing a number in a circle, such as ⑤ for -5. We see this practice used today in scoring games such as pinochle.

Fibonacci in 1225 interpreted a negative solution to a financial problem as a loss instead of a gain, but most medieval mathematicians preferred to ignore the "meaningless" expressions such as $3 - 7$.

The first significant treatment of negative numbers was given by Cardan in 1545 in his *Ars Magna*. Referring to these new numbers as "false," Cardan accepted them as the solutions of equations and stated the rules for their elementary operations.

In 1637 these new quantities were firmly established as numbers by the work of Descartes, who called them "true" and "false" numbers and used them to represent opposite directions.

With the intuitive idea of opposites and the relationship between the positive numbers and the negative numbers on the number line in mind, we now define a negative number as follows.

Definition of $-a$: *If a is any positive rational number, then $-a$ is that unique number for which $a + (-a) = 0$.*

Addition. The definition of the sum of two rational numbers is motivated by their practical use, as outlined in Table 11.3.

TABLE 11.3

DEFINITION	NUMBER EXAMPLE	PRACTICAL EXAMPLE
$(+a) + (+b) = + (a + b)$	$(+5) + (+2) = 7$	A \$5 gain and a \$2 gain results in a \$7 gain
$(-a) + (-b) = - (a + b)$	$(-5) + (-2) = -7$	A \$5 loss and a \$2 loss results in a \$7 loss
If a is larger than b, then $(+a) + (-b) = a - b$	$(+5) + (-2) = 3$	A \$5 gain and a \$2 loss results in a \$3 gain
If b is larger than a, then $(+a) + (-b) = -(b - a)$	$(+2) + (-5) = -3$	A \$2 gain and a \$5 loss results in a \$3 loss

Subtraction

Definition: $a - b \equiv a + (-b)$.

This definition is often stated as a rule for subtraction by saying "Change the sign of the subtrahend and add." For example,

$$
\begin{aligned}
5 - 2 &= 5 + (-2) = 3 \\
5 - (-2) &= 5 + (+2) = 7 \\
-5 - (\ 2) &= -5 + (-2) = -3 \\
-5 - (-2) &= -5 + (+2) = 3
\end{aligned}
$$

With this definition of subtraction we can show that subtraction is the inverse operation for addition.

Theorem: If $a - b = x$ where $a = b + x$, then $x = a + (-b)$.

$a + (-b) = (-b) + a$ by the commutative property of addition
$b + (-b + a) = [b + (-b)] + a$ by the associative property
$b + [a + (-b)] = 0 + a = a$ by the identity property and by substitution
     Thus $x = a + (-b)$

Multiplication and Division. The multiplication and division of rational numbers are defined in keeping with the intuitive idea of opposites and also in requiring that the commutative, associative, and distributive properties continue to be valid.

Definition of multiplication:

$$
\begin{aligned}
(+a) \cdot (+b) &= +ab & \qquad (+6)(+2) &= +12 \\
(-a) \cdot (-b) &= +ab & \qquad (-6)(-2) &= +12 \\
(+a) \cdot (-b) &= -ab & \qquad (+6)(-2) &= -12 \\
(-a) \cdot (+b) &= -ab & \qquad (-6)(+2) &= -12
\end{aligned}
$$

Definition of division:

$$
\frac{+a}{+b} = +\frac{a}{b} \qquad\qquad \frac{+6}{+2} = +3
$$

$$
\frac{-a}{-b} = +\frac{a}{b} \qquad\qquad \frac{-6}{-2} = +3
$$

$$
\frac{+a}{-b} = -\frac{a}{b} \qquad\qquad \frac{+6}{-2} = -3
$$

$$
\frac{-a}{+b} = -\frac{a}{b} \qquad\qquad \frac{-6}{+2} = -3
$$

A convenient rule for summarizing these properties is the following. If the signs are alike, the product or quotient is positive. If the signs are not alike, the product or quotient is negative.

The set of rational numbers is distinguished by the fact that the operations of addition, subtraction, multiplication, and division are closed in this system. This means that any problem that involves only these four operations will have a solution in the set of rational numbers. The properties of this set of numbers will be discussed more fully in a later section.

1:6 Complex Numbers

The universal set of numbers for algebra is the set of complex numbers. This includes the union of the rationals and the irrationals, which are called the real numbers, and also the imaginary numbers, which first arose as the square roots of negative numbers.

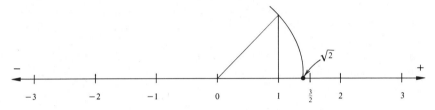

The Real Number Line

One might be tempted to think that the rational points exhaust the points on the number line. However, this is not the case. The irrational number $\sqrt{2}$, for example, can be "squeezed" in between 1.41 and 1.42, and this "squeezing" property can be continued even further. In fact, it can be continued indefinitely to obtain better and better approximations to $\sqrt{2}$ to whatever degree of accuracy the theory or the practical measurements require.

These irrational numbers, such as $\sqrt{2}$, $\sqrt{3}$, $\sqrt[3]{5}$, and so on, are needed to help close the number system with respect to the root-extraction operation. Moreover, once we have extended our number system to include the negative numbers, we must also include a new set of numbers, the imaginary numbers, to assure that our number system is closed under root extraction. For example, we want to consider $\sqrt{-9}$ a number — the number that when multiplied by itself results in -9 ($\sqrt{-9} \times \sqrt{-9} = -9$). The totality of all our numbers, after all these unions, is called the **complex number system.** In more advanced mathematics, it can be shown that every equation obtained by operating on an unknown number by addition, subtraction, multiplication, division, or raising to powers is assured of having its solution in the set of complex numbers. This statement is called the **fundamental theorem of algebra.**

History of the Complex Numbers. The Hindus, Mahavira ca. 850 and Bhaskara ca. 1150, were the first to indicate an awareness of the problem involving the square root of a negative number by writing that a negative number cannot have a square root because a negative cannot be a square.

Cardan, in his *Ars Magna* of 1545, was the first to use the square root of a negative number in a computation. In 1572 Bombelli, in his *Algebra*, introduced a consistent theory of imaginary numbers. Descartes in 1637 in *La Géométrie* classified numbers as "real" and "imaginary" and discussed complex numbers as the solutions of equations.

A graphical representation of complex numbers was originated by John Wallis in his *Algebra* of 1685. He suggested interpreting these new numbers as the sides of negative squares that measure negative areas, since the notion of negative lines for the graphical interpretation of negative numbers had already been accepted.

It was the Norwegian surveyor, Caspar Wessel, however, who in 1797 first presented the modern geometric theory, which involves drawing a perpendicular line, the imaginary axis, to the real number line. Figure 11.3 illustrates the graphical representation of the number $3 + 2\sqrt{-1}$, or $3 + 2i$.

Euler introduced in 1748 the use of the letter i instead of $\sqrt{-1}$ to designate the number whose square is -1. In 1832 Gauss introduced the name "complex number."

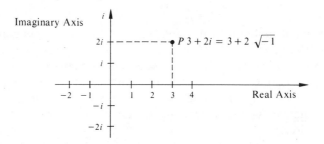

Figure 11.3

The development of complex numbers continued with Hamilton presenting the modern rigorous treatment of these quantities as number pairs in 1835. Later he extended these numbers to a space of three dimensions in his *Lectures on Quaternions* in 1853.

Application of Complex Numbers.   Although complex numbers arose in the theoretical development of algebra, first as solutions of equations and later as numbers needed in proofs of theorems about equations, there are many practical applications of these numbers.

In 1752 the French mathematician, Jean Le Rond D'Alembert (1717–1783), used these numbers in his study of hydrodynamics, which in turn led to the modern theory of aerodynamics.

In 1772 the complex numbers were used by Johann Heinrich Lambert of Germany (1728–1777) in the construction of maps by a technique called "conformal conic projection."

In the twentieth century the American mathematician and electrical engineer, Charles P. Steinmetz (1865–1923), used these numbers to develop the theory of electrical circuits.

DEVELOPMENT OF NAME AND SYMBOLS

2:1 Meaning of Algebra

What we understand today as "elementary algebra" has evolved from subject matter concerned with a set of rules for solving problems about numbers.

Today "elementary algebra" means a deductive system consisting of a set of definitions and assumptions about the set of complex numbers, operations, and relations on this set, and the theorems derived from these definitions and assumptions using the methods of logic.

We also understand that the language of algebra involves the use of symbols, which have gradually replaced words.

The number problems of algebra can be traced to those of the early Egyptians and Babylonians. Later the Greeks solved even more difficult problems and supplied proofs for their results. The Greeks, unfortunately, were limited to the set of positive real numbers, the other numbers not having been discovered. Also they resorted to geometric methods of solution, using very little symbolism.

As the number system developed, so did the symbolism. Gradually the properties of the numbers became better understood and finally, in the twentieth century, elementary algebra emerged as a mathematical system—2000 years after elementary geometry.

2:2 Name "Algebra"

The word "algebra" first appeared in the work "Hisab al-jabr wal-muqabala" by al-Khowarizmi around 825, and it literally meant "reduction" or "restoration." Through this work, "algebra" came to mean the study of equations, the word being adopted by both Arabic and European scholars.

Euler's book, *Vollstaendige Anleitung zur Algebra* ("Complete Introduction to Algebra"), in 1770 became the model of algebra texts and established the name.

The subject of algebra has also been known by other names. Since the unknown number was called *res* (thing) by later Latin writers, the subject was referred to as "die Cosa" (the thing) in Italian, "Die Coss" in German, and "Cossike arte" in English.

In the fifteenth and sixteenth centuries the Italians distinguished algebra from arithmetic by calling algebra the *greater art* and arithmetic the *lesser art*. Thus we have Cardan's *Ars Magna* ("Great Art") of 1545 and the use of *L'arte maggiore* by various Italian writers.

The Moors introduced a more common meaning of the Arabic word *al-jabr* into Spain, with an *algebrista* being a person who reset or "restored" broken bones. From Spain the word passed into Europe and in the sixteenth century in Italy "algebra" meant the art of bonesetting. An algebrista was a barber who also practiced bonesetting and bloodletting as a sideline.

2:3 Development of the Symbols

In the development of its symbols (see Tables 11.4 and 11.5), algebra is said to have passed through three different stages: first, a *rhetorical stage* in which the problems and solutions were stated in words; second, a *syncopated stage* in which a simplification was obtained by using abbreviations for the words; and third, a *symbolic stage* in which the words are replaced by symbols. Historically these stages have not been clearly separated but have overlapped.

The algebra of Diophantus (ca. 250) and Brahmagupta (ca. 625) are considered to be syncopated. Diophantus probably introduced the symbol ⋔ for subtract as a combination of the first two letters of a Greek word meaning "lacking." He indicated the unknown by the symbol *ς*, which probably is a merging of α and ρ, the first two letters of the Greek word *arithmos* ("number").

Brahmagupta and other Hindus selected their words "so much as" and "black," "blue," "yellow," and "red" as the names of the values of the unknowns and then used the initial syllables (ya, ka, ni, and so on) to designate them. Addition was indicated by juxtaposition, subtraction by a dot over the subtrahend, multiplication by writing *bha* (the first syllable of their word for product), and division by writing the divisor below the dividend.

Al-Khowarizmi wrote his equations in the rhetorical form. During the Middle Ages we find abbreviations coming into use, and the symbolism gradually developed after the appearance of printed works. Our present symbolism was essentially established with the work of Descartes in 1637.

The plus sign, +, indicating addition, is a contraction of the Latin word *et* meaning "and." When *et* is written rapidly, it looks like +.

The minus sign, −, indicating subtraction, was used as an equivalent form for "m̄" and "m," the abbreviations of the word "minus."

The marks + and − were used in medieval warehouses on sacks, crates, or barrels to indicate whether the contents was more or less than what it was supposed to be. The signs + and − made their first appearance in print in Widman's *Commercial Arithmetic*, published in 1489.

The symbol × for multiplication was developed in England about 1600, probably by Oughtred. It was not suitable for use in algebra because it resembles the letter *x*, used to designate the unknown. Clavius in 1583 used the dot, writing 3 · 4 for 3 × 4, which became an established practice with its use by Leibniz.

The symbol $\sqrt{}$, used to indicate square-root extraction, was introduced in 1525 by Christoff Rudolff because it resembles a small *r*, the initial letter of *radix* (Latin for "root").

The symbol =, which indicates equality, was introduced in 1557 by Robert Recorde in his work *The Whetstone of Witte* because "noe 2 thynges can be moare equalle." Recorde's parallel lines were not popular at first and we find Descartes in 1637 using ∝ or ∞ for equality. This symbol probably came from *ae*, an abbreviation of *aequales* (Latin for "equal"), although it could have been a purely arbitrary invention.

The unknown and its powers were designated by abbreviations beginning with Diophantus. The Hindus also used this technique, but we see that al-Khowarizmi reverted to the rhetorical stage of using words.

Letters began to be used during the Middle Ages but most writers seemed to prefer abbreviations.

One of the first persons to use letters to represent numbers was the French lawyer François Viète, who was attached to the court of Henry IV. Viète in 1591 improved the symbolism of algebra to such an extent that he is often referred to as the "father of algebra." Viète used capital vowels for the unknowns and successive powers of *A* were written $A, Aq,$ *Acu*, and *Aqq* for $A, A^2, A^3,$ and A^4.

Descartes in 1637 used a notation similar to our own, using the letters *x, y,* and *z* for the unknowns, except he used ∝ or ∞ for = and preferred *xx* and *xxx* to x^2 and x^3, although he introduced both forms. Descartes' influence was so great that his notation became the generally accepted one with the exception of the equal sign. Around 1800 x^2 and x^3 became the established forms.

TABLE 11.4 DEVELOPMENT OF ALGEBRAIC SYMBOLS

Rhetorical (words)	Three multiplied by the cube of the unknown number from which six multiplied by the square of the unknown number is subtracted is equal to the sum of five and the product of four and the unknown number
Syncopated (abbreviations)	3 Cu $\overline{m}$ 6 Sq ae 4 no p 5 (3 cubes minus 6 squares equals 4 numbers plus 5)
Symbolic	
Viète (1591)	$3Acu - 6Aq$ aequatur $4A + 5$
Descartes (1637)	$3xxx - 6xx$ ∞ $4x + 5$
Wallis (1693)	$3x^3 - 6xx = 4x + 5$
Modern	$3x^3 - 6x^2 = 4x + 5$

TABLE 11.5 DEVELOPMENT OF ALGEBRAIC SYMBOLS

CONCEPTS:		Add	Subtract	Multiply	Divide	Equal	Unknown	Square	Cube
MODERN SYMBOLS:		$x+y$	$x-y$	xy or $x \cdot y$	$\dfrac{x}{y}$	$=$	x	x^2	x^3
SOURCE	DATE								
Diophantus (Greek)	250		$\wedge$				ς	Δ^γ	K^γ
Bhaskara (Hindu)	1150		ya 6	ya 6 bha	$\dfrac{6}{2}$		ya, ka		
Pacioli (Italian)	1494	$\bar{p}$	$\bar{m}$				co	ce	cu
Widman (German)	1489	$+$	$-$						
Recorde (England)	1557	$+$	$-$			$=$			
Viète (French)	1591	$+$	$-$	$6A$	$\dfrac{6}{2}$		A (E, O)	Aq	Acu
Harriot (English)	1631	$+$	$-$	$6 \cdot 2$		$=$	a	aa	aaa
Descartes (French)	1637	$+$	$-$	$6x$	$\dfrac{x}{2}$	∞	x	xx x^2	xxx x^3
Wallis (English)	1693	$+$	$-$	$6x$	$\dfrac{x}{2}$	$=$	x	xx	x^3

3. ELEMENTARY ALGEBRA AS AN AXIOMATIC SYSTEM

Today algebra is defined as a mathematical system consisting of an undefined set of objects called numbers, undefined and defined operations and relations, other definitions and axioms (assumptions), and theorems obtained from the definitions and axioms by the methods of logic.

Even though algebra can trace its origins to the counting numbers of primitive man, it has evolved into a subject far more abstract than Euclidean geometry. The development of the number system has reflected the demands of a growing technological society. The development of the symbols and the increasing understanding of the properties of numbers has mirrored man's awareness of himself and his universe.

In presenting the subject of elementary algebra for the first time, the student is gradually introduced to the universal set, the set of complex numbers (Figure 11.4). First he studies the properties of the numbers he met in arithmetic: the counting numbers, zero, the fractions, and perhaps some irrational square roots. Next he learns about the negative numbers and the rationals and learns to solve problems involving linear equations. Then he studies the properties of the irrationals and later the imaginaries, until finally he is familiar with the universal set of complex numbers. At this point he studies quadratic equations and is ready for more advanced problems.

In the following sections we shall briefly overview the subject of elementary algebra in its modern axiomatic setting.

Undefined concepts

A universal set of numbers, *U*
2 operations; add ($x + y$) and multiply (xy or $x \cdot y$)
3 relations; equal (=), less than (<), greater than (>)

Definitions: Four operations: subtract ($x - y$), divide (x/y), raise to a power (x^n), and extract a root ($\sqrt[n]{}$). Other terms to be defined as needed.

The universal set that we have in mind is the set of complex numbers that was developed in previous sections.

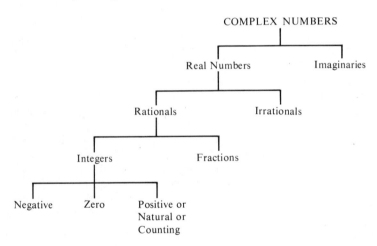

Figure 11.4

Axioms

The equal relation: For all numbers *x*, *y*, and *z* in *U*:

E1. Reflexive property. $x = x$.

E2. Symmetric property. If $x = y$, then $y = x$.

E3. Transitive property. If $x = y$ and $y = z$, then $x = z$.

E4. Addition property. If $x = y$, then $x + z = y + z$.

E5. Multiplication property. If $x = y$, then $xz = yz$.

E6. Substitution property. If $x = y$, then x can be replaced by y in any expression.

EXAMPLES

1. $3 = 3$ (reflexive).
2. If $3 + 4 = 5 + 2$, then $5 + 2 = 3 + 4$ (symmetric).
3. If $3 + 4 = 5 + 2$ and $5 + 2 = 7$, then $3 + 4 = 7$ (transitive).
4. If $3^2 = 9$, then $3^2 + 5 = 9 + 5$ (addition).
5. If $3^2 = 9$, then $5 \cdot 3^2 = 5 \cdot 9$ (multiplication).
6. If $x = 3$ and $x + y = 8$, then $3 + y = 8$ (substitution).

The addition and multiplication operations: For every x, y, z in U, see Table 11.6.

TABLE 11.6

	ADDITION	MULTIPLICATION
01. Closure	$x + y \in U$	$xy \in U$
02. Commutativity	$x + y = y + x$	$xy = yx$
03. Associativity	$(x + y) + z = x + (y + z)$	$(xy)z = x(yz)$
04. Identity	There exists a unique element, 0 in U, so that $x + 0 = 0 + x = x$	There exists a unique element, 1 in U, so that $x \cdot 1 = 1 \cdot x = x$
05. Inverse	For every x in U, there exists a unique element, $-x$ in U, called the **opposite** of x, so that $x + (-x) = 0$	For every x in U except 0, there exists a unique element, $1/x$ in U, called the **reciprocal** of x, so that $x \cdot (1/x) = 1$

06. The distributive property. $x(y + z) = xy + xz$.

Definition: Subtraction: $x - y = x + (-y)$.

Definition: Division: $\dfrac{x}{y} = x \cdot \left(\dfrac{1}{y}\right)$.

In developing our number system, many of the properties that are listed below were accepted intuitively, usually with reference to a geometric figure. However, each of these theorems can be *proved,* that is, derived from the axioms by the methods of logic. The formal proofs of a few of these statements are given below to illustrate this fact.

Theorems

On negatives:

$N1.$ $[x + (-y)] + y = x$ — (subtraction is the inverse operation to addition)

$N2.$ $-(-x) = x$ — (the opposite of an opposite is the original number)

$N3.$ $(-x)y = -xy$

$N4.$ $(-x)(-y) = xy$ — (the rules for the multiplication and division of signed numbers)

$N5.$ $\dfrac{x}{-y} = \dfrac{-x}{y} = -\dfrac{x}{y}$

$N6.$ $\dfrac{-x}{-y} = \dfrac{x}{y}$

On reciprocals:

$R1.$ $\left[x \cdot \left(\dfrac{1}{y}\right)\right] \cdot y = x$ — (division is the inverse operation to multiplication)

$R2.$ $\dfrac{1}{xy} = \dfrac{1}{x} \cdot \dfrac{1}{y}$

$R3.$ $\dfrac{x}{y} \cdot \dfrac{z}{w} = \dfrac{xz}{yw}$ — (how fractions are multiplied)

$R4.$ $\dfrac{1}{1/x} = x$ — (the reciprocal of a reciprocal is the original number)

$R5.$ $\dfrac{xz}{yz} = \dfrac{x}{y}$ — (how fractions are simplified)

$R6.$ $\dfrac{x}{z} + \dfrac{y}{z} = \dfrac{x + y}{z}$ — (how fractions are added)

Theorem N1: Subtraction is the inverse of addition:

$$[x + (-y)] + y = x$$

1. $[x + (-y)] + y = x + [(-y) + y]$ Associative axiom

2. $\qquad\qquad\quad = x + 0$ Inverse axiom

3. $\qquad\qquad\quad = x$ Identity axiom

Theorem R1: Division is the inverse of multiplication:

$$\left[x \cdot \left(\frac{1}{y}\right)\right] \cdot y = x$$

1. $\left[x \cdot \left(\frac{1}{y}\right)\right] \cdot y = x \cdot \left[\left(\frac{1}{y}\right) \cdot y\right]$ Associative axiom

2. $\qquad\qquad\quad = x \cdot 1$ Inverse axiom

3. $\qquad\qquad\quad = x$ Identity axiom

Theorem N2: $-(-x) = x$.

1. $-(-x) = 0 + [-(-x)]$ Identity axiom
2. $\qquad\quad = [x + (-x)] + [-(-x)]$ Inverse axiom
3. $\qquad\quad = x + [(-x) + (-(-x))]$ Associative axiom
4. $\qquad\quad = x + 0$ Inverse axiom
5. $\qquad\quad = x$ Identity axiom

Theorem N3: $(-x)y = -xy$.

1. $(-x)y = (-x)y + [xy + (-xy)]$ Inverse axiom

2. $\qquad = [(-x)y + xy] + (-xy)$ Associative axiom

3. $\qquad = (-x + x)y + (-xy)$ Distributive axiom and Commutative axiom

4. $\qquad = 0 + (-xy)$ Inverse axiom

5. $\qquad = -xy$ Identity axiom

Theorem N4: $(-x)(-y) = xy$.

1. $(-x)(-y) = -[x(-y)]$ Theorem N3

2. $\quad\quad\quad = -[(-y)x]$ Commutative axiom

3. $\quad\quad\quad = -(-yx)$ Theorem N3

4. $\quad\quad\quad = yx$ Theorem N2

5. $\quad\quad\quad = xy$ Commutative axiom

4. SOLUTION OF LINEAR EQUATIONS

Identities. Algebra is concerned with statements that can be classified as true or false but not both.

The axioms and theorems that describe the properties of the numbers in the universal set are statements that are true for every member in the universal set. These statements are called **identities.**

From the special cases $2 + 3 = 3 + 2$ and $8 + 3 = 3 + 8$ we have abstracted the general case $x + 3 = 3 + x$. To generalize and state the number properties, letters of the alphabet are used as the names of unspecified numbers in the universal set. The letters are called **variables** and can be thought of as **placeholders.** When the letter is replaced by the numeral name of a number belonging to the universal set (the numeral names are called **constants**), then it is possible to decide whether the statement is true or false.

To indicate this situation correctly the axioms and theorems (the identities) should always be **quantified** by stating that they are properties of every number in the universal set.

For example, the commutative axiom of addition should be worded as follows.

For every $x \in U$ and for every $y \in U$, $x + y = y + x$. This means that when the symbols x and y are replaced by any numerals that name numbers in U, then $x + y = y + x$ becomes a true statement.

Open Sentences. Algebra is also concerned with sentences that cannot be classified as true or false statements until some additional information is supplied. Such sentences are called **open sentences.**

For example, $x + 3 = 7$ is an open sentence. The letter x is acting as a placeholder.

If x is replaced by 2, we obtain $2 + 3 = 7$, a false statement.

If x is replaced by 4, we obtain $4 + 3 = 7$, a true statement.

Many types of symbols can be used as placeholders. Any letter could be used. In arithmetic, squares, circles, and question marks are often used.

Open sentences have traditionally been called **conditional equations.**

The subset of U, the universal set, for which the conditional equation or open sentence becomes a true statement, is called the **solution set.** The numbers that are members of the solution set are called **solutions** of the equation.

Solving Linear Equations.   One of the objectives of algebra is the solution of conditional equations, that is, to find the set of numbers from the universal set that make a conditional equation (or open sentence) true.

The linear equations are the easiest to solve because they require little more than the application of the addition and multiplication axioms and the concept of "inversion."

EXAMPLE 1. Solve $x - 3 = 5$:

$$x - 3 + 3 = 5 + 3$$ Addition axiom (3 is added to both sides)

$$x + 0 = 8$$ Addition facts

$$x = 8$$ Identity axiom (addition)

Check. $8 - 3 = 5$ is a true statement.

EXAMPLE 2. Solve $3x = 15$:

$$\frac{1}{3} \cdot 3x = \frac{1}{3} \cdot 15$$ Multiplication axiom (both sides are multiplied by $\frac{1}{3}$)

$$1 \cdot x = 5$$ Multiplication facts

$$x = 5$$ Identity axiom (multiplication)

Check. $3 \cdot 5 = 15$ is a true statement.

EXAMPLE 3. Solve $2x - 7 = 5$:

$$2x - 7 + 7 = 5 + 7$$ Addition axiom (7 is added)

$$2x + 0 = 12$$ Addition facts

$$2x = 12$$ Identity axiom (addition)

$$\frac{1}{2} \cdot 2x = \frac{1}{2} \cdot 12$$ Multiplication axiom (both sides are multiplied by $\frac{1}{2}$)

$$x = 6$$ Multiplication facts

Check. $2 \cdot 6 - 7 = 12 - 7 = 5$, a true statement.

EXAMPLE 4. Solve $\dfrac{x}{5} + 4 = 8$:

$$\dfrac{x}{5} = 4 \qquad \text{(−4 is added to both sides)}$$

$$x = 20 \qquad \text{(both sides are multiplied by 5)}$$

Check. $\dfrac{20}{5} + 4 = 4 + 4 = 8$, a true statement.

5. GRAPHS OF LINEAR EQUATIONS

Ordered Pairs. If an open sentence (or conditional equation) contains two letters or variables, then the solution set is a set of ordered pairs.

An **ordered pair** is a set of two elements of which one is named the first and the other the second. In symbols, the elements are enclosed by parentheses and are separated by a comma, the first being written to the left of the second.

For example, (Sacramento, California) is an ordered pair.

Also, (Smith, Jones) is an ordered pair.

Also, (3, 4) is an ordered pair.

The order of the elements in an ordered pair is important; (3, 4) is *not* the same as (4, 3).

Suppose we wish to find all natural numbers x and y so that $2x + y = 10$. The possible choices for x and y are listed in the table below. To obtain the entries, x is replaced by a natural number, starting with 1, and then the equation in one variable, y, is solved:

x	y	
1	8	Solve $2 + y = 10$
2	6	Solve $4 + y = 10$
3	4	Solve $6 + y = 10$
4	2	Solve $8 + y = 10$

STOP! x cannot be replaced by 5 because $10 + y = 10$ does not have a natural number for a solution.

Thus the solution set of $2x + y = 10$, where $x \in N$ and $y \in N$, is the set of ordered pairs: $\{(1, 8), (2, 6), (3, 4), (4, 2)\}$ and it is understood that the first element of each ordered pair is a replacement for x and the second is a replacement for y.

Graphs of Ordered Pairs. Ordered pairs are illustrated geometrically by using a Cartesian coordinate system (invented by René Descartes in 1637).

At the origin of a horizontal real number line, another real number line is drawn perpendicular to the horizontal one. The horizontal line is called the *x*-axis and the vertical line is called the *y*-axis. Parallel horizontal lines and parallel vertical lines are next drawn, forming what is called a **grid** or **lattice** or a **graph** (Figure 11.5).

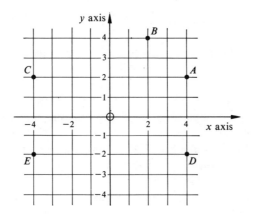

Figure 11.5

Now a one-to-one correspondence is established between the set of ordered pairs of real numbers and the geometric points on this Cartesian plane.

A geometric point is located by starting at the origin and first moving to the position on the *x*-axis indicated by the first element of the ordered pair (to the right if positive and to the left if negative). From this position the point required is reached by moving parallel to the *y*-axis as directed by the second number of the ordered pair (upward if positive and downwards if negative).

The points $A(4, 2)$, $B(2, 4)$, $C(-4, 2)$, $D(4, -2)$, and $E(-4, -2)$ are illustrated in Figure 11.5. Note that the ordered pair $(4, 2)$ is *not* the same as $(2, 4)$.

We have seen that the ordered pairs $\{(1, 8), (2, 6), (3, 4), (4, 2)\}$ form the solution set of the linear equation $2x + y = 10$ when x and y are required to be natural numbers. Now, if we allow x and y to be elements of the set of real numbers, then the solution set of $2x + y = 10$ is an infinite set of ordered pairs. However, with more advanced mathematics, it is possible to show that the graph of this infinite set is a straight line, and moreover the straight line joining the four points of the solution set above.

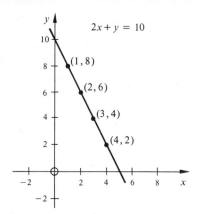

Equations having the pattern $ax + by = c$ are called *linear equations* because their graphs are straight lines. Using the information that the graph of a linear equation is a straight line, the simplest method for graphing a linear equation is the following.

1. Find three ordered pairs of real numbers that satisfy the equation.
2. Graph these three ordered pairs as three geometric points.
3. Draw the straight line through the three points. (Since a straight line is uniquely determined by two points, the third point is used as a check.)

EXAMPLE. Graph $2y - x = 5$.

Solution

x	y
1	3
3	4
5	5

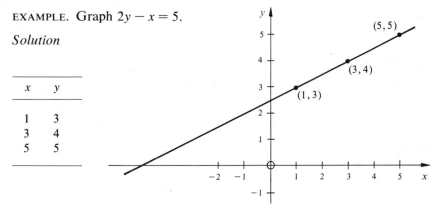

6. SIMULTANEOUS LINEAR EQUATIONS

Some problems in algebra are concerned with the **intersection** of the solution sets of two open sentences that each involve two variables.

This has been referred to traditionally as the solution of two **simultaneous equations** in two variables.

EXAMPLE. Solve graphically the set of simultaneous equations

$$3x + y = 9 \quad \text{and} \quad x - y = 7$$

Solution. The solution set of each equation is graphed separately on the same coordinate system as follows. The geometric point of intersection of the two lines determines the ordered pair that is the algebraic intersection of the two solution sets and thus the solution of the set of equations.

$3x + y = 9$		$x - y = 7$	
x	y	x	y
1	6	7	0
2	3	8	1
3	0	9	2

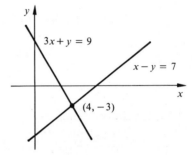

Thus the solution is the ordered pair $(4, -3)$.

Check. $3 \cdot 4 + (-3) = 12 - 3 = 9$, a true statement. $4 - (-3) = 4 + 3 = 7$, a true statement.

EXERCISES

A. EXERCISES ON FRACTIONS

1. Illustrate each of the following with three different geometric models.

   a. $\dfrac{2}{3}$ b. $\dfrac{5}{8}$ c. $\dfrac{3}{5}$ d. $\dfrac{5}{3}$ e. $\dfrac{11}{6}$

2. Simplify each of the following and illustrate with a geometric model.

   a. $\dfrac{15}{20}$ b. $\dfrac{21}{56}$ c. $\dfrac{25}{100}$ d. $\dfrac{8}{12}$ e. $\dfrac{21}{18}$

3. Multiply each of the following and illustrate with a geometric model.

   a. $\dfrac{1}{3}$ by $\dfrac{2}{5}$ b. $\dfrac{3}{4}$ by $\dfrac{2}{5}$ c. $\dfrac{2}{3}$ by $\dfrac{9}{8}$

4. Add each of the following and illustrate with a geometric model.

   a. $\dfrac{1}{3} + \dfrac{5}{8}$ b. $\dfrac{5}{6} + \dfrac{7}{9}$ c. $\dfrac{5}{12} + \dfrac{5}{18}$

5. Change each of the following to decimal fractions.

   a. $\dfrac{3}{8}$ b. $\dfrac{6}{25}$ c. $\dfrac{35}{100}$ d. $\dfrac{7}{16}$ e. $\dfrac{40}{125}$

6. Change each of the following to common fractions.

   a. 0.6   b. 0.025   c. 4.125   d. 23.75   e. 20.375

7. Multiply: a. 45.23 by 7.5   b. 3.028 by 345.23

8. Divide: a. 52.74 by 3.6   b. 3.726 by 0.075

9. Using the fractions $\dfrac{2}{3}, \dfrac{3}{5},$ and $\dfrac{4}{7}$ as x, y, and z, respectively, verify each of the following.
   a. The associative axiom of addition, $x + (y + z) = (x + y) + z$.
   b. The associative axiom of multiplication, $x(yz) = (xy)z$.
   c. The distributive axiom, $x(y + z) = xy + xz$.

B. EXERCISES ON NEGATIVES

1. Determine which of the following would best be measured by signed numbers and which by positive numbers alone.
   a. Population of countries.
   b. Daily change in stock prices.
   c. Daily minimum temperature at Nome, Alaska.
   c. Fat content of milk.
   e. Yards gained by a football team, down by down.
   f. Daily entries on a bank account.

2. If each of the following is positive, name the negative of each.
   a. To the right.   d. A profit.   g. Gain in population.
   b. To the east.   e. Time A.D.   h. Force toward an
   c. Above sea level.   f. Temperature above   object.
                                        zero.

3. If an elevation of 1000 feet above sea level is represented as $+1000$, what signed numbers represent each of the following?
   a. The elevation of a mountain 7850 feet above sea level.
   b. The elevation of Death Valley 280 feet below sea level.
   c. The elevation of the surface of the Pacific Ocean.

4. Explain the meaning of each of the following in terms of signed numbers.
   a. Mr. Smith, owner of a business, said "I am $500 in the red this year."
   b. At the end of a game of cards, Jane's score was 125 while Tom was 50 "in the hole."
5. The following are entries on a monthly bank account. Explain the entries and give the final statement for the month.

+$275.00, +$50.00, −$25.00, −$175.00, +$25.00, −$125.00, −$45.00

6. Add: a. $+15$ b. $+15$ c. -15 d. -15 e. $-7 + 8$ f. $7 + (-8)$
         $\underline{-3}$ $\underline{+3}$ $\underline{+3}$ $\underline{-3}$

7. Subtract: a. $+15$ b. $+15$ c. -15 d. -15 e. $7 - (10)$ f. $7 - (-10)$
              $\underline{+3}$ $\underline{-3}$ $\underline{+3}$ $\underline{-3}$

8. Multiply: a. $(15)(3)$ b. $(15)(-3)$ c. $(-15)(-3)$ d. $(-15)(3)$

9. Divide: a. $\dfrac{15}{-3}$ b. $\dfrac{-15}{-3}$ c. $\dfrac{-15}{3}$ d. $\dfrac{15}{3}$

C. ON TRANSLATIONS

Write an algebraic expression for each of the following.
1. The sum of 5 and the product of 3 and x.
2. Three times the sum of 5 and x.
3. The remainder when one half of y is subtracted from x.
4. The difference when 7 is subtracted from the product of a and b.
5. The quotient when $3N$ is divided by the sum of 3 and the square of N.
6. Eight less than the cube of z.
7. Four diminished by y is multiplied by the sum of 6 and t.
8. Three fourths of x increased by 5 is divided by 8 decreased by x.
9. If 2 is added to five times a number, the result is 17.
10. If the sum of five and a number is multiplied by 2, the result is 17.

D. ON THE AXIOMS

1. An operation $a * b$ is defined on the set of natural numbers as follows:

   $$a * b \equiv ab/2. \text{ (Multiply } a \text{ and } b \text{ and then divide by 2.)}$$

   a. Is this operation closed? Why?
   b. Is this operation commutative? Why?
   c. Is this operation associative? Why?
   d. Does the operation have an identity? Why?

Another operation, $a \# b$, is defined on the set of natural numbers as follows:

$a \# b \equiv 2a + b$. (The second number is added to twice the first.)

   e. Is this operation closed? Why?
   f. Is this operation commutative? Why?
   g. Is a distributive property valid? Why? [Check: $a * (b \# c)$ and $a \# (b * c)$.]
   h. Does either $a * b$ or $a \# b$ have an inverse operation? Why?
2. Prove that multiplication is distributive over subtraction.
3. Prove that division is distributive over addition and subtraction.
4. Cite a counterexample to show that addition is *not* distributive over multiplication.
5. Cite a counterexample to show that addition is *not* distributive over division.

E. SOLVING LINEAR EQUATIONS

Solve and check each of the following.

1. $x - 5 = 7$ 6. $\dfrac{-2x}{3} = 6$

2. $x + 5 = 3$ 7. $6y - 6 = 12$

3. $\dfrac{x}{3} = 5$ 8. $6x + 6 = 4x - 2$

4. $\dfrac{x}{-2} = 6$ 9. $\dfrac{5y}{3} - 2 = 5 + \dfrac{2y}{3}$

5. $12x = 3$ 10. $4 - 2(3 - t) = 8$

F. SIMULTANEOUS LINEAR EQUATIONS

Solve the following graphically.

1. $x + y = 2$ 3. $x - 2y = 11$
    $x - y = -8$ $2x + y = 7$
2. $x + 3y = 13$ 4. $y = x - 4$
    $3x - 2y = 6$ $2x - 3y = 12$

CHAPTER XII

Probability, Calculus, Geometries (Optional)

Nature and Nature's laws lay hid in night:
> God said, "Let Newton be!" and all was light.

> A. Pope

If I have seen farther than Descartes it is by standing on
the shoulders of giants.

> Sir Isaac Newton

Almost everything, which the mathematics of our
century has brought forth in the way of original
scientific ideas, attaches to the name of Gauss.

> Leopold Kronecker (1901)

1. PROBABILITY

1:1 Meaning of Probability

In 1654 a gambler, Chevalier de Méré, asked his friend Blaise Pascal to solve a problem known as the **problem of points,**[1] that is, how to "split the pot" in an unfinished dice game.

Pascal consulted with another French mathematician, Pierre Fermat, and the resulting Pascal-Fermat correspondence became the basis of a new mathematical subject known as the **theory of probability.**

---

[1] This problem also occurs in Pacioli's *Suma* (1494) and in the works of Tartaglia (1556) and Cardan (1539), who also wrote a gambler's manual.

Probability theory is concerned with how likely a particular event is to happen. We are all familiar, perhaps, with statements like the ones below describing the certainty and uncertainty of various events.

1. The earth will turn on its axis tomorrow.
2. There are two things certain in this world—death and taxes.
3. Heads I win—tails you lose!
4. It will probably rain tomorrow.
5. The income tax is likely to be raised this year.
6. The coin will land heads.
7. The earth will stand still tomorrow.
8. He will live forever.
9. All taxes will be abolished next year.

We regard statements 1, 2, and 3 as describing **certain** events and 4, 5, and 6 **uncertain** events. The events in statements 7, 8, and 9 are thought of as **impossible** or as certain *not* to happen.

To compare the likelihoods of events, a number is assigned to an event as a **measure** of its certainty or uncertainty. The certain events are assigned the number 1 and the impossible events the number 0. The uncertain events are assigned numbers between 0 and 1, the more likely event receiving the higher number. Roughly speaking, we can think of a probability as the fraction of the time it is likely to happen. A more precise meaning is provided by the definition below.

Definition: *If s is the number of successes, the number of ways an event can happen, and if f is the number of failures, the number of ways an event can fail to happen, and if each of the s + f ways is equally likely to occur, then the* **mathematical probability** *of the event E, p(E), happening is*

$$p(E) = \frac{s}{s+f}$$

EXAMPLE 1. What is the probability of a coin to land heads?

Solution. $p = \frac{1}{2}$, since there are two ways for the coin to land, heads or tails, and one of these is a success.

EXAMPLE 2. What is the probability of rolling a 4 on a standard die (die is the singular of dice)?

Solution. There are six ways of the die landing, with the number 1, 2, 3, 4, 5, or 6 on top. There is one way for a 4 to be on top. Thus $p = \frac{1}{6}$.

EXAMPLE 3. What is the probability of drawing a heart from a standard playing deck of 52 cards?

Solution. Since there are 13 hearts, there are 13 successes out of 52 possibilities. Thus $p = \frac{13}{52} = \frac{1}{4}$.

1:2 Combination of Events

Not.   An event either happens or it does not happen. Thus if $p(E)$ is the probability that event E does happen and $p(\text{not } E)$ is the probability that event E does not happen, then

$$p(E) + p(\text{not } E) = 1$$

or

$$p(\text{not } E) = 1 - p(E)$$

EXAMPLE. What is the probability of *not* rolling a 4 on a single roll of a die?

Solution. $p(\text{not } 4) = 1 - \frac{1}{6} = \frac{5}{6}$.

And.   *Case 1. E and F are independent:* If E and F are two **independent** events, that is, the probability of either one in no way affects the occurrence of the other, then the probability that both E and F will happen is the *product* of their separate probabilities:

$$p(E \text{ and } F) = p(E) \times p(F)$$

EXAMPLE 1. If two coins are tossed, what is the probability of their both landing heads?

Solution

$$p(E) = p(\text{one coin lands heads}) = \tfrac{1}{2}$$
$$p(F) = p(\text{other coin lands heads}) = \tfrac{1}{2}$$

The toss of one coin is independent of the toss of the other. Thus $p(E \text{ and } F) = p(2 \text{ heads}) = \frac{1}{2} \times \frac{1}{2} = \frac{1}{4}$. Compare this result with the diagram, which pictures all the possible outcomes.

$$\text{(H)} \quad \text{(H)} \quad \text{(T)} \quad \text{(T)}$$
$$\text{(H)} \quad \text{(T)} \quad \text{(H)} \quad \text{(T)}$$

EXAMPLE 2. If two cards are drawn from a standard deck of 52 cards and the first card drawn is replaced before the second is drawn, what is the probability that the first card is a heart and the second an ace?

Solution

$$p(E) = p(\text{draw a heart}) = \frac{13}{52} = \frac{1}{4}$$
$$p(F) = p(\text{draw an ace}) = \frac{4}{52} = \frac{1}{13}$$

Since the first card is replaced, neither drawing affects the other; that is, the drawings are independent and thus

$$p(E \text{ and } F) = p(\text{draw a heart and draw an ace}) = \frac{1}{4} \times \frac{1}{13} = \frac{1}{52}$$

Case 2. E and F are dependent: In some cases, event F depends on the outcome of event E and thus the probability of F occurring after E happens will be different from the probability of F occurring alone. This probability is called a **conditional probability** and is designated in symbols as $p(F/E)$, or the probability that F occurs on the condition that E occurs. Then the probability that E and F occur is the product of the probability of E and the conditional probability of F:

$$p(E \text{ and } F) = p(E) \times p(F/E)$$

EXAMPLE. If two cards are drawn from a standard deck of 52 cards and the first card is *not* replaced before the second card is drawn, what is the probability that the first card is a heart and the second card is a heart?

Solution

$$p(E) = p(\text{draw a heart}) = \frac{13}{52} = \frac{1}{4}$$

$$p(F/E) = p(\text{draw a heart } after \text{ a heart has been drawn}) = \frac{12}{51} = \frac{4}{17}$$

Thus

$$p(E \text{ and } F) = \frac{1}{4} \times \frac{4}{17} = \frac{1}{17}$$

Or. *Case 1. Mutually exclusive events:* If events E and F are mutually exclusive, that is, the alternatives exclude one another or it is impossible for both to happen, then the probability that E or F happens, $p(E \text{ or } F)$, is the *sum* of the probabilities of E and F.

$$p(E \text{ or } F) = p(E) + p(F)$$

EXAMPLE 1. If two coins are tossed, what is the probability that they will both land heads or both land tails?

Solution

$$p(E) = p(\text{both heads}) = \tfrac{1}{4}$$
$$p(F) = p(\text{both tails}) = \tfrac{1}{4}$$

Thus

$$p(E \text{ or } F) = p(\text{both heads or both tails}) = \tfrac{1}{4} + \tfrac{1}{4} = \tfrac{1}{2}$$

EXAMPLE 2. What is the probability of drawing an ace or a king from a standard deck of 52 cards?

Solution

$$p(E) = p(\text{draw an ace}) = \frac{4}{52} = \frac{1}{13}$$

$$p(F) = p(\text{draw a king}) = \frac{4}{52} = \frac{1}{13}$$

Thus

$$p(E \text{ or } F) = p(\text{draw an ace or a king}) = \frac{1}{13} + \frac{1}{13} = \frac{2}{13}$$

Case 2. Events not mutually exclusive: Sometimes the event E and F is included among the possibilities for E and those for F. When this happens, the sum of $p(E)$ and $p(F)$ counts the same event twice, so this common possibility must be subtracted:

$$p(E \text{ or } F) = p(E) + p(F) - p(E \text{ and } F)$$

When the events are mutually exclusive, then $p(E \text{ and } F) = 0$, so the statement above is the general case.

EXAMPLE. What is the probability of drawing a heart or an ace from a standard deck of 52 cards?

Solution

$$p(E) = p(\text{draw a heart}) = \frac{13}{52} = \frac{1}{4}$$

$$p(F) = p(\text{draw an ace}) = \frac{4}{52} = \frac{1}{13}$$

$$p(E \text{ and } F) = p(\text{draw the ace of hearts}) = \frac{1}{52}$$

Thus

$$p(E \text{ or } F) = p(\text{draw heart or ace}) = \frac{1}{4} + \frac{1}{13} - \frac{1}{52}$$

$$= \frac{13}{52} + \frac{4}{52} - \frac{1}{52} = \frac{16}{52} = \frac{4}{13}$$

1:3 Repeated Trials and Pascal's Triangle

If you toss a coin, it lands either heads or tails and thus the probability of its landing heads is $\frac{1}{2}$ and of its landing tails is $\frac{1}{2}$.

If the coin is tossed a second time, or if two coins are tossed together, there are 4 possible outcomes.

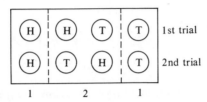

(the number of combinations of two things taken two at a time)

Thus the probability of 2 heads is $\frac{1}{4}$, of 2 tails is $\frac{1}{4}$, and of 1 head and 1 tail is $\frac{1}{4} + \frac{1}{4} = \frac{1}{2}$.

If the coin is tossed a third time, or if three coins are tossed together, then there are 8 possible outcomes (Figure 12.1). The probability of 3 heads is $\frac{1}{8}$ and of 3 tails is $\frac{1}{8}$. The chances of 2 heads and 1 tail is $\frac{3}{8}$ and of 2 tails and 1 head is $\frac{3}{8}$.

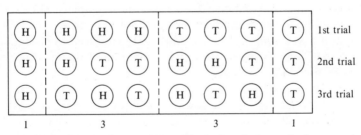

(the number of combinations of two things taken three at a time)

Figure 12.1

As the trials are repeated, different combinations of heads and tails are possible. The French mathematician Blaise Pascal (1623–1662) summarized these different combinations in the form of a triangle, called **Pascal's triangle,** which is illustrated below.

$$
\begin{array}{c}
1 \\
1 \quad 1 \\
1 \quad 2 \quad 1 \\
1 \quad 3 \quad 3 \quad 1 \\
1 \quad 4 \quad 6 \quad 4 \quad 1 \\
1 \quad 5 \quad 10 \quad 10 \quad 5 \quad 1 \\
1 \quad 6 \quad 15 \quad 20 \quad 15 \quad 6 \quad 1 \\
1 \quad 7 \quad 21 \quad 35 \quad 35 \quad 21 \quad 7 \quad 1
\end{array}
$$

. . . .

The triangle may be continued by observing the property that each number is the sum of the two numbers immediately above it.

1:4 Statistical Inference

Although probability theory is still widely used today in analyzing games of chance, its applications in other areas of modern life have become increasingly more significant.

Applications to mortality tables started around 1662 with the work of John Graunt and Edmund Halley in England. In 1699 the first life insurance company was established in London.

Today probability theory is an important part of modern science ranging from agricultural experiments to the biological laws of heredity and the positions of electrons inside the atom. It is used in industry for quality control and for design of equipment. It is used in military tactics, politics, economics, and social sciences in studying behavior.

The French mathematician Pierre Simon de Laplace (1749–1827), who did much to advance the theory of probability with his work *Théorie analytique des probabilitiés* published in 1912, referred to probability as a science that began with games and became one of the most important concerns of human knowledge.

There is an essential difference between probability theory and statistical inference. In probability it is always possible, at least theoretically, to list all the possible outcomes of events being considered. Then the probability of an event determined from these outcomes is used to predict a future occurrence. Probability theory does not tell us that a coin *will* land heads *exactly* 500 times out of 1000, but it does tell us that the number of heads is almost certain to be between 450 and 550. There is no certainty as to an individual case, but when a large number of cases are considered, dependable predictions can be made.

In statistical inference the totality of outcomes is *not* known in advance but is inferred by means of sampling processes using the theory of probability.

One device that is used in analyzing how well the sample represents the total population is the probability curve shown in Figure 12.2.

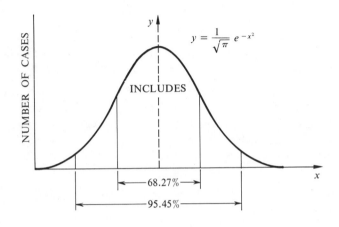

$$y = \frac{1}{\sqrt{\pi}} e^{-x^2}$$

Figure 12.2

This bell-shaped curve is also called the **normal distribution curve** and is typical of many different types of distributions; for example, heights of persons, IQs of students, life span of light bulbs, and the velocities of molecules in a gas.

The great mathematician Carl Friedrich Gauss (1777–1855) derived an equation for the probability curve and analyzed its properties. As a result, experimenters can use the curve to determine how reliable or valid their measurements are. Thus the curve above is also called the **Gaussian curve** and the distributions it describes are referred to as **Gaussian distributions.**

Since the time of Gauss other equations and curves have been studied to describe other types of situations, the "abnormal" situations.

EXERCISES

1. Fermat solved the case of the problem of the points discussed below. *A* needs 2 points to win and *B* needs 3 points to win. There is $64 in

the pot. The money is to be divided between A and B according to their probabilities of winning. How much does each receive?

The total possibilities are listed below, where a is a trial A wins and b is a trial B wins. (Only 4 trials are necessary for A or B to win.)

aaaa	aaab	aabb	baab	abbb	bbbb
	aaba	abab	baba	babb	
	abaa	abba	bbaa	bbab	
	baaa			bbba	

2. What is the probability of drawing a red card from a standard deck of 52 cards?

3. If a letter of the alphabet is chosen at random, what is the probability that it will be
   a. A vowel?   b. A consonant?   c. A letter from a to m?
   d. A vowel and a letter from a to m?
   e. A vowel or a letter from a to m?
   f. Neither a vowel nor a letter from a to m?

4. What is the probability of tossing an even number (2, 4, or 6) on one roll of a die?

5. If a number from 1 to 10 is picked at random, what is the probability that the number is larger than 4?

6. Weather statistics in a certain community show that it rains 73 days out of 365 days. What is the probability of
   a. Rain on Sunday?   b. No rain on Sunday?   c. Rain Saturday and Sunday?   d. Rain Saturday or Sunday?

7. On a multiple-choice test, there are five possible answers for each question. If a student guesses the answer to each question, what is the probability that he guesses
   a. The first answer correctly?   b. The first answer incorrectly?
   c. The first and second answer correctly?   d. The answer to the first or the second correctly?

8. Two prizes are awarded in a raffle. The first ticket drawn is *not* replaced. You have 5 tickets of the 100 that have been sold.
   a. What is your probability of winning the first prize?
   b. If you did not win the first prize, what is your probability of winning the second prize?
   c. What is your probability of winning first and second prize?
   d. What is your probability of winning first or second prize?
   e. What is your probability of not winning either first or second prize?

9. In a certain survey of the lunch habits of 105 persons, the following information was revealed: 70 persons had meat, 75 persons had salad, 50 persons had dessert, 45 had meat and salad, 30 had meat and dessert, 35 had salad and dessert, and 20 had meat, salad, and dessert. What is the probability that a person chosen at random
   a. Orders meat only?   b. Has meat or dessert?   c. Has meat and salad but no dessert?   d. Has dessert if it is known he has salad?

10. What is the probability of throwing 4 heads in a row? 5 heads in a row? n heads in a row?

2. ANALYTIC GEOMETRY AND CALCULUS

2:1 Analytic Geometry

Lord Kelvin remarked, "A single curve, drawn in the manner of the curve of prices of cotton, describes all that the ear can possible hear as the result of the most complicated musical performance . . . that to my mind is a wonderful proof of the potency of mathematics."

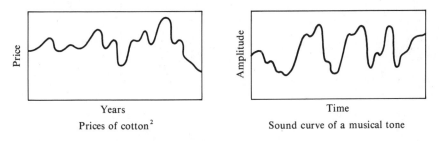

Prices of cotton[2]   Sound curve of a musical tone

Figure 12.3

Analytic geometry is the subject that relates algebra to geometry. A one-to-one correspondence is established between the geometric points of the plane and the algebraic ordered pairs of real numbers. From this there results a correspondence between geometric curves in the plane and algebraic equations in two variables.

The idea of coordinates or a graph can be traced to the ancient Egyptians and later to the Roman surveyors and Greek map makers.

---

[2] Mills, Frederick, *Statistical Methods*, New York: Holt, Rinehart and Winston, Inc., 1939.

The Greek Apollonius investigated very thoroughly the geometry of the quadratic curves in his work *Conic Sections*. He gave them the names **ellipse, parabola,** and **hyperbola.** These curves were not associated with their algebraic equations, however, until a much later date.

Some curves with their equations are illustrated in Figure 12.4.

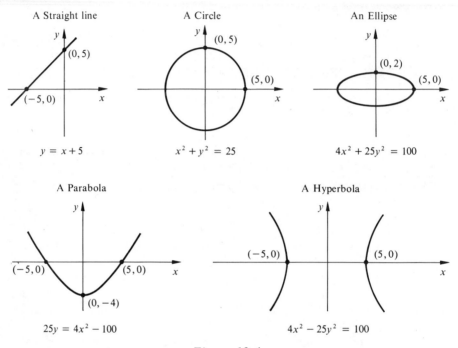

A Straight line

$y = x + 5$

A Circle

$x^2 + y^2 = 25$

An Ellipse

$4x^2 + 25y^2 = 100$

A Parabola

$25y = 4x^2 - 100$

A Hyperbola

$4x^2 - 25y^2 = 100$

Figure 12.4

Although we find some earlier works relating algebra to geometry, the invention of analytic geometry is credited to the French mathematicians Pierre de Fermat (ca. 1601–1665) and René Descartes (1596–1650) with the publication of his work *La Géométrie* in 1637.

During the seventeenth century many new kinds of curves were studied. One curve that received much attention was the **cycloid,** the curve that describes the path of a point on a circle as the circle rolls on a straight line. Galileo, unaware of its mechanical superiority to be proved later, suggested that it be used as an arch for bridges. Pascal devoted much time to the study of the cycloid and discovered many of its properties. Later Huygens, who used the cycloid in the construction of pendulum clocks, showed that the inverted cycloid was the path of shortest time for an object to move from one point to another in the same vertical plane. The properties of the cycloid (Figure 12.5) have been so fascinating and have prompted so many quarrels that the cycloid has been called "the Helen of geometry" (after the lady of Greek and Trojan times). Some other curves of historical interest are illustrated in Figure 12.6.

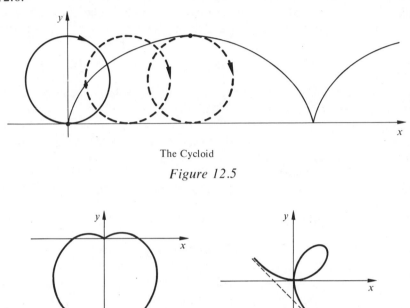

The Cycloid

Figure 12.5

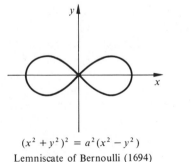

$(x^2 + y^2 - 2ax)^2 = 4a^2(x^2 + y^2)$

Cardioid (heart-shaped)

$x^3 + y^3 = 3axy$

Folium of Descartes

$(x^2 + y^2)^2 = a^2(x^2 - y^2)$

Lemniscate of Bernoulli (1694)

$\sqrt{x^2 + y^2} = a \arctan \frac{y}{x}$ or $r = a\theta$

Spiral of Archimedes

Figure 12.6

2:2 Integral Calculus

The use of an infinite process and the concept of limit form the essence of the subjects of differential and integral calculus.

Suppose we consider the infinite set A, where

$$A = \left\{ 2\frac{1}{2},\ 2\frac{1}{4},\ 2\frac{1}{8},\ 2\frac{1}{16},\ 2\frac{1}{32},\ 2\frac{1}{64},\ \cdots \right\}$$

We observe that the numbers in the set are getting smaller and smaller. We also observe that they are getting closer and closer to 2 but never get smaller than 2. We say that 2 is the **limit** of this set of numbers.

Now let us consider another infinite set B, where

$$B = \{1.9,\ 1.99,\ 1.999,\ 1.9999,\ 1.99999, \cdots \}$$

We see that these numbers are getting larger and larger and also closer and closer to 2. The limit of set B is also 2.

Infinite processes were known to the ancient Greeks. Archimedes used one called the method of exhaustion in determining the areas bounded by parabolas and circles.

One of the techinques that Archimedes used in calculating an area bounded by a parabola is illustrated in Figure 12.7. The shaded area,

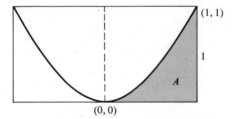

A, under the parabola $y = x^2$ and inside the unit square in the figure above is approximated by rectangles under the area and over the area as indicated in Figure 12.7.

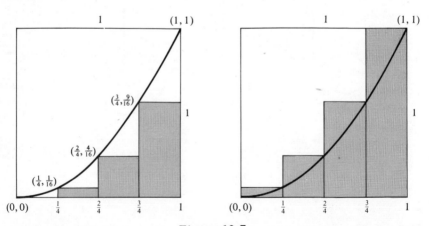

Figure 12.7

Since the equation of the parabola is $y = x^2$, the altitude of each rectangle (the y-value on the curve) is the square of the x-value.

Now let $s =$ the sum of the rectangles under the curve and let $S =$ the sum of the rectangles over the curve. Then

$$s = \frac{1}{4} \cdot \left(\frac{1}{4}\right)^2 + \frac{1}{4} \cdot \left(\frac{2}{4}\right)^2 + \frac{1}{4} \cdot \left(\frac{3}{4}\right)^2 = \frac{1^2 + 2^2 + 3^2}{4^3}$$

and

$$S = \frac{1}{4} \cdot \left(\frac{1}{4}\right)^2 + \frac{1}{4} \cdot \left(\frac{2}{4}\right)^2 + \frac{1}{4} \cdot \left(\frac{3}{4}\right)^2 + \frac{1}{4} \cdot \left(\frac{4}{4}\right)^2 = \frac{1^2 + 2^2 + 3^2 + 4^2}{4^3}$$

Then the area A is larger than s and smaller than S, or

$$\frac{7}{32} = \frac{1^2 + 2^2 + 3^2}{4^3} < A < \frac{1^2 + 2^2 + 3^2 + 4^2}{4^3} = \frac{15}{32}$$

Now this process is repeated by doubling the number of rectangles used as shown in Figure 12.8. This time we obtain

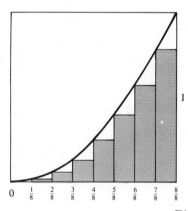 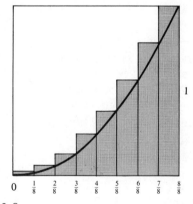

Figure 12.8

$$\frac{35}{128} = \frac{1^2 + 2^2 + 3^2 + 4^2 + 5^2 + 6^2 + 7^2}{8^3}$$

$$< A < \frac{1^2 + 2^2 + 3^2 + 4^2 + 5^2 + 6^2 + 7^2 + 8^2}{8^3} = \frac{51}{128}$$

This process is again repeated by doubling the number of rectangles (Figure 12.9).

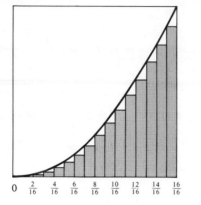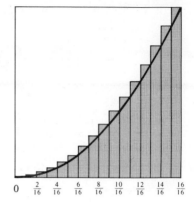

Figure 12.9

This time we obtain

$$s = \frac{1^2 + 2^2 + 3^2 + \cdots + 15^2}{16^3}, \text{ which is smaller than the area } A$$

and $S = \dfrac{1^2 + 2^2 + 3^2 + \cdots + 15^2 + 16^2}{16^3}$, which is larger than the area A

This operation is repeated indefinitely, and the totality of these operations is an infinite process called the **method of exhaustion.** The small areas between the rectangles and the curve are being used up or exhausted as the doubling operation is repeated.

We obtain two sets of numbers: set U, the sums of areas of rectangles under the curve, and set O, the sums of areas of rectangles over the curve:

$$U = \left\{ \frac{1^2 + 2^2 + 3^2}{4^3}, \frac{1^2 + 2^2 + \cdots + 7^2}{8^3}, \frac{1^2 + 2^2 + \cdots + 15^2}{16^3}, \cdots \right\}$$

$$O = \left\{ \frac{1^2 + 2^2 + 3^3 + 4^2}{4^3}, \frac{1^2 + 2^2 + \cdots + 8^2}{8^3}, \frac{1^2 + 2^2 + \cdots + 16^2}{16^3}, \cdots \right\}$$

Archimedes showed that each of the sets had the same limit, $\dfrac{1}{3}$. Thus the limit of set $U = \dfrac{1}{3} = $ limit of set O.

During all this time, the area A has been "squeezed" between values closer and closer to the limit of each set. Thus $\dfrac{1}{3} \leqq A \leqq \dfrac{1}{3}$ or $A = \dfrac{1}{3}$.

When the exhaustion operation is generalized and its properties abstracted as a mathematical system, the system is called **integral calculus,** and the operation is called **integration.** The symbol that is used to indicate an integration is a large letter s, $\int$, invented by Leibniz.

Today, the problem of finding the area under the parabola, $y = x^2$, and inside the unit square would be written as follows:

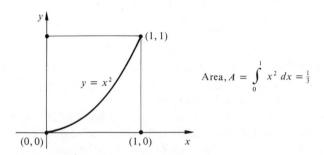

$$\text{Area, } A = \int_0^1 x^2 \, dx = \tfrac{1}{3}$$

Integration has many other interpretations in the real world besides that of determining areas. Some of these applications are concerned with the concepts of volume, work, center of gravity, and force.

2:3 Differential Calculus (The Tangent Problem)

The Greeks were also concerned with another problem that became part of the subject matter of our modern calculus. This was the problem of finding the tangent line to a given curve at a given point.

The circle presented no difficulties. At the point on the circle a line was constructed perpendicular to the radius to the point. This perpendicular was the tangent required, because a tangent line of a circle is perpendicular to the radius at the point of tangency.

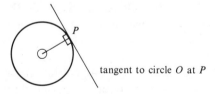

tangent to circle O at P

The Greeks showed that an ellipse was the totality of points whose sum of distances from two fixed points, called the *foci,* was a constant. Then the tangent line to an ellipse was found by using a special property of the ellipse—the fact that its tangent line makes equal angles with the lines joining the point *P* on the ellipse to the foci.

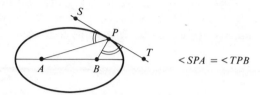

$< SPA = < TPB$

The Greeks considered many tangent problems. Archimedes wrote a complete work on the tangent problem and area problem of a curve that is called the **spiral of Archimedes.**

As more and more curves were studied, finding the tangent line by using a special property of each individual curve proved to be very laborious. There was need for a more general definition of a tangent line. The one that proved most satisfactory defined the tangent line to a curve at a point *P* on the curve as the limiting position of all the lines joining *P* to any other point *Q* on the curve.

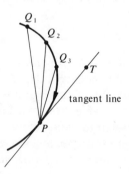

tangent line

As *Q* moves closer and closer to point *P*, the lines PQ_1, PQ_2, PQ_3, $\cdots$ move closer and closer to a line *PT*, which is called the **tangent line.**

Slope.   To make this definition of a tangent line more usable, a number called the **slope** of a line was introduced as a measure of the steepness or direction of a straight line.

Informally, we may describe the slope of a line as the "rise" divided by the "run" or the vertical change divided by the horizontal change.

When a road is said to have a 2 percent grade, this is the same as saying that the slope is $\frac{2}{100}$, or that the change in altitude is 2 feet for every 100 feet moved in the horizontal direction.

Using a coordinate system and the methods of analytic geometry, the slope m of a line through the two points $P_1(x_1, y_1)$ and $P_2(x_2, y_2)$ is defined as follows:

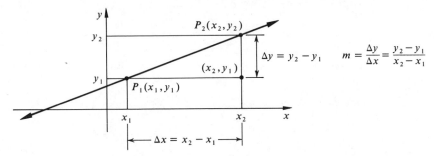

$$\Delta y = y_2 - y_1 \qquad m = \frac{\Delta y}{\Delta x} = \frac{y_2 - y_1}{x_2 - x_1}$$

$$\Delta x = x_2 - x_1$$

EXAMPLE. Find the slope of the line joining the point $A(3, 4)$ to the point $B(5, 8)$.

Solution

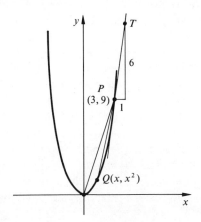

$$8 - 4 = 4 \qquad m = \frac{8 - 4}{5 - 3} = \frac{4}{2} = \frac{2}{1} = 2$$

$$5 - 3 = 2$$

Now the tangent problem can be restated using the concept of slope as follows: At a given point on a curve whose equation is given, find the slope of the tangent line to the curve.

Let us now find the slope of the tangent line to the parabola $y = x^2$ at the point $(3, 9)$ on the parabola.

A general point on the curve can be named (x, x^2) because we are again dealing with the parabola whose y-coordinates are the squares of its x-coordinates. Then the slope of a line joining the point $P(3, 9)$ to any point $Q(x, x^2)$ on the parabola is given by

$$m = \frac{\Delta y}{\Delta x} = \frac{y_2 - y_1}{x_2 - x_1} = \frac{x^2 - 9}{x - 3}$$

By using the distributive property of the set of real numbers, we can see that

$$(x - 3)(x + 3) = (x - 3)x + (x - 3)3 = x^2 - 3x + 3x - 9$$

$$= x^2 - 9$$

Thus

$$\frac{x^2 - 9}{x - 3} = x + 3 \qquad \text{if } x \neq 3$$

Thus the slope of PQ is $x + 3$, or

$$\frac{\Delta y}{\Delta x} = x + 3$$

   Now as the point Q moves closer and closer to P, the slope of line PQ moves closer and closer to $3 + 3 = 6$, because x is moving closer and closer to 3:

x	1	2	2.5	2.9	2.99	2.99999 $\longrightarrow$ 3
$\dfrac{\Delta y}{\Delta x} = x + 3$	4	5	5.5	5.9	5.99	5.99999 $\longrightarrow$ 6

We see that the limiting position of lines PQ is the tangent line at P and the limit of the slopes is 6. Thus the slope of the tangent line to the parabola $y = x^2$ at the point $(3, 9)$ is 6. To construct this tangent line on the graph, we join the point $(3, 9)$ to another point on the tangent line found by moving to the right 1 unit and then upward 6 units.

   This limit process, which is concerned with the limiting value of the ratio of the change of one variable to the change of another variable, is called **differentiation.** The limit value is called the **derivative.** The abstract theory of this limit operation is called **differential calculus.**

   Today differential calculus is applied to many subjects that are involved with rates of change such as biological changes, chemical reactions, and physical concepts. The velocity and acceleration of objects in motion were strong motivating factors in developing the subject of differential calculus.

2:4 Fundamental Theorem of Calculus

Galileo is famous for his work dealing with falling bodies and particularly for his experiments from the leaning tower of Pisa. The genius of this man can perhaps be appreciated even more by knowing that by 1620 he was aware of most of the ideas involved in differential and integral calculus although he had not grasped their complete significance.

The concept of the derivative interpreted as a velocity is illustrated below.

When an object is dropped from a point above the earth, the distance s it drops in t seconds is given by $s = 16t^2$. Figure 12.10 illustrates the fall of an object from a point 1600 feet above the earth's surface.

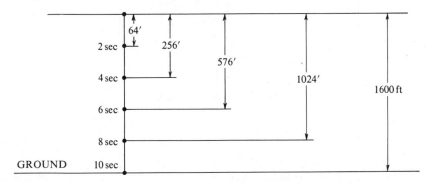

Figure 12.10

With what speed, called the **impact speed,** will the object hit the earth? To answer this question, we start by approximating this speed as the ratio of the change of distance to the change in time (see also Table 12.1).

TABLE 12.1

t	2	4	6	8	9	9.9	9.99	9.999
s	64	256	576	1024	1296	1568.16	1596.8016	1599.6800
$\Delta s = 1600 - s$				576	304	31.84	3.1984	0.31998
$\Delta t = 10 - t$				2	1	0.1	0.01	0.001
$v_{av} = \dfrac{\Delta s}{\Delta t}$				288	304	318.4	319.84	319.98 $\to 320'$

$$\text{Average speed} = \frac{\text{change in distance}}{\text{change in time}} = \frac{\Delta s}{\Delta t} = \frac{1600 - 16t^2}{10 - t}$$

$$\text{Impact speed} = \text{limit of } \frac{\Delta s}{\Delta t} = \lim_{\Delta t \to 0} \frac{\Delta s}{\Delta t} = 320 \text{ ft/sec}$$

(as Δt becomes 0)

Galileo assumed that the velocity of a falling object was the product of a constant $g = 32$ ft/sec^2 near the surface of the earth and the time t it traveled; that is,

$$v = gt \qquad \text{or} \qquad v = 32t$$

Then he stated that the distance the object traveled would have to be the sum of all the verticals above the line $v = 32t$; or the area under this line.

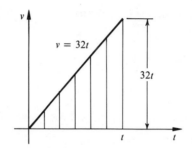

Thus the area $s = \frac{1}{2}(32t){\cdot}t = 16t^2$.

The area problem here involves the limit of a sum of vertical lines and thus involves the concept of integration.

Thus Galileo seemed aware of the following two facts:

1. $32t$ is the derivative of $16t^2$.
2. $16t^2$ is the integral of $32t$.

This relationship generalized and abstracted states that the infinite processes of integration and differentiation are *inverse* operations of each other just as addition and subtraction are inverse operations of each other! Incredible as it might seem, the area problem and the tangent problem are the opposites of each other. This statement that differentiation and integration are inverse operations is called the **fundamental theorem of calculus.**

Newton and Leibniz, both of whom are given equal credit for the invention of the calculus, completely understood the significance of the fundamental theorem and both developed general principles and techniques for solving problems related to the original area and tangent problems. Their mathematical rigor was not very precise, but mathematicians and scientists applied these techniques with great success. Finally, in the nineteenth century the logical foundations of the calculus began to be clarified and improved.

3. GEOMETRIES

3:1 Non-Euclidean Geometries

For over 2000 years geometers attempted to prove Euclid's parallel postulate with no success. Finally around 1830 three mathematicians, Carl Friedrich Gauss (1777–1855) of Germany, Janos Bolyai (1802–1860) of Hungary, and Nicolai Ivanovitch Lobachevsky (1793–1856) of Russia, independently, demonstrated that Euclid's parallel postulate could not be proved from the other postulates and that the replacement of it by another postulate led to a new consistent mathematical system called non-Euclidean geometry. (Gauss originated the name.)

Lobachevsky and Bolyai assumed that through a point there are at least *two* lines parallel to a given line. Some of Euclid's theorems are still true in this system, but those that depend on the parallel postulate are no longer true. For example, in Lobachevsky's geometry, the sum of the angles of a triangle is *less* than 180°, whereas in Euclid's geometry the sum of the angles of a triangle is equal to 180°.

A model for this geometry is the pseudosphere (Figure 12.11), which more or less resembles two trumpets placed end to end except that the surface extends to infinity. The surface curves inward or is said to have "negative curvature."

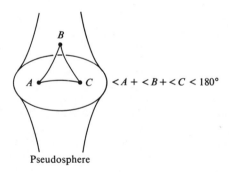

$$< A + < B + < C < 180°$$

Pseudosphere

Figure 12.11

In 1854 the great German mathematician Georg Friedrich Bernhard Riemann (1826–1866), while investigating a still more general class of geometries, found another non-Euclidean geometry. Riemann proposed to substitute for Euclid's parallel postulate the statement that through a point in the plane there is *no* line parallel to a given line.

In this system the sum of the angles of a triangle is larger than 180°. The undefined term *line* is interpreted as a great circle on the surface of a sphere, such as the equator or longitude circles on the earth's surface.

The great circle on the sphere corresponds to the straight line on the Euclidean plane because on a sphere the shortest distance between two points is along the great circle joining them. This fact is used by airlines in establishing certain Arctic polar flights, the routes of least distance (Figure 12.12). The sphere is a surface that curves outward or is said to have "positive curvature."

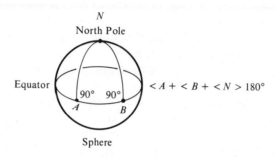

Figure 12.12

In 1871 the mathematician Felix Klein called these three different geometries hyperbolic (Lobachevsky's), parabolic (Euclid's), and elliptic (Riemann's) (Table 12.2).

TABLE 12.2

KIND OF GEOMETRY	NAME OF DISCOVERER	NUMBER OF PARALLELS TO A GIVEN LINE THROUGH A GIVEN POINT	SUM OF THE ANGLES OF A TRIANGLE	CURVATURE OF SURFACE
Hyperbolic	Lobachevsky, Bolyai, Gauss	More than one	Less than 180°	Negative
Parabolic	Euclid	One	Equal to 180°	Zero
Elliptic	Riemann	None	More than 180°	Positive

As a result of certain experiments, scientists believe that space is curved; that is, it has a curvature different from the plane that has zero curvature. According to Einstein's theory of relativity, the mass of a heavenly body, such as a star or planet, creates a warpage or curvature of space just as a heavy rock placed on a tightly stretched rubber sheet would cause the sheet to bulge downward under the rock. Einstein predicted that this curving of space would cause light rays to bend when passing near a star. Scientists verified this prediction during the solar eclipse of 1919. Modern physicists are finding these geometries of extreme importance in dealing with problems in the inner space of the atoms and in the outer space of the stars.

For us, in our everyday world, we could also use the geometries of Lobachevsky and Riemann. However, Euclidean geometry is more consistent with our intuitive ideas and thus is the most convenient one for us to use.

3:2 Topology

What does a doughnut have in common with a coffee cup? This is a question that topologists might ask.

Euclidean and non-Euclidean geometries deal with rigid shapes that do not change their size or shape. However, scientific experiments have shown that objects in motion do undergo a change in shape. Do objects have any geometric properties that are unaffected by continuous changes such as stretching, shrinking, twisting, or bending? Mathematicians have discovered that such properties do exist and **topology** is the mathematical system devoted to the study of geometric properties unchanged after continuous transformations.

Topology began as a branch of geometry in 1847 with the publication of *Vorstudien zur Topologie* ("Studies in Topology") written by the German mathematician Johann Benedict Listing.

The origins go back earlier to observations by Descartes in 1640 of a property of simple polyhedrons that was later expressed in a formula by Euler as

$$V + F = E + 2$$

This states that if V is the number of vertices, F is the number of faces, and E the number of edges of a simple polyhedron, then the sum of the vertices and faces is 2 more than the number of faces. This is illustrated in Figure 12.13 for the five Platonic solids, or regular polyhedra.

In 1736 Leonhard Euler (1707–1783) also solved the **Königsberg Bridges problem.** In the seventeenth century, the German city of Königsberg had its center on an island in the river Pregel. The island was joined to the banks of the river by two bridges to each bank and was joined by a bridge to another island, which in turn was joined to the banks of the river by two bridges. The people of Königsberg liked to stroll across these seven bridges and the problem arose as to whether the seven bridges could be crossed in a continuous walk without recrossing any of them (see Figure 12.14). Euler simplified this problem by replacing it by the network problem, to **traverse** the graph, that is, go along each path exactly once in a continuous way.

Regular Tetrahedron
(4 faces)

Cube
(6 faces)

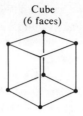

Regular Octahedron
(8 faces)

$$V + F = 4 + 4 = 8 \qquad V + F = 8 + 6 = 14 \qquad V + F = 6 + 8 = 14$$
$$E + 2 = 6 + 2 = 8 \qquad E + 2 = 12 + 2 = 14 \qquad E + 2 = 12 + 2 = 14$$

Dodecahedron
(12 faces)

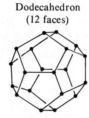

Icosahedron
(20 faces)

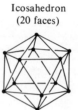

$$V + F = 20 + 12 = 32 \qquad V + F = 12 + 20 = 32$$
$$E + 2 = 30 + 2 = 32 \qquad E + 2 = 30 + 2 = 32$$

Figure 12.13

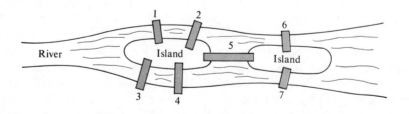

Figure 12.14

A vertex was classified as odd if the number of paths away from it was odd and even if the number of paths away from it was even.

In the network below, the abstraction of the Königsberg Bridges diagram, vertex A is odd (3 paths), B is odd (5 paths), C is odd (3 paths), and D is odd (3 paths).

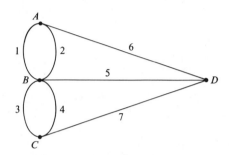

Euler proved the following facts:

1. A network can be traversed if all its vertices are even, and one can start anywhere.
2. A network can be traversed if it has exactly two odd vertices. One must start at one of the odd vertices and end at the other.
3. If a network has more than two odd vertices, it cannot be traversed.

Since the bridges of Königsberg network has four odd vertices, it *cannot* be traversed.

By 1935 an eighth bridge had been built, as shown in Figure 12.15, and then the network became traversable. Vertices A and C became even and only B and D remained odd. Thus one could start at either B or D and traverse the network.

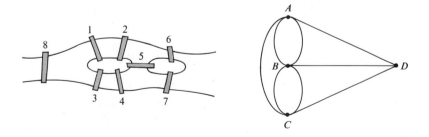

Figure 12.15

Sides.   In 1858 the German mathematician A. F. Möbius discovered a surface that has only one side. This **Möbius band** can be constructed by taking a strip of paper, giving it a half-twist, and then pasting its short edges together (Figure 12.16).

Figure 12.16

An ordinary ring of paper has two sides and the sides can be painted two different colors. This is impossible with the Möbius band because it has only one side.

If you cut along a line running around the middle of the band until you return to your starting point, you will discover a surprising thing. The band remains in one piece after it has been "cut in two."

When the band is cut one third of the way in from the edge all the way around, then there is another unexpected result.

In 1882 Felix Klein discovered another one-sided form, called the **Klein bottle** (Figure 12.17).

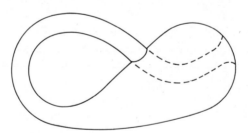

Figure 12.17

The Jordan Curve Theorem.   The **Jordan curve theorem** describes a topological property that has been fundamental in its importance and yet its statement seems almost trivial.

The theorem states that a simple closed curve in a plane (one that does not intersect itself) divides the plane into exactly two domains, an *inside* and an *outside* (Figure 12.18). This statement was first made by the French mathematician Camille Jordan (1838–1922).

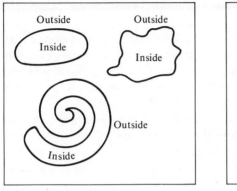

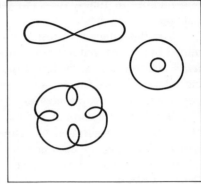

Simple, closed curves   Closed curves, not simple

Figure 12.18

The Jordan theorem seems obvious for familiar figures like the circle or ellipse but it is not so self-evident for more complicated simple closed curves like the one in Figure 12.19. Where is the inside and outside here?

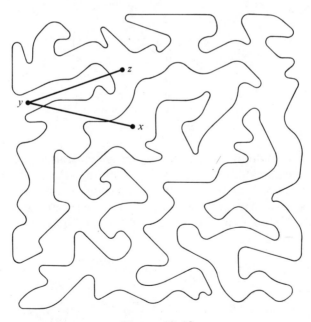

Figure 12.19

A quick way to determine whether x is inside or outside is to draw a line from x to a point clearly outside, such as y. If the straight line crosses the Jordan curve an *even* number of times, then the point is outside; if an odd number of times, then the point is inside. Thus, in the figure, x is outside and z is inside.

Can this concept of inside and outside be extended to regions determined by curves that are not simple and closed? The concept of **connectivity** is introduced to describe these regions. The region inside a simple closed curve is said to be **simply connected.** A domain that is not simply connected is said to be **multiply connected.**

Bernhard Riemann in 1857 used cross cuts, cuts that begin and end at the edge of a surface, to define the connectivity of a surface. Each surface is assigned a **Betti number** or genus, which is the largest number of cross cuts that can be made on a surface without dividing it into more than one piece.

Any cross cut on a disk or circle divides it into two pieces and thus its Betti number is 0.

A ring or a Möbius band requires one cut, so the Betti number of each of these is 1.

A region with 2 holes requires 2 cuts and thus has a Betti number of 2. A Klein bottle also has a Betti number of 2 (Figure 12.20).

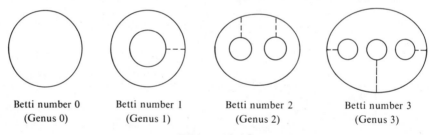

| Betti number 0 | Betti number 1 | Betti number 2 | Betti number 3 |
| (Genus 0) | (Genus 1) | (Genus 2) | (Genus 3) |

Figure 12.20

Now if a multiply connected region is transformed into a simply connected region by this process of cross cuts, then the *inside* and *outside* regions determined by the resulting Jordan curve can be determined. Now it is agreed that the regions that are "inside" after the cut or cuts were "inside" before the cut and those "outside" after were "outside" before (Figure 12.21).

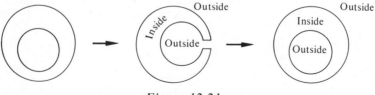

Figure 12.21

In 1895 Henri Poincaré, the French mathematician who is regarded as the father of modern topology, named the Betti number after Enrico Betti, an Italian physicist who in 1871 generalized the connectivity numbers of Riemann.

Before this time, the concept of Betti number was used by two other physicists. The German physicist Gustav Kirchhoff used it in 1847 to characterize the number of independent loop equations involved in certain electric networks. The British physicist James Clerk Maxwell used the concept in 1873 in his famous text *Electricity and Magnetism*.

Topology is a young and rapidly growing branch of mathematics. It deals with many problems that appear simple but are still unsolved. It is expected that in the near future significant developments will be made in this area of modern mathematics, both in the abstract mathematical world and in the real world, an ever-changing world in motion in a probably curved space.

REFERENCES

Bergamini, David, and the Editors of *Life, Mathematics,* New York: Time Incorporated, 1963, Chap. 8, pp. 176–190.

Newman, *The World of Mathematics,* Vol. 1:
   "Commentary," pp. 570–572.
   Leonhard Euler, "The Seven Bridges of Konigsberg."
   Richard Courant and Herbert Robbins, "Topology."

Tucker, Albert S., and Herbert W. Bailey, Jr., "Topology," *Scientific American,* January 1950.

HISTORICAL TIME CHART

PERIOD	DATE	MATHEMATICAL	GENERAL
Prehistoric	−50,000		Early Stone Age. Fire
	−15,000		Middle Stone Age. Artworks
	−5000		Late Stone Age begins
	−5000	4700 Babylonian Calendar	Civilization in valleys of Nile
	to	4241 Egyptian Calendar	and Tigris-Euphrates
Early	−3000	3100 Egyptian mace, numerals	Old Egyptian Empire
Oriental		2900–2700 Great Gizeh Pyramid	Sumerians and Early Babylonia
		2400 Tablets from Ur	Mohenjo-Daro on Indus River
		2200 Tablets from Nippur	Sargon I, 2750; Hammurabi, 2000
		1900–1600 Plimpton 322	Civilization in China
		1850 Moscow papyrus	Amenemhat III in Egypt, 1850
		1650 Rhind papyrus	Cretan Bronze Age
		1600 Tablets in Yale collection	Queen Hatshepsut in Egypt, 1500
		1350 Tablets from Nippur	Rameses II divides land, 1347
Period	−1200	Iron Age replaces Bronze	1200 Achaeans take Greece
of		Alphabet introduced, 1000–900	1055 Israel ruled by David
Transition		Coins introduced, ca. 650	878 Phoenicians found Carthage
			750–606 Assyrian Empire
			753 Rome founded
			900–600 Greek city-states
Greek	−600	Thales (ca. 640–548)	Solon gives laws to Athenians
		Pythagoras (ca. 580–501)	Rise of Persia (Cyrus, Darius,
			Xerxes), 540–480
	−500	Sulvasutras in India, ca. 500	Buddha in India, Confucius in China
		460 Hippocrates of Chios	Rise of Athens under Pericles,
		450 Herodatus (historian)	461–429
		425 Socrates	Golden Age of Athens
			Peloponnesian War (Athens–Sparta),
Logic	−400	375 Theaetetos (irrationals)	431–404
and		370 Eudoxus (proportion)	Philip of Macedonia takes Athens,
Geometry		Plato (ca. 429–348)	338
		Aristotle (ca. 384–322)	Alexander the Great, 336–323
		Eudemus (historian), ca. 335	Alexandria founded, 332
	−300	Euclid—*Elements*, ca. 300	
		Archimedes (287–212)	
		Eratosthenes, ca. 240	
		Apollonius, ca. 225	Syracuse falls to Rome, 212
	−200		Rise of Roman Empire
			Fall of Greece, Carthage, Corinth,
			146
	−100		Mesopotamia falls, 64
			Caesar conquers Gaul, 60–51
	−1		Egypt falls, 30
	1		Birth of Christ, −4 or +7
	100	Ptomely, *Almagest*, 150	Roman Empire
	200	Diophantos, *Arithmetica*, 250	Rules
	300	Pappus, ca. 300	the World
	400	University of Alexandria destroyed	Barbarians attack Roman Empire
			Byzantine Empire, 395 (Constan-
		Proclus (historian) (410–485)	tinople)
		Metrodorus, *Greek Anthology*,	Fall of Rome (western), 476
		ca. 500	Beginning of Papacy

HISTORICAL TIME CHART (*continued*)

Hindu-Arabic	500	Aryabhata, the Elder, ca. 500	Dark Ages in Europe
			Golden Age of India
	600	Brahmagupta in Ujjain, ca. 628	Rise of Arabs (Flight of Mohammed from Mecca, 622)
			Arabs take Alexandria, 630
	700	Zero appears on Indian grant, 738	Arabs in North Africa and Spain, Charles Martel defeats Arabs
Development of our Numerals, Arithmetic, and Algebra		Hindu and Greek classics translated to Arabic in Bagdad, 766 on	at Tours, 732
			Harun al-Rhashid, caliph of Bagdad, patron of mathematics, reigned 786–808
	800		
		Al-Khowarizmi in Bagdad, ca. 825	
		Mahavira in India, ca. 850	
		Zero used at Gwalior, India, 876	
	900	Hindu-Arabic numerals in Spain, 976	
	1000		Norman Conquest, 1066
	1100	Omar Khayyam, ca. 1100	First Crusade proclaimed, 1095
		Bhaskara (Ujjain), ca. 1150	Many Crusades, chivalry
		Greek and Arabic works translated into Latin	Mediterranean, center of trade

---

Early European	1200	Fibonacci (1170–1250) in Pisa	Renaissance begins in Italy
		Rise of European universities, 1250 on	End of Crusades
			Decline of Arab Empire
			Bagdad taken by Mongols
			Chinghiz Khan, 1220
			Kublai Khan, 1260
			Marco Polo begins travels, 1271
	1300	Invention of gunpowder	Black Death in Europe, 1349
		Oresme (1323–1382)	Hundred Years' War, 1337–1453
			Feudal System declines
			Rise of States
			Dante (1265–1321)
	1400	Printing press invented, 1438	Medici in Florence, 1420
Arithmetic, Algebra, Trigonometry		Numerals standardized, 1442	Joan of Arc burned, 1431
		First printed arithmetic, Treviso, Italy, 1478	Turks take Constantinople, 1453 (end of eastern Roman Empire)
		First printing of *Elements*, 1482	Leonardo da Vinci (1452–1519)
	1500	Rudolff (German), decimals, 1530	Age of Discovery
Algebra and Science		Cardan (French), negatives, 1545	Columbus, Magellan
		Recorde (English), = sign, 1557	Queen Elizabeth (1558–1603)
		Bombelli (Italian), complex numbers, 1572	Shakespeare (1564–1616)
			Religious reformations
		Napier (Scotch, 1550–1617), logs	
	1600		Rise of machines
European Modern			
		Viète (1591–1646)	Beginning of science
		Desargues (1593–1662)	Galileo (1564–1642)
Creativity in Many Areas		Descartes (1596–1650)	Colonial period
		Fermat (1601–1665)	European colonies over world
		Pascal (1623–1662)	Religious warfare
		Newton (1643–1727) ⎱ Calculus	
		Leibniz (1646–1716) ⎰	

HISTORICAL TIME CHART (*continued*)

	1700	
Calculus	Euler (1707–1783)	Industrial Revolution
and	Bernoulli family, 1654–1782	Rise of democracies
Applications	Lagrange (1736–1813)	American Revolution, 1776
	Laplace (1749–1827)	French Revolution, 1789
	Legendre (1752–1833)	
	1800 Gauss (1777–1855)	Napoleon (1804–1815)
Foundations	Cauchy (1789–1857)	Beethoven, Goethe, Kant
of	Lobachevsky (1793–1856)	Latin-American revolutions
Mathematics	Bolyai (1802–1860)	Western expansion of U.S.
(Analysis,	Galois (1811–1832)	
Algebra,	Boole (1815–1864)	Industrialization of U.S. and Europe
Geometry)	Weierstrass (1815–1864)	
	Riemann (1826–1866)	Colonial empires
	1900 Dedekind (1831–1916)	World War I, 1914–1918
	Cantor (1845–1918)	Communist Revolution, 1917
Foundations	Poincaré (1854–1912)	Great Depression, 1929
of Topology	Peano (1858–1932)	World War II, 1939–1945
and	Hilbert (1862–1943)	Nuclear energy
Probability	Whitehead (1861–1947)	Aviation, electronics
	Russell (1872–),	Advances in medicine, psychology,
	Principia Mathematica,	social sciences
	1910–1913	Emergence of Africa
	Brouwer (1881–)	Electronic computers mass
		produced, 1951
	Goedel (1906–)	

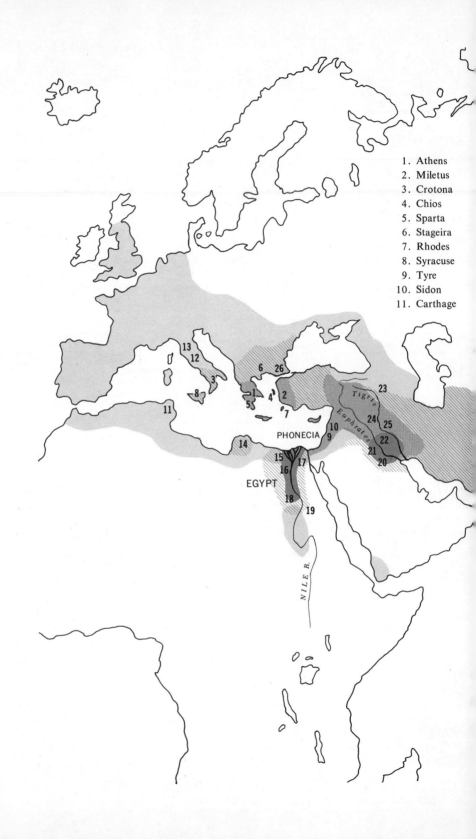

1. Athens
2. Miletus
3. Crotona
4. Chios
5. Sparta
6. Stageira
7. Rhodes
8. Syracuse
9. Tyre
10. Sidon
11. Carthage

13
12
6   26
1   4   2
5   23
3
8   7   *Tigris*
11   24
10   25
PHONECIA   22
9   21
14   20
15 *Euphrates*
16 17
EGYPT
18
19

N I L E   R.

CITIES OR SITES ON MAPS

12. Rome	23. Ninevah
13. Pisa	24. Assur
14. Cyrene	25. Bagdad
15. Alexandria	26. Constantinople (Istanbul)
16. Memphis	27. Mohenjo-Daro on Indus
17. Cairo (Gizeh)	28. Ujjain
18. Thebes (Karnak, Luxor)	29. Mysore
19. Syene (Aswan)	30. Nana Ghat (75 miles from Poona)
20. Ur	31. Patua
21. Nippur	32. Calcutta
22. Babylon	

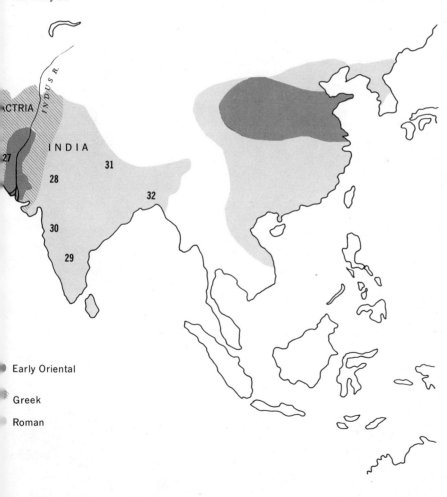

Early Oriental

Greek

Roman

ANSWERS TO SELECTED EXERCISES

Chapter 1

1. **a.** For each piece of candy that one child has, the other has exactly one, and conversely. They both have the same number of pieces.
   c. Each player is matched with exactly one number and each number on a jersey is matched with exactly one player.
2. **a.** L I M E
   ↕ ↕ ↕ ↕.
   M I L E
3. **a.** No.
   b. No, if team is complete roster. Yes, if team is the men in action.
   c. Yes.
5. 6 ways (NOW, NWO, ONW, OWN, WNO, WON).
7. **a.** Numeral.   **b.** Neither.   **c.** Number.
9. **a.** 27 cups.   **b.** 7 quarts, 1 pint, 1 cup.   **c.** 2.
11. **a.** Dot dot dit, dot dot dot, dot dot dot dit, dot dot dot dot, dot dot dot dot dit, dot dot dot dot dot. Base 2.
    c. Mo mo, eeny mo mo, meeny mo mo. Base 4.
13. **a.** 3 dots, 3 ots   **b.** 2 lots, 2 bots, 3 ots.   **c.** 4 lots.
    d. 5 lots, 1 dot, 3 cots, 3 bots.

Chapter 2

1. a, c, d, f, g.
2. **a.** {Washington, Oregon, California, Alaska, Hawaii}.
   c. {1, 2, 3, 4, 5, 6, 10, 12, 15, 20, 30, 60}.
   f. $\{\frac{1}{2}, \frac{1}{3}, \frac{1}{4}, \cdots\}$.   **g.** { } or $\varnothing$.
3. **a.** The coins of United States currency.
   c. The different letters in the word "college."
4. a, b, e.
5. **a.** The set of all colors. (Other sets are also possible.)
   c. The items on a menu. (Other sets are also possible.)
6. $\varnothing$, {Bird}, {Cat}, {Dog}, {Bird, Dog}, {Bird, Cat}, {Cat, Dog}, {Bird, Cat, Dog}.
7. $C \subset B \subset A$ and $C \subset B \subset D$. (Note: $A = D$.)
9. Equal: $A = C$, $B = E$.
   Equivalent: $A \leftrightarrow C$, $B \leftrightarrow E$, $A \leftrightarrow D$, $C \leftrightarrow D$, $B \leftrightarrow G$, $G \leftrightarrow E$.
11. **a.** A.   **b.** D.   **c.** $B = C$.   **d.** $C \leftrightarrow D$ or $B \leftrightarrow D$.

13.

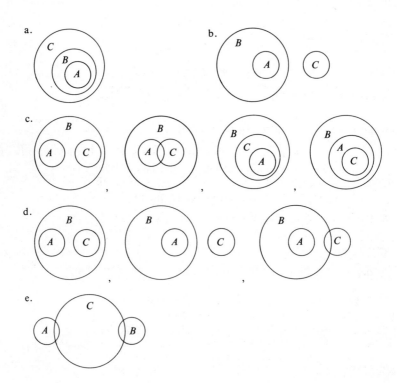

15.

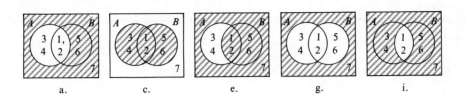

a. c. e. g. i.

17.

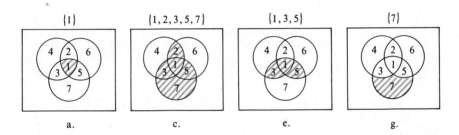

a. c. e. g.

19. a. 135.   **b.** 10.   **c.** 30.   **d.** 25.
21. a. 25.   **b.** 40.   **c.** 45.   **d.** 25.   **e.** 10.
22. a. Ordinal.   **c.** Cardinal.   **e.** Ordinal.   **g.** Ordinal.
23. a. 4.   **b.** 2.
25. a. 1, 2, 3, 4, 5, 6, 8, 9, 10, 12, 13, 14.
      b. 2, 5, 9, 13.   **c.** 5, 9.   **d.** 9.   **e.** 2.

Chapter 3

1. 41,026.   **3.** 55.   **5.** 2752.   **7.** 789.
9. The numerals for decimal 59 are:

a.   b.   c.   d.   e.

11. Decimal 3649 is

Decimal 5780 is

12. b. 3589. **d.** 9,040,021.

13. b. ♥λℙ. **d.** ϴℳσ∝.

14. a. 240. **c.** 865.

15. Decimal 637 is

16. Advantages: Avoids repetition, economizes symbols.
  Disadvantages: Memory work increased, numerals confused with words.

17. Advantages: Avoids repetition, economizes symbols.
  Disadvantages: More memory work.

19. $347 = (2 \times 125) + (3 \times 25) + (4 \times 5) + 2$.
  a. ɸ ɸ ▢▢▢ ★★★★ ‖. **b.** ‖ ℙ ‖‖‖▢ ‖‖‖ ★ ‖. **c.** ℓɸℂ▢ ℓ★ℓ.
  d. ℳℛℏℓ (using $125 = m$, $250 = n$, $375 = o$, $500 = p$).

21. a. 92,551. **c.** 8888. **e.** 167.

22. The number four hundred four is written as:

404.   ‖‖‖O‖‖‖ ·   ‖‖ ⋘ ‖‖
‖‖ ⟨ ‖ ·   · · · · ·
  a.   **b.**   **c.**   **d.**

23. Economizes symbols; easier to write large numbers; best for computations.

24. More memory required for computations, more abstract.

25. Base ten and addition principle.

26. a. Base 60, unciphered, no zero symbol, no separation point.
  b. Base 20, unciphered. **c.** Unciphered.

27. The decimal numeral $197 = (3 \times 64) + (0 \times 16) + (1 \times 4) + 1$ is written as
  follows:

  a. CCCA1. **b.** 111C1A1. **c.** 3C1A1. **d.** 111 1 1 or $\begin{matrix}111\\1\end{matrix}$.

  e. 3 11. **f.** 3011.

Chapter 4

1. a. 4735. **c.** 980. **e.** 90,106.

2. a. $(4 \times 10^3) + (5 \times 10^2) + (6 \times 10) + (7 \times 1)$.
  c. $(3 \times 10^4) + (4 \times 10^3)$. **e.** $(3 \times 10^4) + (2 \times 10^3) + (1 \times 10)$.

3. a. 53. **c.** 375. **e.** 140. **g.** 152. **i.** 295.

4. 200 base 10 is **a.** 11,001,000. **b.** 21,102. **c.** 3020. **d.** 1300.
 e. 532. **f.** 404. **g.** 310. **h.** 242. **i.** 148. **j.** 10, 0.
 k. 3, 20.
5. **a.** 101,101 base 2 = 55 base 8.
 c. 11,101,010 base 2 = 352 base 8.
 e. 1,000,000 base 2 = 100 base 8.
6. **a.** 11,000. **c.** 110. **e.** 1,000,001. **f.** 1101.
7. **a.** 412. **c.** 123. **e.** 22,322.
8. **a.** 1253. **b.** 19e. **c.** 255e. **d.** $628\frac{1e}{27}$.
9. **a.** ⚄△∠ **b.** ☆☆☆ **c.** |○△ ⚄☆ **d.** ⚄⚄
12. **a.** $\frac{1}{2}$ base 10 = 0.1 base 2, $\frac{3}{4}$ base 10 = 0.11 base 2.
 b. $\frac{4}{5}$ base 10 = 0.4 base 5.
 d. $\frac{1}{2}$ base 10 = 0.6 base 12, $\frac{5}{6}$ base 10 = 0.t base 12.
 e. $\frac{1}{2}$ base 10 = 0.30, base 60, $\frac{3}{4}$ base 10 = 0.45, base 60.
13. **a.** $\frac{7}{8}$. **b.** $\frac{26}{125}$. **e.** $\frac{41}{120}$.
14. **a.** 63¢ requires 6 coins base 2, 7 coins base 5, 9 coins base 10; 99¢
 requires 4 coins base 2, 11 coins base 5, 18 coins base 10.
 b. Modified base 2 because 2 is used as a multiplier most of the time.
 c. and **d.** Base 2, requires least number of coins or measuring standards.

Chapter 5

1. **a.** LXVII. **c.** |9⚄.

2. **a.** XXXIII. **c.** |∩∩∩9.

3. **a.**

I	XXXVI
II	LXXII
IIII	CXXXXIIII
VIII	CCLXXXVIII
XVI	DLXXVI
XVII	DCXII

4. **a.**

1	$\frac{1}{9}$
2	$\frac{1}{6} + \frac{1}{18}$
4	$\frac{1}{3} + \frac{1}{9}$
8	$\frac{2}{3} + \frac{1}{6} + \frac{1}{18}$
16	$1\frac{1}{3} + \frac{1}{3} + \frac{1}{9}$
32	$3\frac{1}{3} + \frac{1}{6} + \frac{1}{18}$
34	$3 + \frac{2}{3} + \frac{1}{9}$

5. **a.** Try 9. Then 9 + 1 = 10 and 10 × 3 = 30. Thus, $N = 9 \times 3 = 27$.
6. **a.** 7. **c.** 5.5.
7. About 7 years, 4 months.
8. For 14,25,25 triangle, **a.** between 84 and 88 is a good estimate.
 b. 175 **c.** 168.
9. **i. a.** about 108. **b.** 108. **c.** 108.
 ii. a. about 108. **b.** 117. **c.** 108.
10. **a.** 243. **b.** 256. **c.** 254.5.
11. 147.
12. **b.** If $p = 3$, $q = 2$, then 5, 12, 13, 25 + 144 = 169.
 If $p = 4$, $q = 1$, then 15, 8, 17, 225 + 64 = 289.

Chapter 6

1. a, b, e, f, h, j, l, m, n, p, q, r.
2. **a.** $P \lor Q$.   **c.** $P \to Q$.   **e.** $P \lor \bar{P}$.   **g.** $P \land Q$.   **i.** $\bar{P}$.
   k. $(P \lor Q) \to \bar{R}$.   **m.** $P \to Q$.   **o.** $P \to Q$.   **q.** $P \land Q$.
   s. $P \to \bar{Q}$.
3. **a.** Paris is not in Italy. True.
   c. Paris is in Italy and London is in England. False.
   e. Paris is not in Italy and London is in England. True.
   g. If Paris is in Italy, then London is in England. True.
   i. If Paris is in Italy, then London is not in England. True.
   k. Paris is in Italy or London is not in England. False.
   m. Paris is not in Italy or London is not in England. True.
   o. It is not the case that Paris is in Italy or London is in England. False.
4. **b.** 1. exclusive, 3. inclusive, 5. inclusive, 7. exclusive.

5. **a.**

P	Q	$P * Q$
T	T	F
T	F	F
F	T	F
F	F	T

b.

$\bar{P}$	$\bar{Q}$	$\bar{P} \land \bar{Q}$	$(\bar{P} * Q) \leftrightarrow (\bar{P} \land \bar{Q})$
F	F	F	T
F	T	F	T
T	F	F	T
T	T	T	T

c. Neither roses are red nor snow is white if and only if roses are not red and snow is not white.

6. **a.**

P	Q	$P \land Q$	$\overline{P \land Q}$	$\leftrightarrow$	$\bar{P} \lor \bar{Q}$	$\bar{P}$	$\bar{Q}$
T	T	T	F	T	F	F	F
T	F	F	T	T	T	F	T
F	T	F	T	T	T	T	F
F	F	F	T	T	T	T	T

c.

P	Q	$P \to Q$	$\leftrightarrow$	$\bar{P} \lor Q$	$\bar{P}$	Q
T	T	T	T	T	F	T
T	F	F	T	F	F	F
F	T	T	T	T	T	T
F	F	T	T	T	T	F

7. **a.** If I do not pass, then I do not study.
   c. If I am happy, then I am invited.
   e. If we don't have trouble, then Jane does not come or John does.
   g. If the baby is not hungry and he is well, then he does not cry.
   i. If I do not fly, then I go by boat.

9. a.

P	Q	P/Q
T	T	F
T	F	T
F	T	T
F	F	T

b.

P	P/P	$\overline{P}$
T	F	F
F	T	T

c.

P	Q	P/P	Q/Q	(P/P)/(Q/Q)	P ∨ Q
T	T	F	F	T	T
T	F	F	T	T	T
F	T	T	F	T	T
F	F	T	T	F	F

10. a. Valid, direct. **b.** Invalid, converse. **c.** Invalid, inverse.
 d. Valid, indirect or contrapositive. **i.** Valid, indirect.
 j. Invalid, inverse. **k.** Invalid, converse. **l.** Valid, direct.
 q. Invalid, converse. **s.** Invalid, converse.
 u. Valid, indirect chain.
11. a. Valid. **c.** Valid. **e.** Invalid. **g.** Invalid. **i.** Valid.
12. a. If a man is successful, then he is happy. **c.** No conclusion.
 e. All birds have wings. **f.** All lemons contain acid.

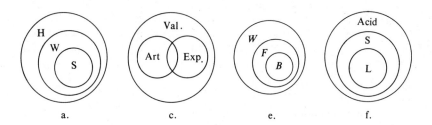

a.   c.   e.   f.

 g. No conclusion. **i.** No conclusion. **k.** Fattening food is sweet.

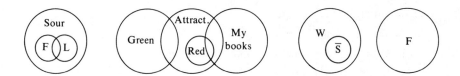

 m. No conclusion.
 o. I did not park overtime and I did not park in a red zone.
 q. I know the author. **s.** I stopped in Hawaii.
13. a. None of my poultry are officers.
 c. None of these apples were grown in the shade.
 e. Eggs of the Great Auk cannot be had for a song.

Chapter 7

2. a. No general category.   **b.** No specialization.   **c.** Redundant.

3. Yes. Define educated man.

5. a. No.   **c.** Yes.   **e.** No.

6. a. Yes.   **c.** No.   **e.** No.

7. a. Falling out of love.   **c.** 20° rise in temperature.   **e.** No inverse.
   g. No inverse.   **i.** Relaxing a rubber band.

8. a. $I = 5$. Yes.   **c.** $I = 0$. Yes.   **e.** No identity.

9. a. 4.   **c.** 6.   **e.** 10.   **g.** 8.   **i.** Impossible.

10. a. $2 - 3 = 4, 3 - 2 = 1, 4 \div 3 = 3, 3 \div 4 = 2$.
   c. $2 + (3 + 4) = 2 + 2 = 4$ and $(2 + 3) + 4 = 0 + 4 = 4$.
   $2 \times (3 \times 4) = 2 \times 2 = 4$ and $(2 \times 3) \times 4 = 1 \times 4 = 4$.
   $2 \times (3 + 4) = 2 \times 2 = 4$ and $(2 \times 3) + (2 \times 4) = 1 + 3 = 4$.

11. a.

+	0	1	2	3	4	5		×	0	1	2	3	4	5
0	0	1	2	3	4	5		0	0	0	0	0	0	0
1	1	2	3	4	5	0		1	0	1	2	3	4	5
2	2	3	4	5	0	1		2	0	2	4	0	2	4
3	3	4	5	0	1	2		3	0	3	0	3	0	3
4	4	5	0	1	2	3		4	0	4	2	0	4	2
5	5	0	1	2	3	4		5	0	5	4	3	2	1

   c. 0, 2, 3, 4.
   e. Closure; addition, multiplication, subtraction.
   Commutativity; addition and multiplication.
   Identity; all.
   Inverse; addition and subtraction.
   Associativity; addition and multiplication.

12. a. Friday.   **c.** Tuesday.

13. a. Each element in the table is in S.

   b. Each table is symmetrical about its main diagonal.

   c. D for $\oplus$ and A for $\odot$.

   d. D appears exactly once in each row.

   e. B and D.

14. a. Not commutative.   **c.** Not closed.

   e. Not all elements have inverses.

15. a. $(A + B)C$.   **c.** ABC.   **e.** $\overline{A + B}$.   **g.** $\overline{A} \cdot \overline{B}$.

16. $a = b, d = h, e = g$.

17.

a.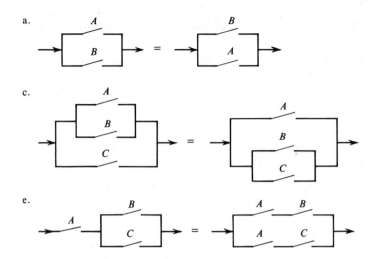

c.

e.

18. **a.** (1) There is at least one line.
(2) Each point is on exactly two lines.
(3) Every line has exactly two points on it.
(4) Every line has exactly two lines parallel to it.
Parallel lines are lines that do not have the same point on both lines.
b. Theorem 1. There is at least one point on the plane.
(1) There is at least one line. (Axiom 1)
(2) This line has a point on it. (Axiom 3)
Theorem 3. There are exactly five lines.
(1) There is one line, a. (Axiom 1)
(2) Line a has exactly two lines intersecting it, b and c. (Theorem 2)
(3) Line a has exactly two lines parallel to it, d and e. (Axiom 4)
Thus, a total of 5 lines.
c. (1) There is at least one politician in the room.
(2) Every committee has exactly two committees intersecting it.
(3) There are exactly five committees.
(4) There are exactly five politicians.
d.   Towns: A, B, C, D, E
Roads: AB, BC, CD, DE, EA

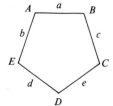

Chapter 8

1. Two circles will intersect if the line segment joining their centers is less than or equal to the sum of their radii.

3. **a.** $\overline{PS}$.   **c.** $\overline{PR}$.   **e.** $\overline{PQ}$.   **g.** $\overline{QR}$.   **i.** $\overleftrightarrow{PQ}$.   **k.** Q.   **m.** $\overrightarrow{PQ}$.   **o.** $\overrightarrow{RQ}$.

4. **a.** $\angle QPR$.   **c.** $\angle QPR \cup \overrightarrow{PV}$.   **e.** $\overrightarrow{PV}$.   **g.** $Q \cup \overrightarrow{PV}$.   **i.** $\overrightarrow{QS} \cup \overrightarrow{RT} - (Q \cup R)$.   **k.** $\triangle PQR$.

5. **1.** Given.
   2. Symmetric Property.
   3. Reflexive Property.
   4. $ASA \cong ASA$.
   5. Corresponding sides of congruent triangles are congruent.

7. The man. The triangles are congruent by SAS.

11. Area of trapezoid $ABCD = \dfrac{1}{2}$ area of $ABFE$.

13. Area of trapezoid = sum of areas of three triangles

$$(a + b)^2 = \frac{ab}{2} + \frac{ab}{2} + \frac{c^2}{2}$$

15. 96,250 square miles.
17. 16 feet, 8 inches.

Chapter 9

1. **a.** 3, 6, 10, 15, 21.   **c.** 5, 12, 22, 35, 41.
   b. 4, 9, 16, 25, 36.   **d.** 6, 15, 28.

3. **a.**

6

12

20

b. Each n by $n + 1$ rectangle can be split into two congruent equilateral triangles, with the length of each side $= n$.

$$n(n + 1) = \frac{n(n + 1)}{2} + \frac{n(n + 1)}{2}.$$

4. **a.** 6.   **c.** 12.   **e.** 1.   **g.** 65.   **i.** 23.
5. **a.** $\frac{2}{3}$.   **c.** $\frac{5}{7}$.   **e.** $\frac{43}{92}$.   **g.** $\frac{7}{13}$.   **i.** $\frac{75}{112}$.

7. $1184 = 2^5 \times 37$ and $1210 = 2 \times 5 \times 11 \times 11$.

Divisors:		Divisors:	
1		1	
2	592	2	605
4	296	5	242
8	148	10	121
16	74	11	110
32	37	22	55
63	1147	51	1133

$63 + 1147 = 1210$ $51 + 1133 = 1184$

8. $2^4(2^5 - 1) = 16 \times 31 = 496$
$496 = 1 + 2 + 4 + 8 + 16 + 31 + 62 + 124 + 248.$

10. a. Prime. **c.** Prime. **e.** $29 \times 13.$ **g.** $3 \times 3 \times 17.$

11. 25 primes less than 100, 46 primes less than 200.

12. 14 pairs: (3, 5), (5, 7), (11, 13), (17, 19), (29, 31), (41, 43), (59, 61), (71, 73), (101, 103), (107, 109), (137, 139), (149, 151), (191, 193), (197, 199).

13.

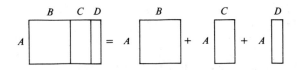

15.

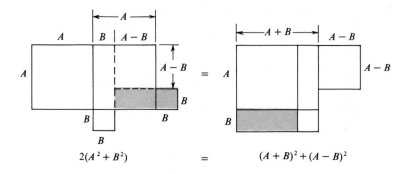

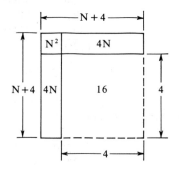

16. $N^2 + 8N + 16 = 9 + 16 = 25$
$(N + 4)^2 = 25$
$N + 4 = 5$
$N = 1.$

18. $N = 3$, (3, 4, 5); $N = 5$, (5, 12, 13); $N = 7$, (7, 24, 25).

19. a. $x = N$, $y = 2N - 5$; (3, 1), (4, 3), (5, 5).

20. (2, 1), (7, 4), (26, 15); $x + y \sqrt{3} = (2 + \sqrt{3})^N$, $N =$ any natural number.

Chapter 10

A.1. MCCCLXX.   **2.** DCLXVII.   **3.** MMMMCCCCXXXXVI.

B.1. **a.** Sum of units   15   **b.**   20
     tens   100   190
     hundreds 2000   1800
   Sum of sums   2115   2010

2. a.   73   *Check* 943   **b.** 75   *Check* 255
  1622   789   641   496
  789   1732   496   751
  943   255

3. a. 177.   **b.** 1729.
  4   72

4. a. 682   *Check* 444   **b.** 831   *Check* 797
  444   208   797   34
  208   652   34   831

5. a. 714   *Check* 286   **b.** 1000   *Check* 593
  286   428   593   407
  39   714   60   1000
  428   407

6. a.   31   Ans. 1311   *Check*   23
  29   57
  151   161
  10|57| 115
  23   1311
  23

 b.   7   Ans. 11,760   *Check*   48   245
  15   245   48
  10260   240   1960
  962   192   980
  8|245| 96   11760
  48   11760
  48
  48

7. a.   Ans. 3450   *Check*   46
         75
         230
         322
         3450

 b.   Ans. 22,372   *Check*   94
         238
         752
         282
         188
         22372

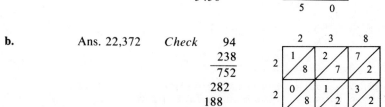

8. a.

```
        6  8      Check   27
        2  7              68
     ┌──┬──┬──┐           216
     │4 │7 │6 │           162
  ┌──┼──┼──┼──┘          1836
  │1 │3 │6 │
  └──┴──┴──┘
  1  8  3  6
```

b.

```
           5  3  6      Check    204
           2  0  4               536
        ┌──┬──┬──┬──┐           1224
        │2 │1 │4 │4 │            612
     ┌──┼──┼──┼──┼──┘          1020
     │1 │0 │7 │2 │0 │         109344
     └──┴──┴──┴──┴──┘
     1  0  9 , 3  4  4
```

9. a.
```
    1̸          Check
   2̸2̸            75
   9̸7̸8̸  │ 13    13
   7̸8̸  │       225
   7̸8̸           75
               975
```

b.
```
    1̸1̸          Check
   1̸4̸6̸           154
   3̸8̸4̸2̸ │ 23    23
   1̸8̸4̸ │       462
   1̸8̸4̸          308
               3542
```

10. a. 86)6364(74   *Check*
```
     56              86
     ──              74
     76             344
     42             602
    ───            6364
    344
     32
    ───
     24
     24
     ──
```

b. 45)9876(219$\frac{21}{45}$ *Check*
```
     90             219
     ──              45
     87            1095
     45             876
    ───            9855
    426              21
    360            9876
    ───
     66
     45
    ───
     21
```

C 1.

Divide by 7	③ answer
Add 5	21
Square	16
Subtract 6	4
Multiply by 2	10
Extract square root	5
25	25

2.

Add 2	⑤ answer
Square root	3
Subtract 5	9
Multiply by 7	14
Divide by 18	2
Square	36
Result, 6	6

Chapter 11

A. 1. a. $\frac{2}{3}$

b. $\frac{5}{8}$.

c. $\frac{3}{5}$.

d. $\frac{5}{3}$.

e. $\frac{11}{6}$.

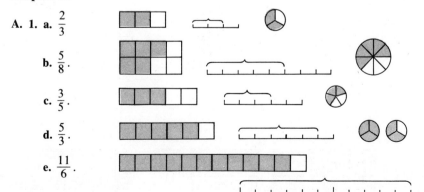

2. a. $\dfrac{15}{20} = \dfrac{3 \times 5}{4 \times 5} = \dfrac{3}{4}$.

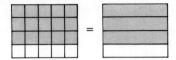

b. $\dfrac{21}{56} = \dfrac{3 \times 7}{8 \times 7} = \dfrac{3}{8}$.

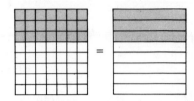

d. $\dfrac{8}{12} = \dfrac{2 \times 4}{3 \times 4} = \dfrac{2}{3}$.

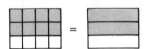

e. $\dfrac{21}{18} = \dfrac{7 \times 3}{6 \times 3} = \dfrac{7}{6}$.

3. a. $\dfrac{1}{3} \cdot \dfrac{2}{5} = \dfrac{2}{15}$.

b. $\dfrac{3}{4} \cdot \dfrac{2}{5} = \dfrac{6}{20} = \dfrac{3}{10}$.

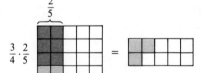

c. $\dfrac{2}{3} \cdot \dfrac{9}{8} = \dfrac{18}{24} = \dfrac{3}{4}$.

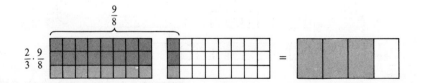

4. a. $\frac{1}{3} + \frac{5}{8} = \frac{8 + 15}{24} = \frac{23}{24}$.

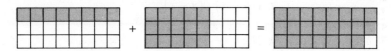

b. $\frac{5}{6} + \frac{7}{9} = \frac{15}{18} + \frac{14}{18} = \frac{29}{18}$.

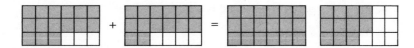

c. $\frac{5}{12} + \frac{5}{18} = \frac{15}{36} + \frac{10}{36} = \frac{25}{36}$.

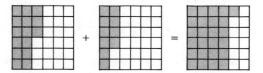

5. a. .375. **b.** .24. **c.** .35. **d.** .4375. **e.** .32.

6. a. $\frac{3}{5}$. **b.** $\frac{1}{40}$. **c.** $4\frac{1}{8} = \frac{33}{8}$. **d.** $23\frac{3}{4} = \frac{95}{4}$. **e.** $20\frac{3}{8} = \frac{163}{8}$.

7. a. 339.225. **b.** 1045.35644.

8. a. 14.65. **b.** 49.68.

9. a. $\frac{2}{3} + \left(\frac{3}{5} + \frac{4}{7}\right) = \frac{2}{3} + \left(\frac{41}{35}\right) = \frac{193}{105}$ and $\left(\frac{2}{3} + \frac{3}{5}\right) + \frac{4}{7} = \frac{19}{15} + \frac{4}{7} = \frac{193}{105}$.

b. $\frac{2}{3} \cdot \left(\frac{3}{5} \cdot \frac{4}{7}\right) = \frac{2}{3} \cdot \frac{\overset{4}{\cancel{12}}}{35} = \frac{8}{35}$ and $\left(\frac{2}{3} \cdot \frac{3}{5}\right) \cdot \frac{4}{7} = \frac{2}{5} \cdot \frac{4}{7} = \frac{8}{35}$.

c. $\frac{2}{3}\left(\frac{3}{5} + \frac{4}{7}\right) = \frac{2}{3} \cdot \frac{41}{35} = \frac{82}{105}$ and $\frac{2}{3} \cdot \frac{3}{5} + \frac{2}{3} \cdot \frac{4}{7} = \frac{6}{15} + \frac{8}{21} = \frac{82}{105}$.

B. 1. Signed numbers b, c, e, f.

2. a. To the left. **e.** Time B.C.
   b. To the west. **f.** Temperature below zero.
   c. Below sea level. **g.** Loss in population.
   d. A loss. **h.** Force away from an object.

3. a. +7850. **b.** −280. **c.** 0.

4. a. −500. **b.** −50.

5. + deposits, − withdrawals, final statement = −$20. (Account overdrawn by $20.)

6. a. +12. **b.** +18. **c.** −12. **d.** −18. **e.** +1. **f.** −1.

7. a. +12. **b.** +18. **c.** −18. **d.** −12. **e.** −3. **f.** +17.

8. a. 45. **b.** −45. **c.** +45. **d.** −45.

9. a. −5. **b.** +5. **c.** −5. **d.** +5.

C. 1. $5 + 3x$.

2. $3(5 + x)$.

3. $x - y/2$.

4. $ab - 7$.

5. $3n/(3 + n^2.)$

6. $z^3 - 8$.

7. $(4 - y)(6 + t)$.

8. $\left(\dfrac{3x}{4} + 5\right)\Big/\left(8 - x\right)$.

9. $2 + 5x = 17$.

10. $2(5 + x) = 17$.

D. 1. a. No, $(1 \cdot 1)/2 = \dfrac{1}{2}$ is not a natural number.

b. Yes, $ab = ba$ for $a \in N$ and $b \in N$.

c. Yes, $(ab)c = a(bc)$.

d. Yes, $I = 2$, $(a \cdot 2)/2 = a$ for all a.

e. Yes, because addition and multiplication are closed for natural numbers.

f. No, $2 \cdot 5 + 4 = 14$ and $2 \cdot 4 + 5 = 13$ and $14 \neq 13$.

g. $a * (b \text{ \# } c) = \dfrac{a(b \text{ \# } c)}{2} = \dfrac{a(2b + c)}{2} = \dfrac{2ab + ac}{2} = ab + \dfrac{ac}{2}$.

$(a * b) \text{ \# } (a * c) = 2\dfrac{ab}{2} + \dfrac{ac}{2} = ab + \dfrac{ac}{2}$ [* distributes over #].

$a \text{ \# } (b * c) = 2a + \dfrac{bc}{2}$, $(a \text{ \# } b) * (a \text{ \# } c) = \dfrac{(2a + b)(2a + c)}{2}$

$$= \dfrac{4a^2 + 2ab + 2ac + bc}{2}.$$

No.

h. For $a * b$, no, because $\dfrac{a \cdot a'}{2} = 2 \to aa' = 4 \to a' = \dfrac{4}{a}$ and division is not closed for natural numbers. For $a \text{ \# } b$, no, because there is no identity.

2. $a(b - c) = a(b + (-c)) = ab + a(-c) = ab + (-ac) = ab - ac$.

3. $\dfrac{b + c}{a} = \dfrac{1}{a}(b + c) = \dfrac{1}{a}(b) + \dfrac{1}{a}(c) = \dfrac{b}{a} + \dfrac{c}{a}$.

$\dfrac{b - c}{a} = \dfrac{1}{a}(b - c) = \dfrac{1}{a}(b) - \dfrac{1}{a}(c) = \dfrac{b}{a} - \dfrac{c}{a}$.

4. $a + bc \neq (a + b)(a + c)$.

$2 + 3 \cdot 4 = 2 + 12 = 14$ and $(2 + 3)(2 + 4) = 5 \cdot 6 = 30$.

5. $a + \dfrac{b}{c} \neq (a + b) \div (a + c)$.

$3 + \dfrac{10}{2} = 3 + 5 = 8$ and $\dfrac{3 + 10}{3 + 2} = \dfrac{13}{5} = 2\dfrac{3}{5}$.

E. **1.** 12.
   2. −2.
   3. 15.
   4. −12.
   5. $\frac{1}{4}$.
   6. −9.
   7. 3.
   8. −4.
   9. 7.
   10. $4 - 6 + 2t = 8$
   $\qquad -2 + 2t = 8$
   $\qquad\qquad 2t = 10$
   $\qquad\qquad\ t = 5.$

F. 1.

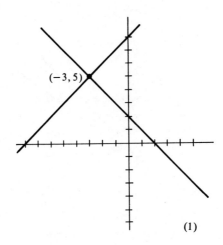

(1)

F. 2.

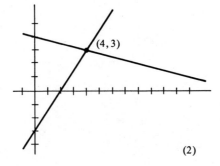

(2)

F. 3.

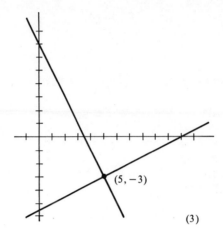

(5, −3)

(3)

F. 4.

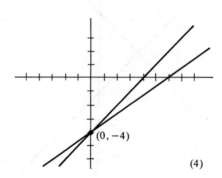

(0, −4)

(4)

Chapter 12

1. $p(A \text{ wins}) = \dfrac{11}{16}$. Thus, \$44 for A.

$p(B \text{ wins}) = \dfrac{5}{16}$. Thus, \$20 for B.

2. $\frac{1}{2}$.

3. a. $\frac{5}{26}$.   **b.** $\frac{21}{26}$.   **c.** $\frac{1}{2}$.   **d.** $\frac{3}{26}$.   **e.** $\frac{15}{26}$.   **f.** $\frac{11}{26}$.

4. $\frac{1}{2}$.

5. $\frac{3}{5}$.

6. a. $\frac{1}{5}$.   **b.** $\frac{4}{5}$.   **c.** $\frac{1}{25}$.   **d.** $\frac{9}{25}$.

7. a. $\frac{1}{5}$.   **b.** $\frac{4}{5}$.   **c.** $\frac{1}{25}$.   **d.** $\frac{9}{25}$.

8. a. $\frac{1}{20}$.   **b.** $\frac{5}{99}$.   **c.** $\frac{1}{495}$.   **d.** $\frac{97}{990}$.   **e.** $\frac{893}{990}$.

9. a. $\frac{1}{7}$.   **b.** $\frac{6}{7}$.   **c.** $\frac{5}{21}$.   **d.** $\frac{7}{21}$.

10. a. $\frac{1}{16}$.   **b.** $\frac{1}{32}$.   **c.** $1/2^n$.

INDEX